*Chanson de Roland*

*From the painting by Gaston Bussiere*

THE HARVARD CLASSICS
EDITED BY CHARLES W ELIOT LL D

# EPIC AND SAGA

BEOWULF
THE SONG OF ROLAND
THE DESTRUCTION OF DA DERGA'S HOSTEL
THE STORY OF THE VOLSUNGS
AND NIBLUNGS

WITH INTRODUCTIONS AND NOTES

VOLUME 49

P F COLLIER & SON
NEW YORK

Designed, Printed, and Bound at
The Collier Press, New York

# CONTENTS

TRANSLATED BY EIRÍKR MAGNÚSSON AND WILLIAM MORRIS

## INTRODUCTORY NOTE

WHEN our Teutonic ancestors migrated to Britain from the Continent of Europe, they brought with them the heroic songs in which their minstrels were accustomed to celebrate the deeds of their kings and warriors. In Section xvi of "Beowulf" will be found a short description of the recitation at a feast of this kind of lay. Perhaps as early as the seventh century of our era, after the introduction of Christianity, an unknown poet gathered material from these lays and composed the epic of "Beowulf." Besides the stories, he took from the older songs their metrical form and many features of style; but how far he retained their actual language there is no longer any means of knowing. A good deal of comment and reflection he must have added; and the structure of the epic is certainly due to him. He did not sing or chant to a harp as his predecessors in the treatment of this material had done; he wrote a book to be read. "Beowulf" is thus not folk-song, but belongs to a much more conscious and developed stage of art than the popular ballad.

The exploits narrated in the poem belong to the life of Germanic peoples before they crossed the North Sea, and at least one of the characters can be identified with a historical personage. Hygelac was the Danish king Chochilaicus, who was killed in a raid into the countries near the mouth of the Rhine, not far from 520 A.D.; and as he was the uncle of Beowulf, this fixes approximately the date for the historical prototype of our hero. But the events of the poem are legendary, not historic. The fights with monsters and dragons, which occupy so much of the poem, are clear evidence of the large extent to which the marvels of popular tradition had attached themselves to figures whose historical identity had already become shadowy. Some scholars have even tried to interpret the persons and events of the poem as mythology; and while one can not deny that mythical elements may have become interwoven, yet the poet believed his hero to be thoroughly human, and his foes to be such ghosts and monsters as are still believed in by the peasantry in many parts of Europe.

From Professor Gummere's translation, which preserves with great skill the essential metrical features of the original, accent

3

*and alliteration, one can get a good idea of the rhythmic vigor of the old English. The translation is made from the solitary text which has come down to us, a manuscript of the tenth century, now in the British Museum.*

*Although, as has been said, the chief materials of the poem must have come from the Continent, much of the detail giving a picture of life at an old Germanic court is likely to have been drawn from the England of the writer's own day. "Beowulf" thus comes to have, in addition to its interest as the earliest extended imaginative work extant among the Teutonic peoples, a special value for the light it throws on the culture and ideals of character prevalent during the first centuries of the English occupation of Britain.*

# BEOWULF

TRANSLATED BY

## FRANCIS B. GUMMERE

### PRELUDE OF THE FOUNDER OF THE DANISH HOUSE

LO, praise of the prowess of people-kings
    of spear-armed Danes, in days long sped,
    we have heard, and what honor the athelings
      won!
Oft Scyld the Scefing from squadroned foes,
from many a tribe, the mead-bench tore,
awing the earls. Since erst he lay
friendless, a foundling, fate repaid him:
for he waxed under welkin, in wealth he throve,
till before him the folk, both far and near,
who house by the whale-path, heard his mandate,
gave him gifts: a good king he!
To him an heir was afterward born,
a son in his halls, whom heaven sent
to favor the folk, feeling their woe
that erst they had lacked an earl for leader
so long a while; the Lord endowed him,
the Wielder of Wonder, with world's renown.
Famed was this Beowulf:[1] far flew the boast of him,
son of Scyld, in the Scandian lands.
So becomes it a youth to quit him well
with his father's friends, by fee and gift,
that to aid him, agéd, in after days,
come warriors willing, should war draw nigh,
liegemen loyal: by lauded deeds
shall an earl have honor in every clan.

---

[1] Not, of course, Beowulf the Great, hero of the epic.

Forth he fared at the fated moment,
sturdy Scyld to the shelter of God.
Then they bore him over to ocean's billow,
loving clansmen, as late he charged them,
while wielded words the winsome Scyld,
the leader belovéd who long had ruled. . . .
In the roadstead rocked a ring-dight vessel,
ice-flecked, outbound, atheling's barge:
there laid they down their darling lord
on the breast of the boat, the breaker-of-rings,[2]
by the mast the mighty one. Many a treasure
fetched from far was freighted with him.
No ship have I known so nobly dight
with weapons of war and weeds of battle,
with breastplate and blade: on his bosom lay
a heapéd hoard that hence should go
far o'er the flood with him floating away.
No less these loaded the lordly gifts,
thanes' huge treasure, than those had done
who in former time forth had sent him
sole on the seas, a suckling child.
High o'er his head they hoist the standard,
a gold-wove banner; let billows take him,
gave him to ocean. Grave were their spirits,
mournful their mood. No man is able
to say in sooth, no son of the halls,
no hero 'neath heaven,—who harbored that freight!

## I

Now Beowulf bode in the burg of the Scyldings,
leader belovéd, and long he ruled
in fame with all folk, since his father had gone
away from the world, till awoke an heir,
haughty Healfdene, who held through life,
sage and sturdy, the Scyldings glad.
Then, one after one, there woke to him,
to the chieftain of clansmen, children four:

---

[2] Kenning for king or chieftain of a *comitatus:* he breaks off gold from
the spiral rings—often worn on the arm—and so rewards his followers.

Heorogar, then Hrothgar, then Halga brave;
and I heard that —— was ——'s queen,
the Heathoscylfing's helpmate dear.
To Hrothgar was given such glory of war,
such honor of combat, that all his kin
obeyed him gladly till great grew his band
of youthful comrades. It came in his mind
to bid his henchmen a hall uprear,
a master mead-house, mightier far
than ever was seen by the sons of earth,
and within it, then, to old and young
he would all allot that the Lord had sent him,
save only the land and the lives of his men.
Wide, I heard, was the work commanded,
for many a tribe this mid-earth round,
to fashion the folkstead. It fell, as he ordered,
in rapid achievement that ready it stood there,
of halls the noblest: Heorot[1] he named it
whose message had might in many a land.
Not reckless of promise, the rings he dealt,
treasure at banquet: there towered the hall,
high, gabled wide, the hot surge waiting
of furious flame.[2] Nor far was that day
when father and son-in-law stood in feud
for warfare and hatred that woke again.[3]

    With envy and anger an evil spirit
endured the dole in his dark abode,

[1] That is, "The Hart," or "Stag," so called from decorations in the gables that resembled the antlers of a deer. This hall has been carefully described in a pamphlet by Heyne. The building was rectangular, with opposite doors—mainly west and east—and a hearth in the middle of the single room. A row of pillars down each side, at some distance from the walls, made a space which was raised a little above the main floor, and was furnished with two rows of seats. On one side, usually south, was the high-seat, midway between the doors. Opposite this, on the other raised space, was another seat of honor. · At the banquet soon to be described, Hrothgar sat in the south or chief high-seat, and Beowulf opposite to him. The scene for a flying (see below, v. 499) was thus very effectively set. Planks on trestles—the "board" of later English literature—formed the tables just in front of the long rows of seats, and were taken away after banquets, when the retainers were ready to stretch themselves out for sleep on the benches.

[2] Fire was the usual end of these halls. See v. 781, below. One thinks of the splendid scene at the end of the *Nibelungen*, of the *Nialssaga*, of Saxo's story of Amlethus, and many a less famous instance.

[3] It is to be supposed that all hearers of this poem knew how Hrothgar's hall was burnt,—perhaps in the unsuccessful attack made on him by his son-in-law Ingeld.

that he heard each day the din of revel
high in the hall: there harps rang out,
clear song of the singer.  He sang who knew[4]
tales of the early time of man,
how the Almighty made the earth,
fairest fields enfolded by water,
set, triumphant, sun and moon
for a light to lighten the land-dwellers,
and braided bright the breast of earth
with limbs and leaves, made life for all
of mortal beings that breathe and move.

So lived the clansmen in cheer and revel
a winsome life, till one began
to fashion evils, that field of hell.
Grendel this monster grim was called,
march-riever[5] mighty, in moorland living,
in fen and fastness; fief of the giants
the hapless wight a while had kept
since the Creator his exile doomed.
On kin of Cain was the killing avenged
by sovran God for slaughtered Abel.
Ill fared his feud,[6] and far was he driven,
for the slaughter's sake, from sight of men.
Of Cain awoke all that woful breed,
Etins[7] and elves and evil-spirits,
as well as the giants that warred with God
weary while: but their wage was paid them!

## II

WENT he forth to find at fall of night
that haughty house, and heed wherever
the Ring-Danes, outrevelled, to rest had gone.
Found within it the atheling band

---

[4] A skilled minstrel.  The Danes are heathens, as one is told presently; but this lay of beginnings is taken from Genesis.
[5] A disturber of the border, one who sallies from his haunt in the fen and roams over the country near by.  This probably pagan nuisance is now furnished with biblical credentials as a fiend or devil in good standing, so that all Christian Englishmen might read about him.  " Grendel " may mean one who grinds and crushes.    [6] Cain's.    [7] Giants.

asleep after feasting and fearless of sorrow,
of human hardship. Unhallowed wight,
grim and greedy, he grasped betimes,
wrathful, reckless, from resting-places,
thirty of the thanes, and thence he rushed
fain of his fell spoil, faring homeward,
laden with slaughter, his lair to seek.
Then at the dawning, as day was breaking,
the might of Grendel to men was known;
then after wassail was wail uplifted,
loud moan in the morn. The mighty chief,
atheling excellent, unblithe sat,
labored in woe for the loss of his thanes,
when once had been traced the trail of the fiend,
spirit accurst: too cruel that sorrow,
too long, too loathsome. Not late the respite;
with night returning, anew began
ruthless murder; he recked no whit,
firm in his guilt, of the feud and crime.
They were easy to find who elsewhere sought
in room remote their rest at night,
bed in the bowers,[1] when that bale was shown
was seen in sooth, with surest token,—
the hall-thane's[2] hate. Such held themselves
far and fast who the fiend outran!
Thus ruled unrighteous and raged his fill
one against all; until empty stood
that lordly building, and long it bode so.
Twelve years' tide the trouble he bore,
sovran of Scyldings, sorrows in plenty,
boundless cares. There came unhidden
tidings true to the tribes of men,
in sorrowful songs, how ceaselessly Grendel
harassed Hrothgar, what hate he bore him,
what murder and massacre, many a year,
feud unfading,—refused consent
to deal with any of Daneland's earls,
make pact of peace, or compound for gold:

---

[1] The smaller buildings within the main enclosure but separate from the hall.    [2] Grendel.

still less did the wise men ween to get
great fee for the feud from his fiendish hands.
But the evil one ambushed old and young,
death-shadow dark, and dogged them still,
lured, or lurked in the livelong night
of misty moorlands: men may say not
where the haunts of these Hell-Runes [3] be.
Such heaping of horrors the hater of men,
lonely roamer, wrought unceasing,
harassings heavy. O'er Heorot he lorded,
gold-bright hall, in gloomy nights;
and ne'er could the prince [4] approach his throne,
—'twas judgment of God,—or have joy in his hall.
Sore was the sorrow to Scyldings'-friend,
heart-rending misery. Many nobles
sat assembled, and searched out counsel
how it were best for bold-hearted men
against harassing terror to try their hand.
Whiles they vowed in their heathen fanes
altar-offerings, asked with words [5]
that the slayer-of-souls would succor give them
for the pain of their people. Their practice this,
their heathen hope; 'twas Hell they thought of
in mood of their mind. Almighty they knew not,
Doomsman of Deeds and dreadful Lord,
nor Heaven's-Helmet heeded they ever,
Wielder-of-Wonder.—Woe for that man
who in harm and hatred hales his soul
to fiery embraces;—nor favor nor change
awaits he ever. But well for him
that after death-day may draw to his Lord,
and friendship find in the Father's arms!

### III

Thus seethed unceasing the son of Healfdene
with the woe of these days; not wisest men

[3] " Sorcerers-of-hell."
[4] Hrothgar, who is the " Scyldings'-friend " of 170.
[5] That is, in formal or prescribed phrase.

assuaged his sorrow; too sore the anguish,
loathly and long, that lay on his folk,
most baneful of burdens and bales of the night.

This heard in his home Hygelac's thane,
great among Geats, of Grendel's doings.
He was the mightiest man of valor
in that same day of this our life,
stalwart and stately. A stout wave-walker
he bade make ready. Yon battle-king, said he,
far o'er the swan-road he fain would seek,
the noble monarch who needed men!
The prince's journey by prudent folk
was little blamed, though they loved him dear;
they whetted the hero, and hailed good omens.
And now the bold one from bands of Geats
comrades chose, the keenest of warriors
e'er he could find; with fourteen men
the sea-wood[1] he sought, and, sailor proved,
led them on to the land's confines.
    Time had now flown;[2] afloat was the ship,
boat under bluff. On board they climbed,
warriors ready; waves were churning
sea with sand; the sailors bore
on the breast of the bark their bright array,
their mail and weapons: the men pushed off,
on its willing way, the well-braced craft.
Then moved o'er the waters by might of the wind
that bark like a bird with breast of foam,
till in season due, on the second day,
the curvéd prow such course had run
that sailors now could see the land,
sea-cliffs shining, steep high hills,
headlands broad. Their haven was found,
their journey ended. Up then quickly
the Weders'[3] clansmen climbed ashore,
anchored their sea-wood, with armor clashing
and gear of battle: God they thanked

[1] Ship.
[2] That is, since Beowulf selected his ship and led his men to the harbor.
[3] One of the auxiliary names of the Geats.

for passing in peace o'er the paths of the sea.

Now saw from the cliff a Scylding clansman,
a warden that watched the water-side,
how they bore o'er the gangway glittering shields,
war-gear in readiness; wonder seized him
to know what manner of men they were.
Straight to the strand his steed he rode,
Hrothgar's henchman; with hand of might
he shook his spear, and spake in parley.
"Who are ye, then, ye arméd men,
mailéd folk, that yon mighty vessel
have urged thus over the ocean ways,
here o'er the waters? A warden I,
sentinel set o'er the sea-march here,
lest any foe to the folk of Danes
with harrying fleet should harm the land.
No aliens ever at ease thus bore them,
linden-wielders :[4] yet word-of-leave
clearly ye lack from clansmen here,
my folk's agreement.—A greater ne'er saw I
of warriors in world than is one of you,—
yon hero in harness! No henchman he
worthied by weapons, if witness his features,
his peerless presence! I pray you, though, tell
your folk and home, lest hence ye fare
suspect to wander your way as spies
in Danish land. Now, dwellers afar,
ocean-travellers, take from me
simple advice: the sooner the better
I hear of the country whence ye came."

IV

To him the stateliest spake in answer;
the warriors' leader his word-hoard unlocked:—
"We are by kin of the clan of Geats,
and Hygelac's own hearth-fellows we.
To folk afar was my father known,

[4] Or: Not thus openly ever came warriors hither; yet . . .

noble atheling, Ecgtheow named.
Full of winters, he fared away
agéd from earth; he is honored still
through width of the world by wise men all.
To thy lord and liege in loyal mood
we hasten hither, to Healfdene's son,
people-protector: be pleased to advise us!
To that mighty-one  come we on mickle errand,
to the lord of the Danes; nor deem I right
that aught be hidden.  We hear—thou knowest
if sooth it is—the saying of men,
that amid the Scyldings a scathing monster,
dark ill-doer, in dusky nights
shows terrific his rage unmatched,
hatred and murder.  To Hrothgar I
in greatness of soul would succor bring,
so the Wise-and-Brave[1] may worst his foes,—
if ever the end of ills is fated,
of cruel contest, if cure shall follow,
and the boiling care-waves cooler grow;
else ever afterward anguish-days
he shall suffer in sorrow while stands in place
high on its hill that house unpeered!"
Astride his steed, the strand-ward answered,
clansman unquailing: "The keen-souled thane
must be skilled to sever and sunder duly
words and works, if he well intends.
I gather, this band is graciously bent
to the Scyldings' master.  March, then, **bearing**
weapons and weeds the way I show you.
I will bid my men your boat meanwhile
to guard for fear lest foemen come,—
your new-tarred ship by shore of ocean
faithfully watching till once again
it waft o'er the waters those well-loved thanes,
—winding-neck'd wood,—to Weders' bounds,
heroes such as the hest of fate
shall succor and save from the shock of war."
They bent them to march,—the boat lay still,

[1] Hrothgar.

fettered by cable and fast at anchor,
broad-bosomed ship.—Then shone the boars[2]
over the cheek-guard; chased with gold,
keen and gleaming, guard it kept
o'er the man of war, as marched along
heroes in haste, till the hall they saw,
broad of gable and bright with gold:
that was the fairest, 'mid folk of earth,
of houses 'neath heaven, where Hrothgar lived,
and the gleam of it lightened o'er lands afar.
The sturdy shieldsman showed that bright ·
burg-of-the boldest; bade them go
straightway thither; his steed then turned,
hardy hero, and hailed them thus:—
"'Tis time that I fare from you.  Father Almighty
in grace and mercy guard you well,
safe in your seekings.  Seaward I go,
'gainst hostile warriors hold my watch."


**V**


STONE-BRIGHT the street:[1] it showed the way
to the crowd of clansmen.  Corselets glistened
hand-forged, hard; on their harness bright
the steel ring sang, as they strode along
in mail of battle, and marched to the hall.
There, weary of ocean, the wall along
they set their bucklers, their broad shields, down,
and bowed them to bench: the breastplates clanged,
war-gear of men; their weapons stacked,
spears of the seafarers stood together,
gray-tipped ash: that iron band
was worthily weaponed!—A warrior proud

[2] Beowulf's helmet has several boar-images on it; he is the "man of war"; and the boar-helmet guards him as typical representative of the marching party as a whole.  The boar was sacred to Freyr, who was the favorite god of the Germanic tribes about the North Sea and the Baltic.  Rude representations of warriors show the boar on the helmet quite as large as the helmet itself.

[1] Either merely paved, the *strata via* of the Romans, or else thought of as a sort of mosaic, an extravagant touch like the reckless waste of gold on the walls and roofs of a hall.

asked of the heroes their home and kin.
" Whence, now, bear ye burnished shields,
harness gray and helmets grim,
spears in multitude?  Messenger, I,
Hrothgar's herald!  Heroes so many
ne'er met I as strangers of mood so strong.
'Tis plain that for prowess, not plunged into exile,
for high-hearted valor, Hrothgar ye seek!"
Him the sturdy-in-war bespake with words,
proud earl of the Weders answer made,
hardy 'neath helmet:—" Hygelac's, we,
fellows at board; I am Beowulf named.
I am seeking to say to the son of Healfdene
this mission of mine, to thy master-lord,
the doughty prince, if he deign at all
grace that we greet him, the good one, now."
Wulfgar spake, the Wendles' chieftain,
whose might of mind to many was known,
his courage and counsel: " The king of Danes,
the Scyldings' friend, I fain will tell,
the Breaker-of-Rings, as the boon thou askest,
the faméd prince, of thy faring hither,
and, swiftly after, such answer bring
as the doughty monarch may deign to give."
Hied then in haste to where Hrothgar sat
white-haired and old, his earls about him,
till the stout thane stood at the shoulder there
of the Danish king: good courtier he!
Wulfgar spake to his winsome lord:—
" Hither have fared to thee far-come men
o'er the paths of ocean, people of Geatland;
and the stateliest there by his sturdy band
is Beowulf named.  This boon they seek,
that they, my master, may with thee
have speech at will: nor spurn their prayer
to give them hearing, gracious Hrothgar!
In weeds of the warrior worthy they,
methinks, of our liking; their leader most surely,
a hero that hither his henchmen has led."

## VI

Hrothgar answered, helmet of Scyldings:—
" I knew him of yore in his youthful days;
his agéd father was Ecgtheow named,
to whom, at home, gave Hrethel the Geat
his only daughter. Their offspring bold
fares hither to seek the steadfast friend.
And seamen, too, have said me this,—
who carried my gifts to the Geatish court,
thither for thanks,—he has thirty men's
heft of grasp in the gripe of his hand,
the bold-in-battle. Blesséd God
out of his mercy this man hath sent
to Danes of the West, as I ween indeed,
against horror of Grendel. I hope to give
the good youth gold for his gallant thought.
Be thou in haste, and bid them hither,
clan of kinsmen, to come before me;
and add this word,—they are welcome guests
to folk of the Danes."

[To the door of the hall
Wulfgar went] and the word declared:—
" To you this message my master sends,
East-Danes' king, that your kin he knows,
hardy heroes, and hails you all
welcome hither o'er waves of the sea!
Ye may wend your way in war-attire,
and under helmets Hrothgar greet;
but let here the battle-shields bide your parley,
and wooden war-shafts wait its end."

Uprose the mighty one, ringed with his men,
brave band of thanes: some bode without,
battle-gear guarding, as bade the chief.
Then hied that troop where the herald led them,
under Heorot's roof: [the hero strode,]
hardy 'neath helm, till the hearth he neared.
Beowulf spake,—his breastplate gleamed,
war-net woven by wit of the smith:—

" Thou Hrothgar, hail! Hygelac's I,
kinsman and follower. Fame a plenty
have I gained in youth! These Grendel-deeds
I heard in my home-land heralded clear.
Seafarers say how stands this hall,
of buildings best, for your band of thanes
empty and idle, when evening sun
in the harbor of heaven is hidden away.
So my vassals advised me well,—
brave and wise, the best of men,—
O sovran Hrothgar, to seek thee here,
for my nerve and my might they knew full well.
Themselves had seen me from slaughter come
blood-flecked from foes, where five I bound,
and that wild brood worsted. I' the waves I slew
nicors[1] by night, in need and peril
avenging the Weders,[2] whose woe they sought,—
crushing the grim ones. Grendel now,
monster cruel, be mine to quell
in single battle! So, from thee,
thou sovran of the Shining-Danes,
Scyldings'-bulwark, a boon I seek,—
and, Friend-of-the-folk, refuse it not,
O Warriors'-shield, now I've wandered far,—
that I alone with my liegemen here,
this hardy band, may Heorot purge!
More I hear, that the monster dire,
in his wanton mood, of weapons recks not;
hence shall I scorn—so Hygelac stay,
king of my kindred, kind to me!—
brand or buckler to bear in the fight,
gold-colored targe: but with gripe alone
must I front the fiend and fight for life,
foe against foe. Then faith be his
in the doom of the Lord whom death shall take.
Fain, I ween, if the fight he win,

---

[1] The *nicor*, says Bugge, is a hippopotamus; a walrus, says ten Brink.
But that water-goblin who covers the space from Old Nick of jest to the
Neckan and Nix of poetry and tale, is all one needs, and Nicor is a good
name for him.

[2] His own people, the Geats.

in this hall of gold my Geatish band
will he fearless eat,—as oft before,—
my noblest thanes.  Nor need'st thou then
to hide my head;[3] for his shall I be,
dyed in gore, if death must take me;
and my blood-covered body he'll bear as prey,
ruthless devour it, the roamer-lonely,
with my life-blood redden his lair in the fen:
no further for me need'st food prepare!
To Hygelac send, if Hild[4] should take me,
best of war-weeds, warding my breast,
armor excellent, heirloom of Hrethel
and work of Wayland.[5]  Fares Wyrd[6] as she must."


## VII

HROTHGAR spake, the Scyldings'-helmet:—
"For fight defensive, Friend my Beowulf,
to succor and save, thou hast sought us here.
Thy father's combat[1] a feud enkindled
when Heatholaf with hand he slew
among the Wylfings; his Weder kin
for horror of fighting feared to hold him.
Fleeing, he sought our South-Dane folk,
over surge of ocean the Honor-Scyldings,
when first I was ruling the folk of Danes,
wielded, youthful, this widespread realm,
this hoard-hold of heroes.  Heorogar was dead,
my elder brother, had breathed his last,
Healfdene's bairn: he was better than I!
Straightway the feud with fee[2] I settled,
to the Wylfings sent, o'er watery ridges,
treasures olden: oaths he[3] swore me.

---

[3] That is, cover it as with a face-cloth.  "There will be no need of funeral rites."     [4] Personification of Battle.
[5] The Germanic Vulcan.
[6] This mighty power, whom the Christian poet can still revere, has here the general force of " Destiny."
[1] There is no irrelevance here. Hrothgar sees in Beowulf's mission a heritage of duty, a return of the good offices which the Danish king rendered to Beowulf's father in time of dire need.
[2] Money, for wergild, or man-price.          [3] Ecgtheow, Beowulf's sire.

Sore is my soul to say to any
of the race of man what ruth for me
in Heorot Grendel with hate hath wrought,
what sudden harryings.  Hall-folk fail me,
my warriors wane; for Wyrd hath swept them
into Grendel's grasp.  But God is able
this deadly foe from his deeds to turn!
Boasted full oft, as my beer they drank,
earls o'er the ale-cup, arméd men,
that they would bide in the beer-hall here,
Grendel's attack with terror of blades.
Then was this mead-house at morning tide
dyed with gore, when the daylight broke,
all the boards of the benches blood-besprinkled,
gory the hall: I had heroes the less,
doughty dear-ones that death had reft.
—But sit to the banquet, unbind thy words,
hardy hero, as heart shall prompt thee."

Gathered together, the Geatish men
in the banquet-hall on bench assigned,
sturdy-spirited, sat them down,
hardy-hearted.  A henchman attended,
carried the carven cup in hand,
served the clear mead.  Oft minstrels sang
blithe in Heorot.  Heroes revelled,
no dearth of warriors, Weder and Dane.


## VIII

UNFERTH spake, the son of Ecglaf,
who sat at the feet of the Scyldings' lord,
unbound the battle-runes.[1]—Beowulf's quest,
sturdy seafarer's, sorely galled him;
ever he envied that other men
should more achieve in middle-earth
of fame under heaven than he himself.—
"Art thou that Beowulf, Breca's rival,

---

[1] " Began the fight."

who emulous swam on the open sea,
when for pride the pair of you proved the floods,
and wantonly dared in waters deep
to risk your lives? No living man,
or lief or loath, from your labor dire
could you dissuade, from swimming the main.
Ocean-tides with your arms ye covered,
with strenuous hands the sea-streets measured,
swam o'er the waters. Winter's storm
rolled the rough waves. In realm of sea
a sennight strove ye. In swimming he topped thee,
had more of main! Him at morning-tide
billows bore to the Battling Reamas,
whence he hied to his home so dear,
beloved of his liegemen, to land of Brondings,
fastness fair, where his folk he ruled,
town and treasure. In triumph o'er thee
Beanstan's bairn[2] his boast achieved.
So ween I for thee a worse adventure
—though in buffet of battle thou brave hast been,
in struggle grim,—if Grendel's approach
thou darst await through the watch of night!"

Beowulf spake, bairn of Ecgtheow:—
"What a deal hast uttered, dear my Unferth,
drunken with beer, of Breca now,
told of his triumph! Truth I claim it,
that I had more of might in the sea
than any man else, more ocean-endurance.
We twain had talked, in time of youth,
and made our boast,—we were merely boys,
striplings still,—to stake our lives
far at sea: and so we performed it.
Naked swords, as we swam along,
we held in hand, with hope to guard us
against the whales. Not a whit from me
could he float afar o'er the flood of waves,
haste o'er the billows; nor him I abandoned.
Together we twain on the tides abode

[2] Breca.

five nights full till the flood divided us,
churning waves and chillest weather,
darkling night, and the northern wind
ruthless rushed on us: rough was the surge.
Now the wrath of the sea-fish rose apace;
yet me 'gainst the monsters my mailéd coat,
hard and hand-linked, help afforded,—
battle-sark braided my breast to ward,
garnished with gold. There grasped me firm
and haled me to bottom the hated foe,
with grimmest gripe. 'Twas granted me, though,
to pierce the monster with point of sword,
with blade of battle: huge beast of the sea
was whelmed by the hurly through hand of mine.

IX

ME thus often the evil monsters
thronging threatened. With thrust of my sword,
the darling, I dealt them due return!
Nowise had they bliss from their booty then
to devour their victim, vengeful creatures,
seated to banquet at bottom of sea;
but at break of day, by my brand sore hurt,
on the edge of ocean up they lay,
put to sleep by the sword. And since, by them
on the fathomless sea-ways sailor-folk
are never molested.—Light from east,
came bright God's beacon; the billows sank,
so that I saw the sea-cliffs high,
windy walls. For Wyrd oft saveth
earl undoomed if he doughty be!
And so it came that I killed with my sword
nine of the nicors. Of night-fought battles
ne'er heard I a harder 'neath heaven's dome,
nor adrift on the deep a more desolate man!
Yet I came unharmed from that hostile clutch,
though spent with swimming. The sea upbore me,
flood of the tide, on Finnish land,

the welling waters.  No wise of thee
have I heard men tell such terror of falchions,
bitter battle.  Breca ne'er yet,
not one of you pair, in the play of war
such daring deed has done at all
with bloody brand,—I boast not of it!—
though thou wast the bane[1] of thy brethren dear,
thy closest kin, whence curse of hell
awaits thee, well as thy wit may serve!
For I say in sooth, thou son of Ecglaf,
never had Grendel these grim deeds wrought,
monster dire, on thy master dear,
in Heorot such havoc, if heart of thine
were as battle-bold as thy boast is loud!
But he has found no feud will happen;
from sword-clash dread of your Danish clan
he vaunts him safe, from the Victor-Scyldings.
He forces pledges, favors none
of the land of Danes, but lustily murders,
fights and feasts, nor feud he dreads
from Spear-Dane men.  But speedily now
shall I prove him the prowess and pride of the Geats,
shall bid him battle.  Blithe to mead
go he that listeth, when light of dawn
this morrow morning o'er men of earth,
ether-robed sun from the south shall beam!"

Joyous then was the Jewel-giver,
hoar-haired, war-brave; help awaited
the Bright-Danes' prince, from Beowulf hearing,
folk's good shepherd, such firm resolve.
Then was laughter of liegemen loud resounding
with winsome words.  Came Wealhtheow forth,
queen of Hrothgar, heedful of courtesy,
gold-decked, greeting the guests in hall;
and the high-born lady handed the cup
first to the East-Danes' heir and warden,
bade him be blithe at the beer-carouse,
the land's beloved one.  Lustily took he
banquet and beaker, battle-famed king.

[1] Murderer.

Through the hall then went the Helmings' Lady,
to younger and older everywhere
carried the cup, till come the moment
when the ring-graced queen, the royal-hearted,
to Beowulf bore the beaker of mead.
She greeted the Geats' lord, God she thanked,
in wisdom's words, that her will was granted,
that at last on a hero her hope could lean
for comfort in terrors. The cup he took,
hardy-in-war, from Wealhtheow's hand,
and answer uttered the eager-for-combat.
Beowulf spake, bairn of Ecgtheow:—
" This was my thought, when my thanes and I
bent to the ocean and entered our boat,
that I would work the will of your people
fully, or fighting fall in death,
in fiend's gripe fast. I am firm to do
an earl's brave deed, or end the days
of this life of mine in the mead-hall here."
Well these words to the woman seemed,
Beowulf's battle-boast.—Bright with gold
the stately dame by her spouse sat down.
Again, as erst, began in hall
warriors' wassail and words of power,
the proud-band's revel, till presently
the son of Healfdene hastened to seek
rest for the night; he knew there waited
fight for the fiend in that festal hall,
when the sheen of the sun they saw no more,
and dusk of night sank darkling nigh,
and shadowy shapes came striding on,
wan under welkin. The warriors rose.
Man to man, he made harangue,
Hrothgar to Beowulf, bade him hail,
let him wield the wine hall: a word he added:—
" Never to any man erst I trusted,
since I could heave up hand and shield,
this noble Dane-Hall, till now to thee.
Have now and hold this house unpeered;
remember thy glory; thy might declare;

watch for the foe! No wish shall fail thee
if thou bidest the battle with bold-won life."


## X

THEN Hrothgar went with his hero-train,
defence-of-Scyldings, forth from hall;
fain would the war-lord Wealhtheow seek,
couch of his queen. The King-of-Glory
against this Grendel a guard had set,
so heroes heard, a hall-defender,
who warded the monarch and watched for the mon-
     ster.
In truth, the Geats' prince gladly trusted
his mettle, his might, the mercy of God!
Cast off then his corselet of iron,
helmet from head; to his henchman gave,—
choicest of weapons,—the well-chased sword,
bidding him guard the gear of battle.
Spake then his Vaunt the valiant man,
Beowulf Geat, ere the bed be sought:—
"Of force in fight no feebler I count me,
in grim war-deeds, than Grendel deems him.
Not with the sword, then, to sleep of death
his life will I give, though it lie in my power.
No skill is his to strike against me,
my shield to hew though he hardy be,
bold in battle; we both, this night,
shall spurn the sword, if he seek me here,
unweaponed, for war. Let wisest God,
sacred Lord, on which side soever
doom decree as he deemeth right."
Reclined then the chieftain, and cheek-pillows held
the head of the earl, while all about him
seamen hardy on hall-beds sank.
None of them thought that thence their steps
to the folk and fastness that fostered them,
to the land they loved, would lead them back!
Full well they wist that on warriors many

battle-death seized, in the banquet-hall,
of Danish clan.   But comfort and help,
war-weal weaving, to Weder folk
the Master gave, that, by might of one;
over their enemy all prevailed,
by single strength.  In sooth 'tis told
that highest God o'er human kind
hath wielded ever!—Thro' wan night striding,
came the walker-in-shadow.  Warriors slept
whose hest was to guard the gabled hall,—
all save one.  'Twas widely known
that against God's will the ghostly ravager
him[1] could not hurl to haunts of darkness;
wakeful, ready, with warrior's wrath,
bold he bided the battle's issue.


XI

THEN from the moorland, by misty crags,
with God's wrath laden, Grendel came.
The monster was minded of mankind now
sundry to seize in the stately house.
Under welkin he walked, till the wine-palace there,
gold-hall of men, he gladly discerned,
flashing with fretwork.  Not first time, this,
that he the home of Hrothgar sought,—
yet ne'er in his life-day, late or early,
such hardy heroes, such hall-thanes, found!
To the house the warrior walked apace,
parted from peace;[2] the portal opended,
though with forged bolts fast, when his fists had
     struck it,
and baleful he burst in his blatant rage,
the house's mouth.  All hastily, then,
o'er fair-paved floor the fiend trod on,
ireful he strode; there streamed from his eyes
fearful flashes, like flame to see.

---

[1] Beowulf,—the " one."
[2] That is, he was a " lost soul," doomed to hell.

He spied in hall the hero-band,
kin and clansmen clustered asleep,
hardy liegemen. Then laughed his heart;
for the monster was minded, ere morn should dawn,
savage, to sever the soul of each,
life from body, since lusty banquet
waited his will! But Wyrd forbade him
to seize any more of men on earth
after that evening. Eagerly watched
Hygelac's kinsman his cursed foe,
how he would fare in fell attack.
Not that the monster was minded to pause!
Straightway he seized a sleeping warrior
for the first, and tore him fiercely asunder,
the bone-frame bit, drank blood in streams,
swallowed him piecemeal: swiftly thus
the lifeless corse was clear devoured,
e'en feet and hands. Then farther he hied;
for the hardy hero with hand he grasped,
felt for the foe with fiendish claw,
for the hero reclining,—who clutched it boldly,
prompt to answer, propped on his arm.
Soon then saw that shepherd-of-evils
that never he met in this middle-world,
in the ways of earth, another wight
with heavier hand-gripe; at heart he feared,
sorrowed in soul,—none the sooner escaped!
Fain would he flee, his fastness seek,
the den of devils: no doings now
such as oft he had done in days of old!

Then bethought him the hardy Hygelac-thane
of his boast at evening: up he bounded,
grasped firm his foe, whose fingers cracked.
The fiend made off, but the earl close followed.
The monster meant—if he might at all—
to fling himself free, and far away
fly to the fens,—knew his fingers' power
in the gripe of the grim one. Gruesome march
to Heorot this monster of harm had made!
Din filled the room; the Danes were bereft,

castle-dwellers and clansmen all,
earls, of their ale. Angry were both
those savage hall-guards: the house resounded.
Wonder it was the wine-hall firm
in the strain of their struggle stood, to earth
the fair house fell not; too fast it was
within and without by its iron bands
craftily clamped; though there crashed from sill
many a mead-bench—men have told me—
gay with gold, where the grim foes wrestled.
So well had weened the wisest Scyldings
that not ever at all might any man
that bone-decked, brave house break asunder,
crush by craft,—unless clasp of fire
in smoke engulfed it.—Again uprose
din redoubled. Danes of the North
with fear and frenzy were filled, each one,
who from the wall that wailing heard,
God's foe sounding his grisly song,
cry of the conquered, clamorous pain
from captive of hell. Too closely held him
he who of men in might was strongest
in that same day of this our life.

### XII

Not in any wise would the earls'-defence[1]
suffer that slaughterous stranger to live,
useless deeming his days and years
to men on earth. Now many an earl
of Beowulf brandished blade ancestral,
fain the life of their lord to shield,
their praiséd prince, if power were theirs;
never they knew,— as they neared the foe,
hardy-hearted heroes of war,
aiming their swords on every side
the accursed to kill,—no keenest blade,
no farest of falchions fashioned on earth,

[1] Kenning for Beowulf.

could harm or hurt that hideous fiend!
He was safe, by his spells, from sword of battle,
from edge of iron.  Yet his end and parting
on that same day of this our life
woful should be, and his wandering soul
far off flit to the fiends' domain.
Soon he found, who in former days,
harmful in heart and hated of God,
on many a man such murder wrought,
that the frame of his body failed him now.
For him the keen-souled kinsman of Hygelac
held in hand; hateful alive
was each to other.  The outlaw dire
took mortal hurt; a mighty wound
showed on his shoulder, and sinews cracked,
and the bone-frame burst.  To Beowulf now
the glory was given, and Grendel thence
death-sick his den in the dark moor sought,
noisome abode: he knew too well
that here was the last of life, an end
of his days on earth.—To all the Danes
by that bloody battle the boon had come.
From ravage had rescued the roving stranger
Hrothgar's hall; the hardy and wise one
had purged it anew.  His night-work pleased him,
his deed and its honor.  To Eastern Danes
had the valiant Geat his vaunt made good,
all their sorrow and ills assuaged,
their bale of battle borne so long,
and all the dole they erst endured,
pain a-plenty.—'Twas proof of this,
when the hardy-in-fight a hand laid down,
arm and shoulder,—all, indeed,
of Grendel's gripe,—'neath the gabled roof.


XIII

MANY at morning, as men have told me,
warriors gathered the gift-hall round,
folk-leaders faring from far and near,

o'er wide-stretched ways, the wonder to view,
trace of the traitor.  Not troublous seemed
the enemy's end to any man
who saw by the gait of the graceless foe
how the weary-hearted, away from thence,
baffled in battle and banned, his steps
death-marked dragged to the devils' mere.
Bloody the billows were boiling there,
turbid the tide of tumbling waves
horribly seething, with sword-blood hot,
by that doomed one dyed, who in den of the moor
laid forlorn his life adown,
his heathen soul,—and hell received it.

Home then rode the hoary clansmen
from that merry journey, and many a youth,
on horses white, the hardy warriors,
back from the mere.  Then Beowulf's glory
eager they echoed, and all averred
that from sea to sea, or south or north,
there was no other in earth's domain,
under vault of heaven, more valiant found,
of warriors none more worthy to rule!
(On their lord beloved they laid no slight,
gracious Hrothgar: a good king he!)

From time to time, the tried-in-battle
their gray steeds set to gallop amain,
and ran a race when the road seemed fair.
From time to time, a thane of the king,
who had made many vaunts, and was mindful of
    verses,
stored with sagas and songs of old,
bound word to word in well-knit rime,
welded his lay; this warrior soon
of Beowulf's quest right cleverly sang,
and artfully added an excellent tale,
in well-ranged words, of the warlike deeds
he had heard in saga of Sigemund.
Strange the story: he said it all,—
the Wælsing's wanderings wide, his struggles,
which never were told to tribes of men,

the feuds and the frauds, save to Fitela only,
when of these doings he deigned to speak,
uncle to nephew; as ever the twain
stood side by side in stress of war,
and multitude of the monster kind
they had felled with their swords.    Of Sigemund
    grew,
when he passed from life, no little praise;
for the doughty-in-combat a dragon killed
that herded the hoard:[1] under hoary rock
the atheling dared the deed alone,
fearful quest, nor was Fitela there.
Yet so it befell, his falchion pierced
that wondrous worm;—on the wall it struck,
best blade; the dragon died in its blood.
Thus had the dread-one by daring achieved
over the ring-hoard to rule at will,
himself to pleasure; a sea-boat he loaded,
and bore on its bosom the beaming gold,
son of Wæls; the worm was consumed.
He had of all heroes the highest renown
among races of men, this refuge-of-warriors,
for deeds of daring that decked his name
since the hand and heart of Heremod
grew slack in battle.  He, swiftly banished
to mingle with monsters at mercy of foes,
to death was betrayed; for torrents of sorrow
had lamed him too long; a load of care
to earls and athelings all he proved.
Oft indeed, in earlier days,
for the warrior's wayfaring wise men mourned,
who had hoped of him help from harm and bale,
and had thought their sovran's son would thrive,
follow his father, his folk protect,
the hoard and the stronghold, heroes' land,
home of Scyldings.—But here, thanes said,
the kinsman of Hygelac kinder seemed
to all: the other[2] was urged to crime!

---

[1] "Guarded the treasure."
[2] *Sc.* Heremod.

And afresh to the race,[3] the fallow roads
by swift steeds measured! The morning sun
was climbing higher. Clansmen hastened
to the high-built hall, those hardy-minded,
the wonder to witness. Warden of treasure,
crowned with glory, the king himself,
with stately band from the bride-bower strode;
and with him the queen and her crowd of maidens
measured the path to the mead-house fair.

## XIV

HROTHGAR spake,—to the hall he went,
stood by the steps, the steep roof saw,
garnished with gold, and Grendel's hand:—
"For the sight I see to the Sovran Ruler
be speedy thanks! A throng of sorrows
I have borne from Grendel; but God still works
wonder on wonder, the Warden-of-Glory.
It was but now that I never more
for woes that weighed on me waited help
long as I lived, when, laved in blood,
stood sword-gore-stained this stateliest house,—
widespread woe for wise men all,
who had no hope to hinder ever
foes infernal and fiendish sprites
from havoc in hall. This hero now,
by the Wielder's might, a work has done
that not all of us erst could ever do
by wile and wisdom. Lo, well can she say
whoso of women this warrior bore
among sons of men, if still she liveth,
that the God of the ages was good to her
in the birth of her bairn. Now, Beowulf, thee,
of heroes best, I shall heartily love
as mine own, my son; preserve thou ever

---

[3] The singer has sung his lays, and the epic resumes its story. The time-relations are not altogether good in this long passage which describes the rejoicings of "the day after"; but the present shift from the riders on the road to the folk at the hall is not very violent, and is of a piece with the general narrative style.

this kinship new: thou shalt never lack
wealth of the world that I wield as mine!
Full oft for less have I largess showered,
my precious hoard, on a punier man,
less stout in struggle. Thyself hast now
fulfilled such deeds, that thy fame shall endure
through all the ages. As ever he did,
well may the Wielder reward thee still!"
Beowulf spake, bairn of Ecgtheow:—
"This work of war most willingly
we have fought, this fight, and fearlessly dared
force of the foe. Fain, too, were I
hadst thou but seen himself, what time
the fiend in his trappings tottered to fall!
Swiftly, I thought, in strongest gripe
on his bed of death to bind him down,
that he in the hent of this hand of mine
should breathe his last: but he broke away.
Him I might not—the Maker willed not—
hinder from flight, and firm enough hold
the life-destroyer: too sturdy was he,
the ruthless, in running! For rescue, however,
he left behind him his hand in pledge,
arm and shoulder; nor aught of help
could the cursèd one thus procure at all.
None the longer liveth he, loathsome fiend,
sunk in his sins, but sorrow holds him
tightly grasped in gripe of anguish,
in baleful bonds, where bide he must,
evil outlaw, such awful doom
as the Mighty Maker shall mete him out."

More silent seemed the son of Ecglaf[1]
in boastful speech of his battle-deeds,
since athelings all, through the earl's great prowess,
beheld that hand, on the high roof gazing,
foeman's fingers,—the forepart of each
of the sturdy nails to steel was likest,—
heathen's "hand-spear," hostile warrior's

---

[1] Unferth, Beowulf's sometime opponent in the flyting.

claw uncanny. 'Twas clear, they said,
that him no blade of the brave could touch,
how keen soever, or cut away
that battle-hand bloody from baneful foe.


### XV

THERE was hurry and hest in Heorot now
for hands to bedeck it, and dense was the throng
of men and women the wine-hall to cleanse,
the guest-room to garnish. Gold-gay shone the
    hangings
that were wove on the wall, and wonders many
to delight each mortal that looks upon them.
Though braced within by iron bands,
that building bright was broken sorely;[1]
rent were its hinges; the roof alone
held safe and sound, when, seared with crime,
the fiendish foe his flight essayed,
of life despairing.—No light thing that,
the flight for safety,—essay it who will!
Forced of fate, he shall find his way
to the refuge ready for race of man,
for soul-possessors, and sons of earth;
and there his body on bed of death
shall rest after revel.
          Arrived was the hour
when to hall proceeded Healfdene's son:
the king himself would sit to banquet.
Ne'er heard I of host in haughtier throng
more graciously gathered round giver-of-rings!
Bowed then to bench those bearers-of-glory,
fain of the feasting. Featly received
many a mead-cup the mighty-in-spirit,
kinsmen who sat in the sumptuous hall,
Hrothgar and Hrothulf. Heorot now

[1] There is no horrible inconsistency here such as the critics strive and cry about. In spite of the ruin that Grendel and Beowulf had made within the hall, the framework and roof held firm, and swift repairs made the interior habitable. Tapestries were hung on the walls, and willing hands prepared the banquet.

was filled with friends; the folk of Scyldings
ne'er yet had tried the traitor's deed.

To Beowulf gave the bairn of Healfdene
a gold-wove banner, guerdon of triumph,
broidered battle-flag, breastplate and helmet;
and a splendid sword was seen of many
borne to the brave one. Beowulf took
cup in hall:[2] for such costly gifts
he suffered no shame in that soldier throng.
For I heard of few heroes, in heartier mood,
with four such gifts, so fashioned with gold,
on the ale-bench honoring others thus!
O'er the roof of the helmet high, a ridge,
wound with wires, kept ward o'er the head,
lest the relict-of-files[3] should fierce invade,
sharp in the strife, when that shielded hero
should go to grapple against his foes.
Then the earls'-defence[4] on the floor[5] bade lead
coursers eight, with carven head-gear,
adown the hall: one horse was decked
with a saddle all shining and set in jewels;
'twas the battle-seat of the best of kings,
when to play of swords the son of Healfdene
was fain to fare. Ne'er failed his valor
in the crush of combat when corpses fell.
To Beowulf over them both then gave
the refuge-of-Ingwines right and power,
o'er war-steeds and weapons: wished him joy of them.
Manfully thus the mighty prince,
hoard-guard for heroes, that hard fight repaid
with steeds and treasures contemned by none
who is willing to say the sooth aright.

---

[2] From its formal use in other places, this phrase, to take cup in hall, or " on the floor," would seem to mean that Beowulf stood up to receive his gifts, drink to the donor, and say thanks.

[3] Kenning for sword.

[4] Hrothgar. He is also the " refuge of the friends of Ing," below. Ing belongs to myth.

[5] Horses are frequently led or ridden into the hall where folk sit at banquet: so in Chaucer's *Squire's Tale*, in the ballad of *King Estmere*, and in the romances.

## XVI

AND the lord of earls, to each that came
with Beowulf over the briny ways,
an heirloom there at the ale-bench gave,
precious gift; and the price[1] bade pay
in gold for him whom Grendel erst
murdered,—and fain of them more had killed,
had not wisest God their Wyrd averted,
and the man's[2] brave mood.  The Maker then
ruled human kind, as here and now.
Therefore is insight always best,
and forethought of mind. How much awaits him
of lief and of loath, who long time here,
through days of warfare this world endures!


Then song and music mingled sounds
in the presence of Healfdene's head-of-armies[3]
and harping was heard with the hero-lay
as Hrothgar's singer the hall-joy woke
along the mead-seats, making his song
of that sudden raid on the sons of Finn.[4]
  Healfdene's hero, Hnæf the Scylding,
was fated to fall in the Frisian slaughter.[5]
Hildeburh needed not hold in value

[1] Man-price, *wergild*.          [2] Beowulf's.          [3] Hrothgar.
[4] There is no need to assume a gap in the *Ms*. As before about Sigemund
and Heremod, so now, though at greater length, about Finn and his feud,
a lay is chanted or recited; and the epic poet, counting on his readers'
familiarity with the story,—a fragment of it still exists,—simply gives the
headings.
[5] The exact story to which this episode refers in summary is not to be
determined, but the following account of it is reasonable and has good
support among scholars.  Finn, a Frisian chieftain, who nevertheless has
a " castle " outside the Frisian border, marries Hildeburh, a Danish princess; and her brother, Hnæf, with many other Danes, pays Finn a visit.
Relations between the two peoples have been strained before.  Something
starts the old feud anew; and the visitors are attacked in their quarters.
Hnæf is killed; so is a son of Hildeburh.  Many fall on both sides.  Peace
is patched up; a stately funeral is held; and the surviving visitors become
in a way vassals or liegemen of Finn, going back with him to Frisia.  So
matters rest a while.  Hengest is now leader of the Danes; but he is set
upon revenge for his former lord, Hnæf.  Probably he is killed in feud;
but his clansmen, Guthlaf and Oslaf, gather at their home a force of
sturdy Danes, come back to Frisia, storm Finn's stronghold, kill him, and
carry back their kinswoman Hildeburh.

her enemies' honor![6]   Innocent both
were the loved ones she lost at the linden-play,
bairn and brother; they bowed to fate,
stricken by spears; 'twas a sorrowful woman!
None doubted why the daughter of Hoc
bewailed her doom when dawning came,
and under the sky she saw them lying,
kinsmen murdered, where most she had kenned
of the sweets of the world! By war were swept, too,
Finn's own liegemen, and few were left;
in the parleying-place[7] he could ply no longer
weapon, nor war could he wage on Hengest,
and rescue his remnant by right of arms
from the prince's thane. A pact he offered:
another dwelling the Danes should have,
hall and high-seat, and half the power
should fall to them in Frisian land;
and at the fee-gifts, Folcwald's son
day by day the Danes should honor,
the folk of Hengest favor with rings,
even as truly, with treasure and jewels,
with fretted gold, as his Frisian kin
he meant to honor in ale-hall there.
Pact of peace they plighted further
on both sides firmly. Finn to Hengest
with oath, upon honor, openly promised
that woful remnant, with wise-men's aid,
nobly to govern, so none of the guests
by word or work should warp the treaty,[8]
or with malice of mind bemoan themselves
as forced to follow their fee-giver's slayer,
lordless men, as their lot ordained.
Should Frisian, moreover, with foeman's taunt,
that murderous hatred to mind recall,
then edge of the sword must seal his doom.

---

[6] The "enemies" must be the Frisians.

[7] Battlefield.—Hengest is the "prince's thane," companion of Hnæf. "Folcwald's son" is Finn.

[8] That is, Finn would govern in all honor the few Danish warriors who were left, provided, of course, that none of them tried to renew the quarrel or avenge Hnæf their fallen lord. If, again, one of Finn's Frisians began a quarrel, he should die by the sword.

Oaths were given, and ancient gold
heaped from hoard.—The hardy Scylding,
battle-thane best,[9] on his balefire lay.
All on the pyre were plain to see
the gory sark, the gilded swine-crest,
boar of hard iron, and athelings many
slain by the sword: at the slaughter they fell.
It was Hildeburh's hest, at Hnæf's own pyre
the bairn of her body on brands to lay,
his bones to burn, on the balefire placed,
at his uncle's side.  In sorrowful dirges
bewept them the woman: great wailing ascended.
Then wound up to welkin the wildest of death-fires,
roared o'er the hillock:[10] heads all were melted,
gashes burst, and blood gushed out
from bites[11] of the body.  Balefire devoured,
greediest spirit, those spared not by war
out of either folk: their flower was gone.

## XVII

THEN hastened those heroes their home to see,
friendless, to find the Frisian land,
houses and high burg.  Hengest still
through the death-dyed winter dwelt with Finn,
holding pact, yet of home he minded,
though powerless his ring-decked prow to drive
over the waters, now waves rolled fierce
lashed by the winds, or winter locked them
in icy fetters.  Then fared another
year to men's dwellings, as yet they do,
the sunbright skies, that their season ever
duly await.  Far off winter was driven;
fair lay earth's breast; and fain was the rover,
the guest, to depart, though more gladly he pondered
on wreaking his vengeance than roaming the deep,
and how to hasten the hot encounter

[9] Hnæf.
[10] The high place chosen for the funeral: see description of Beowulf's
funeral-pile at the end of the poem.                    [11] Wounds.

where sons of the Frisians were sure to be.
So he escaped not the common doom,
when Hun with " Lafing," the light-of-battle,
best of blades, his bosom pierced:
its edge was famed with the Frisian earls.
On fierce-heart Finn there fell likewise,
on himself at home, the horrid sword-death;
for Guthlaf and Oslaf of grim attack
had sorrowing told, from sea-ways landed,
mourning their woes.[1] Finn's wavering spirit
bode not in breast. The burg was reddened
with blood of foemen, and Finn was slain,
king amid clansmen; the queen was taken.
To their ship the Scylding warriors bore
all the chattels the chieftain owned,
whatever they found in Finn's domain
of gems and jewels. The gentle wife
o'er paths of the deep to the Danes they bore,
led to her land.

The lay was finished,
the gleeman's song. Then glad rose the revel;
bench-joy brightened. Bearers draw
from their " wonder-vats" wine. Comes Wealhtheow
  forth,
under gold-crown goes where the good pair sit,
uncle and nephew, true each to the other one,
kindred in amity. Unferth the spokesman
at the Scylding lord's feet sat: men had faith in his
  spirit,
his keenness of courage, though kinsmen had found
  him
unsure at the sword-play. The Scylding queen spoke:
" Quaff of this cup, my king and lord,
breaker of rings, and blithe be thou,
gold-friend of men; to the Geats here speak
such words of mildness as man should use.
Be glad with thy Geats; of those gifts be mindful,
or near or far, which now thou hast.

[1] That is, these two Danes, escaping home, had told the story of the attack on Hnæf, the slaying of Hengest, and all the Danish woes. Collecting a force, they return to Frisia and kill Finn in his home.

Men say to me, as son thou wishest
yon hero to hold. Thy Heorot purged,
jewel-hall brightest, enjoy while thou canst,
with many a largess; and leave to thy kin
folk and realm when forth thou goest
to greet thy doom. For gracious I deem
my Hrothulf,[2] willing to hold and rule
nobly our youths, if thou yield up first,
prince of Scyldings, thy part in the world.
I ween with good he will well requite
offspring of ours, when all he minds
that for him we did in his helpless days
of gift and grace to gain him honor!"
Then she turned to the seat where her sons were
      placed,
Hrethric and Hrothmund, with heroes' bairns,
young men together: the Geat, too, sat there,
Beowulf brave, the brothers between.


XVIII

A CUP she gave him, with kindly greeting
and winsome words. Of wounden gold,
she offered, to honor him, arm-jewels twain,
corselet and rings, and of collars the noblest
that ever I knew the earth around.
Ne'er heard I so mighty, 'neath heaven's dome,
a hoard-gem of heroes, since Hama bore
to his bright-built burg the Brisings' necklace,
jewel and gem casket.—Jealousy fled he,
Eormenric's hate: chose help eternal.
Hygelac Geat, grandson of Swerting,
on the last of his raids this ring bore with him,

[2] Nephew to Hrothgar, with whom he subsequently quarrels, and elder
cousin to the two young sons of Hrothgar and Wealhtheow,—their natural
guardian in the event of the king's death. There is something finely femi-
nine in this speech of Wealhtheow's, apart from its somewhat irregular and
irrelevant sequence of topics. Both she and her lord probably distrust
Hrothulf; but she bids the king to be of good cheer, and, turning to the
suspect, heaps affectionate assurances on his probity. " My own Hrothulf "
will surely not forget those favors and benefits of the past, but will repay
them to the orphaned boy.

under his banner the booty defending,
the war-spoil warding; but Wyrd o'erwhelmed him
what time, in his daring, dangers he sought,
feud with Frisians. Fairest of gems
he bore with him over the beaker-of-waves,
sovran strong: under shield he died.
Fell the corpse of the king into keeping of Franks,
gear of the breast, and that gorgeous ring;
weaker warriors won the spoil,
after gripe of battle, from Geatland's lord,
and held the death-field.

                         Din rose in hall.
Wealhtheow spake amid warriors, and said:—
"This jewel enjoy in thy jocund youth,
Beowulf lov'd, these battle-weeds wear,
a royal treasure, and richly thrive!
Preserve thy strength, and these striplings here
counsel in kindness: requital be mine.
Hast done such deeds, that for days to come
thou art famed among folk both far and near,
so wide as washeth the wave of Ocean
his windy walls. Through the ways of life
prosper, O prince! I pray for thee
rich possessions. To son of mine
be helpful in deed and uphold his joys!
Here every earl to the other is true,
mild of mood, to the master loyal!
Thanes are friendly, the throng obedient,
liegemen are revelling: list and obey!"
  Went then to her place.—That was proudest of
    feasts;
flowed wine for the warriors. Wyrd they knew not,
destiny dire, and the doom to be seen
by many an earl when eve should come,
and Hrothgar homeward hasten away,
royal, to rest. The room was guarded
by an army of earls, as erst was done.
They bared the bench-boards; abroad they spread
beds and bolsters.—One beer-carouser
in danger of doom lay down in the hall.—

At their heads they set their shields of war,
bucklers bright; on the bench were there
over each atheling, easy to see,
the high battle-helmet, the haughty spear,
the corselet of rings. 'Twas their custom so
ever to be for battle prepared,
at home, or harrying, which it were,
even as oft as evil threatened
their sovran king.—They were clansmen good.

## XIX

THEN sank they to sleep. With sorrow one bought
his rest of the evening,—as ofttime had happened
when Grendel guarded that golden hall,
evil wrought, till his end drew nigh,
slaughter for sins. 'Twas seen and told
how an avenger survived the fiend,
as was learned afar. The livelong time
after that grim fight, Grendel's mother,
monster of women, mourned her woe.
She was doomed to dwell in the dreary waters,
cold sea-courses, since Cain cut down
with edge of the sword his only brother,
his father's offspring: outlawed he fled,
marked with murder, from men's delights
warded the wilds.—There woke from him
such fate-sent ghosts as Grendel, who,
war-wolf horrid, at Heorot found
a warrior watching and waiting the fray,
with whom the grisly one grappled amain.
But the man remembered his mighty power,
the glorious gift that God had sent him,
in his Maker's mercy put his trust
for comfort and help: so he conquered the foe,
felled the fiend, who fled abject,
reft of joy, to the realms of death,
mankind's foe. And his mother now,
gloomy and grim, would go that quest

of sorrow, the death of her son to avenge.
To Heorot came she, where helmeted Danes
slept in the hall. Too soon came back
old ills of the earls, when in she burst,
the mother of Grendel. Less grim, though, that terror,
e'en as terror of woman in war is less,
might of maid, than of men in arms
when, hammer-forgéd, the falchion hard,
sword gore-stained, through swine of the helm,
crested, with keen blade carves amain.
Then was in hall the hard-edge drawn,
the swords on the settles,[1] and shields a-many
firm held in hand: nor helmet minded
nor harness of mail, whom that horror seized.

Haste was hers; she would hie afar
and save her life when the liegemen saw her.
Yet a single atheling up she seized
fast and firm, as she fled to the moor.
He was for Hrothgar of heroes the dearest,
of trusty vassals betwixt the seas,
whom she killed on his couch, a clansman famous,
in battle brave.—Nor was Beowulf there;
another house had been held apart,
after giving of gold, for the Geat renowned.—
Uproar filled Heorot; the hand all had viewed,
blood-flecked, she bore with her; bale was returned,
dole in the dwellings: 'twas dire exchange
where Dane and Geat were doomed to give
the lives of loved ones. Long-tried king,
the hoary hero, at heart was sad
when he knew his noble no more lived,
and dead indeed was his dearest thane.
To his bower was Beowulf brought in haste,
dauntless victor. As daylight broke,
along with his earls the atheling lord,
with his clansmen, came, where the king abode
waiting to see if the Wielder-of-All
would turn this tale of trouble and woe.
Strode o'er floor the famed-in-strife,

[1] They had laid their arms on the benches near where they slept.

with his hand-companions,—the hall resounded,—
wishing to greet the wise old king,
Ingwines' lord; he asked if the night
had passed in peace to the prince's mind.


## XX

HROTHGAR spake, helmet-of-Scyldings:—
"Ask not of pleasure! Pain is renewed
to Danish folk. Dead is Æschere,
of Yrmenlaf the elder brother,
my sage adviser and stay in council,
shoulder-comrade in stress of fight
when warriors clashed and we warded our heads,
hewed the helm-boars; hero famed
should be every earl as Æschere was!
But here in Heorot a hand hath slain him
of wandering death-sprite. I wot not whither,[1]
proud of the prey, her path she took,
fain of her fill. The feud she avenged
that yesternight, unyieldingly,
Grendel in grimmest grasp thou killedst,—
seeing how long these liegemen mine
he ruined and ravaged. Reft of life,
in arms he fell. Now another comes,
keen and cruel, her kin to avenge,
faring far in feud of blood:
so that many a thane shall think, who e'er
sorrows in soul for that sharer of rings,
this is hardest of heart-bales. The hand lies low
that once was willing each wish to please.
Land-dwellers here[2] and liegemen mine,
who house by those parts, I have heard relate
that such a pair they have sometimes seen,

---

[1] He surmises presently where she is.
[2] The connection is not difficult. The words of mourning, of acute grief, are said; and according to Germanic sequence of thought, inexorable here, the next and only topic is revenge. But is it possible? Hrothgar leads up to his appeal and promise with a skilful and often effective description of the horrors which surround the monster's home and await the attempt of an avenging foe.

march-stalkers mighty the moorland haunting,
wandering spirits: one of them seemed,
so far as my folk could fairly judge,
of womankind; and one, accursed,
in man's guise trod the misery-track
of exile, though huger than human bulk.
Grendel in days long gone they named him,
folk of the land; his father they knew not,
nor any brood that was born to him
of treacherous spirits. Untrod is their home;
by wolf-cliffs haunt they and windy headlands,
fenways fearful, where flows the stream
from mountains gliding to gloom of the rocks,
underground flood. Not far is it hence
in measure of miles that the mere expands,
and o'er it the frost-bound forest hanging,
sturdily rooted, shadows the wave.
By night is a wonder weird to see,
fire on the waters. So wise lived none
of the sons of men, to search those depths!
Nay, though the heath-rover, harried by dogs,
the horn-proud hart, this holt should seek,
long distance driven, his dear life first
on the brink he yields ere he brave the plunge
to hide his head: 'tis no happy place!
Thence the welter of waters washes up
wan to welkin when winds bestir
evil storms, and air grows dusk,
and the heavens weep. Now is help once more
with thee alone! The land thou knowst not,
place of fear, where thou findest out
that sin-flecked being. Seek if thou dare!
I will reward thee, for waging this fight,
with ancient treasure, as erst I did,
with winding gold, if thou winnest back."

### XXI

Beowulf spake, bairn of Ecgtheow:
" Sorrow not, sage! It beseems us better

friends to avenge than fruitlessly mourn them.
Each of us all must his end abide
in the ways of the world; so win who may
glory ere death! When his days are told,
that is the warrior's worthiest doom.
Rise, O realm-warder! Ride we anon,
and mark the trail of the mother of Grendel.
No harbor shall hide her—heed my promise!—
enfolding of field or forested mountain
or floor of the flood, let her flee where she will!
But thou this day endure in patience,
as I ween thou wilt, thy woes each one."
Leaped up the graybeard: God he thanked,
mighty Lord, for the man's brave words.
For Hrothgar soon a horse was saddled
wave-maned steed. The sovran wise
stately rode on; his shield-armed men
followed in force. The footprints led
along the woodland, widely seen,
a path o'er the plain, where she passed, and trod
the murky moor; of men-at-arms
she bore the bravest and best one, dead,
him who with Hrothgar the homestead ruled.

On then went the atheling-born
o'er stone-cliffs steep and strait defiles,
narrow passes and unknown ways,
headlands sheer, and the haunts of the Nicors.
Foremost he[1] fared, a few at his side
of the wiser men, the ways to scan,
till he found in a flash the forested hill
hanging over the hoary rock,
a woful wood: the waves below
were dyed in blood. The Danish men
had sorrow of soul, and for Scyldings all,
for many a hero, 'twas hard to bear,
ill for earls, when Æschere's head
they found by the flood on the foreland there.
Waves were welling, the warriors saw,
hot with blood; but the horn sang oft

[1] Hrothgar is probably meant.

battle-song bold.  The band sat down,
and watched on the water worm-like things,
sea-dragons strange that sounded the deep,
and nicors that lay on the ledge of the ness—
such as oft essay at hour of morn
on the road-of-sails their ruthless quest,—
and sea-snakes and monsters.  These started away,
swollen and savage that song to hear,
that war-horn's blast.  The warden of Geats,
with bolt from bow, then balked of life,
of wave-work, one monster; amid its heart
went the keen war-shaft; in water it seemed
less doughty in swimming whom death had seized.
Swift on the billows, with boar-spears well
hooked and barbed, it was hard beset,
done to death and dragged on the headland,
wave-roamer wondrous.  Warriors viewed
the grisly guest.

        Then girt him Beowulf
in martial mail, nor mourned for his life.
His breastplate broad and bright of hues,
woven by hand, should the waters try;
well could it ward the warrior's body
that battle should break on his breast in vain
nor harm his heart by the hand of a foe.
And the helmet white that his head protected
was destined to dare the deeps of the flood,
through wave-whirl win: 'twas wound with chains,
decked with gold, as in days of yore
the weapon-smith worked it wondrously,
with swine-forms set it, that swords nowise,
brandished in battle, could bite that helm.
Nor was that the meanest of mighty helps
which Hrothgar's orator offered at need:
"Hrunting" they named the hilted sword,
of old-time heirlooms easily first;
iron was its edge, all etched with poison,
with battle-blood hardened, nor blenched it at fight
in hero's hand who held it ever,
on paths of peril prepared to go

to folkstead² of foes.   Not first time this
it was destined to do a daring task.
For he bore not in mind, the bairn of Ecglaf
sturdy and strong, that speech he had made,
drunk with wine, now this weapon he lent
to a stouter swordsman.   Himself, though, durst not
under welter of waters wager his life
as loyal liegeman.   So lost he his glory,
honor of earls.   With the other not so,
who girded him now for the grim encounter.


### XXII

BEOWULF spake, bairn of Ecgtheow:—
" Have mind, thou honored offspring of Healfdene,
gold-friend of men, now I go on this quest,
sovran wise, what once was said:
if in thy cause it came that I
should lose my life, thou wouldst loyal bide
to me, though fallen, in father's place!
Be guardian, thou, to this group of my thanes,
my warrior-friends, if War should seize me;
and the goodly gifts thou gavest me,
Hrothgar beloved, to Hygelac send!
Geatland's king may ken by the gold,
Hrethel's son see, when he stares at the treasure,
that I got me a friend for goodness famed,
and joyed while I could in my jewel-bestower.
And let Unferth wield this wondrous sword,
earl far-honored, this heirloom precious,
hard of edge: with Hrunting I
seek doom of glory, or Death shall take me."

After these words the Weder-Geat lord
boldly hastened, biding never
answer at all: the ocean floods
closed o'er the hero. Long while of the day
fled ere he felt the floor of the sea.

² Meeting-place.

Soon found the fiend who the flood-domain
sword-hungry held these hundred winters,
greedy and grim, that some guest from above,
some man, was raiding her monster-realm.
She grasped out for him with grisly claws,
and the warrior seized; yet scathed she not
his body hale; the breastplate hindered,
as she strove to shatter the sark of war,
the linkéd harness, with loathsome hand.
Then bore this brine-wolf, when bottom she touched,
the lord of rings to the lair she haunted,
whiles vainly he strove, though his valor held,
weapon to wield against wondrous monsters
that sore beset him; sea-beasts many
tried with fierce tusks to tear his mail,
and swarmed on the stranger. But soon he marked
he was now in some hall, he knew not which,
where water never could work him harm,
nor through the roof could reach him ever
fangs of the flood. Firelight he saw,
beams of a blaze that brightly shone.
Then the warrior was ware of that wolf-of-the-deep,
mere-wife monstrous. For mighty stroke
he swung his blade, and the blow withheld not.
Then sang on her head that seemly blade
its war-song wild. But the warrior found
the light-of-battle[1] was loath to bite,
to harm the heart: its hard edge failed
the noble at need, yet had known of old
strife hand to hand, and had helmets cloven,
doomed men's fighting-gear. First time, this,
for the gleaming blade that its glory fell.

Firm still stood, nor failed in valor,
heedful of high deeds, Hygelac's kinsman;
flung away fretted sword, featly jewelled,
the angry earl; on earth it lay
steel-edged and stiff. His strength he trusted,
hand-gripe of might. So man shall do

---

[1] Kenning for "sword." Hrunting is bewitched, laid under a spell of
uselessness, along with all other swords.

whenever in war he weens to earn him
lasting fame, nor fears for his life!
Seized then by shoulder, shrank not from combat,
the Geatish war-prince Grendel's mother.
Flung then the fierce one, filled with wrath,
his deadly foe, that she fell to ground.
Swift on her part she paid him back
with grisly grasp, and grappled with him.
Spent with struggle, stumbled the warrior,
fiercest of fighting-men, fell adown.
On the hall-guest she hurled herself, hent her short
    sword,
broad and brown-edged,[2] the bairn to avenge,
the sole-born son.—On his shoulder lay
braided breast-mail, barring death,
withstanding entrance of edge or blade.
Life would have ended for Ecgtheow's son,
under wide earth for that earl of Geats,
had his armor of war not aided him,
battle-net hard, and holy God
wielded the victory, wisest Maker.
The Lord of Heaven allowed his cause;
and easily rose the earl erect.


### XXIII

'MID the battle-gear saw he a blade triumphant,
old-sword of Eotens, with edge of proof,
warriors' heirloom, weapon unmatched,
—save only 'twas more than other men
to bandy-of-battle could bear at all—
as the giants had wrought it, ready and keen.
Seized then its chain-hilt the Scyldings' chieftain,
bold and battle-grim, brandished the sword,
reckless of life, and so wrathfully smote
that it gripped her neck and grasped her hard,
her bone-rings breaking: the blade pierced through

---

[2] This brown of swords, evidently meaning burnished, bright, continues to
be a favorite adjective in the popular ballads.

that fated-one's flesh: to floor she sank.
Bloody the blade: he was blithe of his deed.
Then blazed forth light. 'Twas bright within
as when from the sky there shines unclouded
heaven's candle. The hall he scanned.
By the wall then went he; his weapon raised
high by its hilts the Hygelac-thane,
angry and eager. That edge was not useless
to the warrior now. He wished with speed
Grendel to guerdon for grim raids many,
for the war he waged on Western-Danes
oftener far than an only time,
when of Hrothgar's hearth-companions
he slew in slumber, in sleep devoured,
fifteen men of the folk of Danes,
and as many others outward bore,
his horrible prey. Well paid for that
the wrathful prince! For now prone he saw
Grendel stretched there, spent with war,
spoiled of life, so scathed had left him
Heorot's battle. The body sprang far
when after death it endured the blow,
sword-stroke savage, that severed its head.

Soon,[1] then, saw the sage companions
who waited with Hrothgar, watching the flood,
that the tossing waters turbid grew,
blood-stained the mere. Old men together,
hoary-haired, of the hero spake;
the warrior would not, they weened, again,
proud of conquest, come to seek
their mighty master. To many it seemed
the wolf-of-the-waves had won his life.
The ninth hour came. The noble Scyldings
left the headland; homeward went
the gold-friend of men.[2] But the guests sat on,
stared at the surges, sick in heart,
and wished, yet weened not, their winsome lord
again to see.

[1] After the killing of the monster and Grendel's decapitation.
[2] Hrothgar.

          Now that sword began,
from blood of the fight, in battle-droppings,[3]
war-blade, to wane: 'twas a wondrous thing
that all of it melted as ice is wont
when frosty fetters the Father loosens,
unwinds the wave-bonds, wielding all
seasons and times: the true God he!
  Nor took from that dwelling the duke of the Geats
precious things, though a plenty he saw,
save only the head and that hilt withal
blazoned with jewels: the blade had melted,
burned was the bright sword, her blood was so hot,
so poisoned the hell-sprite who perished within
    there.
Soon he was swimming who safe saw in combat
downfall of demons; up-dove through the flood.
The clashing waters were cleansèd now,
waste of waves, where the wandering fiend
her life-days left and this lapsing world.
Swam then to strand the sailors'-refuge,
sturdy-in-spirit, of sea-booty glad,
of burden brave he bore with him.
Went then to greet him, and God they thanked,
the thane-band choice of their chieftain blithe,
that safe and sound they could see him again.
Soon from the hardy one helmet and armor
deftly they doffed: now drowsed the mere,
water 'neath welkin, with war-blood stained.
  Forth they fared by the footpaths thence,
merry at heart the highways measured,
well-known roads. Courageous men
carried the head from the cliff by the sea,
an arduous task for all the band,
the firm in fight, since four were needed
on the shaft-of-slaughter[4] strenuously
to bear to the gold-hall Grendel's head.
So presently to the palace there
foemen fearless, fourteen Geats,
marching came. Their master-of-clan

---

[3] The blade slowly dissolves in blood-stained drops like icicles.    [4] Spear.

mighty amid them the meadow-ways trod.
Strode then within the sovran thane
fearless in fight, of fame renowned,
hardy hero, Hrothgar to greet.
And next by the hair into hall was borne
Grendel's head, where the henchmen were drinking,
an awe to clan and queen alike,
a monster of marvel: the men looked on.

## XXIV

BEOWULF spake, bairn of Ecgtheow:—
" Lo, now, this sea-booty, son of Healfdene,
Lord of Scyldings, we've lustily brought thee,
sign of glory; thou seest it here.
Not lightly did I with my life escape!
In war under water this work I essayed
with endless effort; and even so
my strength had been lost had the Lord not shielded
    me.
Not a whit could I with Hrunting do
in work of war, though the weapon is good;
yet a sword the Sovran of Men vouchsafed me
to spy on the wall there, in splendor hanging,
old, gigantic,—how oft He guides
the friendless wight!—and I fought with that brand,
felling in fight, since fate was with me,
the house's wardens.   That war-sword then
all burned, bright blade, when the blood gushed o'er it,
battle-sweat hot; but the hilt I brought back
from my foes.  So avenged I their fiendish deeds,
death-fall of Danes, as was due and right.
And this is my hest, that in Heorot now
safe thou canst sleep with thy soldier band,
and every thane of all thy folk
both old and young; no evil fear,
Scyldings' lord, from that side again,
aught ill for thy earls, as erst thou must ! "
Then the golden hilt, for that gray-haired leader,

hoary hero, in hand was laid,
giant-wrought, old.   So owned and enjoyed it
after downfall of devils, the Danish lord,
wonder-smiths' work, since the world was rid
of that grim-souled fiend, the foe of God,
murder-marked, and his mother as well.
Now it passed into power of the people's king,
best of all that the oceans bound
who have scattered their gold o'er Scandia's isle.
Hrothgar spake—the hilt he viewed,
heirloom old, where was etched the rise
of that far-off fight when the floods o'erwhelmed,
raging waves, the race of giants
(fearful their fate!), a folk estranged
from God Eternal: whence guerdon due
in that waste of waters the Wielder paid them.
So on the guard of shining gold
in runic staves it was rightly said
for whom the serpent-traced sword was wrought,
best of blades, in bygone days,
and the hilt well wound.—The wise-one spake,
son of Healfdene; silent were all:—
  "Lo, so may he say who sooth and right
follows 'mid folk, of far times mindful,
a land-warden old,[1] that this earl belongs
to the better breed!  So, borne aloft,
thy fame must fly, O friend my Beowulf,
far and wide o'er folksteads many.  Firmly thou
      shalt all maintain,
mighty strength with mood of wisdom.  Love of
      mine will I assure thee,
as, awhile ago, I promised; thou shalt prove a stay
      in future,
in far-off years, to folk of thine,
to the heroes a help.  Was not Heremod thus
to offspring of Ecgwela, Honor-Scyldings,
nor grew for their grace, but for grisly slaughter,
for doom of death to the Danishmen.

[1] That is, "whoever has as wide authority as I have and can remember
so far back so many instances of heroism, may well say, as I say, that no
better hero ever lived than Beowulf."

He slew, wrath-swollen, his shoulder-comrades,
companions at board! So he passed alone,
chieftain haughty, from human cheer.
Though him the Maker with might endowed,
delights of power, and uplifted high
above all men, yet blood-fierce his mind,
his breast-hoard, grew; no bracelets gave he
to Danes as was due; he endured all joyless
strain of struggle and stress of woe,
long feud with his folk. Here find thy lesson!
Of virtue advise thee! This verse I have said
    for thee,
wise from lapsed winters. Wondrous seems
how to sons of men Almighty God
in the strength of His spirit sendeth wisdom,
estate, high station: He swayeth all things.
Whiles He letteth right lustily fare
the heart of the hero of high-born race,—
in seat ancestral assigns him bliss,
his folk's sure fortress in fee to hold,
puts in his power great parts of the earth,
empire so ample, that end of it
this wanter-of-wisdom weeneth none.
So he waxes in wealth; nowise can harm him
illness or age; no evil cares
shadow his spirit; no sword-hate threatens
from ever an enemy: all the world
wends at his will; no worse he knoweth,
till all within him obstinate pride
waxes and wakes while the warden slumbers,
the spirit's sentry; sleep is too fast
which masters his might, and the murderer nears,
stealthily shooting the shafts from his bow!

XXV

"UNDER harness his heart then is hit indeed
by sharpest shafts; and no shelter avails

from foul behest of the hellish fiend.[1]
Him seems too little what long he possessed.
Greedy and grim, no golden rings
he gives for his pride; the promised future
forgets he and spurns, with all God has sent
    him,
Wonder-Wielder, of wealth and fame.
Yet in the end it ever comes
that the frame of the body fragile yields,
fatéd falls; and there follows another
who joyously the jewels divides,
the royal riches, nor recks of his forebear.
Ban, then, such baleful thoughts, Beowulf dearest,
best of men, and the better part choose,
profit eternal; and temper thy pride,
warrior famous! The flower of thy might
lasts now a while: but erelong it shall be
that sickness or sword thy strength shall minish,
or fang of fire, or flooding billow,
or bite of blade, or brandished spear,
or odious age; or the eyes' clear beam
wax dull and darken: Death even thee
in haste shall o'erwhelm, thou hero of war!
So the Ring-Danes these half-years a hundred I
    ruled,
wielded 'neath welkin, and warded them bravely
from mighty-ones many o'er middle-earth,
from spear and sword, till it seemed for me
no foe could be found under fold of the sky.
Lo, sudden the shift! To me seated secure
came grief for joy when Grendel began
to harry my home, the hellish foe;
for those ruthless raids, unresting I suffered
heart-sorrow heavy. Heaven be thanked,
Lord Eternal, for life extended
that I on this head all hewn and bloody,
after long evil, with eyes may gaze!
—Go to the bench now! Be glad at banquet,

---

[1] That is, he is now undefended by conscience from the temptations
(shafts) of the devil.

warrior worthy! A wealth of treasure
at dawn of day, be dealt between us!"
   Glad was the Geats' lord, going betimes
to seek his seat, as the Sage commanded.
Afresh, as before, for the famed-in-battle,
for the band of the hall, was a banquet dight
nobly anew. The Night-Helm darkened
dusk o'er the drinkers.
                        The doughty ones rose:
for the hoary-headed would hasten to rest,
agéd Scylding; and eager the Geat,
shield-fighter sturdy, for sleeping yearned.
Him wander-weary, warrior-guest
from far, a hall-thane heralded forth,
who by custom courtly cared for all
needs of a thane as in those old days
warrior-wanderers wont to have.
So slumbered the stout-heart. Stately the hall
rose gabled and gilt where the guest slept on
till a raven black the rapture-of-heaven[2]
blithe-heart boded. Bright came flying
shine after shadow. The swordsmen hastened,
athelings all were eager homeward
forth to fare; and far from thence
the great-hearted guest would guide his keel.
   Bade then the hardy-one Hrunting be brought
to the son of Ecglaf, the sword bade him take,
excellent iron, and uttered his thanks for it,
quoth that he counted it keen in battle,
"war-friend" winsome: with words he slandered not
edge of the blade: 'twas a big-hearted man!
Now eager for parting and armed at point
warriors waited, while went to his host
that Darling of Danes. The doughty atheling
to high-seat hastened and Hrothgar greeted.

---

[2] Kenning for the sun.—This is a strange rôle for the raven. He is the warrior's bird of battle, exults in slaughter and carnage; his joy here is a compliment to the sunrise.

## XXVI

BEOWULF spake, bairn of Ecgtheow:—
"Lo, we seafarers say our will,
far-come men, that we fain would seek
Hygelac now. We here have found
hosts to our heart: thou hast harbored us well.
If ever on earth I am able to win me
more of thy love, O lord of men,
aught anew, than I now have done,
for work of war I am willing still!
If it come to me ever across the seas
that neighbor foemen annoy and fright thee,—
as they that hate thee erewhile have used,—
thousands then of thanes I shall bring,
heroes to help thee. Of Hygelac I know,
ward of his folk, that, though few his years,
the lord of the Geats will give me aid
by word and by work, that well I may serve thee,
wielding the war-wood to win thy triumph
and lending thee might when thou lackest men.
If thy Hrethric should come to court of Geats,
a sovran's son, he will surely there
find his friends. A far-off land
each man should visit who vaunts him brave."
  Him then answering, Hrothgar spake:—
"These words of thine the wisest God
sent to thy soul! No sager counsel
from so young in years e'er yet have I heard.
Thou art strong of main and in mind art wary,
art wise in words! I ween indeed
if ever it hap that Hrethel's heir
by spear be seized, by sword-grim battle,
by illness or iron, thine elder and lord,
people's leader,—and life be thine,—
no seemlier man will the Sea-Geats find
at all to choose for their chief and king,
for hoard-guard of heroes, if hold thou wilt
thy kinsman's kingdom! Thy keen mind pleases me
the longer the better, Beowulf loved!

Thou hast brought it about that both our peoples,
sons of the Geat and Spear-Dane folk,
shall have mutual peace, and from murderous strife,
such as once they waged, from war refrain.
Long as I rule this realm so wide,
let our hoards be common, let heroes with gold
each other greet o'er the gannet's-bath,
and the ringed-prow bear o'er rolling waves
tokens of love. I trow my landfolk
towards friend and foe are firmly joined,
and honor they keep in the olden way."

To him in the hall, then, Healfdene's son
gave treasures twelve, and the trust-of-earls
bade him fare with the gifts to his folk beloved,
hale to his home, and in haste return.
Then kissed the king of kin renowned,
Scyldings' chieftain, that choicest thane,
and fell on his neck. Fast flowed the tears
of the hoary-headed. Heavy with winters,
he had chances twain, but he clung to this,[1]—
that each should look on the other again,
and hear him in hall. Was this hero so dear to him,
his breast's wild billows he banned in vain;
safe in his soul a secret longing,
locked in his mind, for that lovéd man
burned in his blood. Then Beowulf strode,
glad of his gold-gifts, the grass-plot o'er,
warrior blithe. The wave-roamer bode
riding at anchor, its owner awaiting.
As they hastened onward, Hrothgar's gift
they lauded at length.—'Twas a lord unpeered,
every way blameless, till age had broken
—it spareth no mortal—his splendid might.

### XXVII

CAME now to ocean the ever-courageous
hardy henchmen, their harness bearing,

[1] That is, he might or might not see Beowulf again. Old as he was, the
latter chance was likely; but he clung to the former, hoping to see his
young friend again " and exchange brave words in the hall."

woven war-sarks. The warden marked,
trusty as ever, the earl's return.
From the height of the hill no hostile words
reached the guests as he rode to greet them;
but " Welcome ! " he called to that Weder clan
as the sheen-mailed spoilers to ship marched on.
Then on the strand, with steeds and treasure
and armor their roomy and ring-dight ship
was heavily laden: high its mast
rose over Hrothgar's hoarded gems.
A sword to the boat-guard Beowulf gave,
mounted with gold; on the mead-bench since
he was better esteemed, that blade possessing,
heirloom old.—Their ocean-keel boarding,
they drove through the deep, and Daneland left.
A sea-cloth was set, a sail with ropes,
firm to the mast; the flood-timbers moaned;[1]
nor did wind over billows that wave-swimmer blow
across from her course. The craft sped on,
foam-necked it floated forth o'er the waves,
keel firm-bound over briny currents,
till they got them sight of the Geatish cliffs,
home-known headlands. High the boat,
stirred by winds, on the strand updrove.
Helpful at haven the harbor-guard stood,
who long already for loved companions
by the water had waited and watched afar.
He bound to the beach the broad-bosomed ship
with anchor-bands, lest ocean-billows
that trusty timber should tear away.
Then Beowulf bade them bear the treasure,
gold and jewels; no journey far
was it thence to go to the giver of rings,
Hygelac Hrethling: at home he dwelt
by the sea-wall close, himself and clan.
Haughty that house, a hero the king,
high the hall, and Hygd[2] right young,
wise and wary, though winters few

[1] With the speed of the boat.
[2] Queen to Hygelac. She is praised by contrast with the antitype, Thryth,
just as Beowulf was praised by contrast with Heremod.

in those fortress walls she had found a home,
Hæreth's daughter.  Nor humble her ways,
nor grudged she gifts to the Geatish men,
of precious treasure.  Not Thryth's pride showed she,
folk-queen famed, or that fell deceit.
Was none so daring that durst make bold
(save her lord alone) of the liegemen dear
that lady full in the face to look,
but forgéd fetters he found his lot,
bonds of death!  And brief the respite;
soon as they seized him, his sword-doom was spoken,
and the burnished blade a baleful murder
proclaimed and closed.  No queenly way
for woman to practise, though peerless she,
that the weaver-of-peace[8] from warrior dear
by wrath and lying his life should reave!
But Hemming's kinsman hindered this.—

For over their ale men also told
that of these folk-horrors fewer she wrought,
onslaughts of evil, after she went,
gold-decked bride, to the brave young prince,
atheling haughty, and Offa's hall
o'er the fallow flood at her father's bidding
safely sought, where since she prospered,
royal, thronéd, rich in goods,
fain of the fair life fate had sent her,
and leal in love to the lord of warriors.
He, of all heroes I heard of ever
from sea to sea, of the sons of earth,
most excellent seemed.  Hence Offa was praised
for his fighting and feeing by far-off men,
the spear-bold warrior; wisely he ruled
over his empire.  Eomer woke to him,
help of heroes, Hemming's kinsman,
grandson of Garmund, grim in war.

[8] Kenning for " wife."

## XXVIII

Hastened the hardy one, henchmen with him,
sandy strand of the sea to tread
and widespread ways. The world's great candle,
sun shone from south. They strode along
with sturdy steps to the spot they knew.
where the battle-king young, his burg within,
slayer of Ongentheow, shared the rings,
shelter-of-heroes. To Hygelac
Beowulf's coming was quickly told,—
that there in the court the clansmen's refuge,
the shield-companion sound and alive,
hale from the hero-play homeward strode.
With haste in the hall, by highest order,
room for the rovers was readily made.
By his sovran he sat, come safe from battle,
kinsman by kinsman. His kindly lord
he first had greeted in gracious form,
with manly words. The mead dispensing,
came through the high hall Hæreth's daughter,
winsome to warriors, wine-cup bore
to the hands of the heroes. Hygelac then
his comrade fairly with question plied
in the lofty hall, sore longing to know
what manner of sojourn the Sea-Geats made.
"What came of thy quest, my kinsman Beowulf,
when thy yearnings suddenly swept thee yonder
battle to seek o'er the briny sea,
combat in Heorot? Hrothgar couldst thou
aid at all, the honored chief,
in his wide-known woes? With waves of care
my sad heart seethed; I sore mistrusted
my loved one's venture: long I begged thee
by no means to seek that slaughtering monster,
but suffer the South-Danes to settle their feud
themselves with Grendel. Now God be thanked
that safe and sound I can see thee now!"
    Beowulf spake, the bairn of Ecgtheow:—
"'Tis known and unhidden, Hygelac Lord,

to many men, that meeting of ours,
struggle grim between Grendel and me,
which we fought on the field where full too many
sorrows he wrought for the Scylding-Victors,
evils unending. These all I avenged.
No boast can be from breed of Grendel,
any on earth, for that uproar at dawn,
from the longest-lived of the loathsome race
in fleshly fold!—But first I went
Hrothgar to greet in the hall of gifts,
where Healfdene's kinsman high-renowned,
soon as my purpose was plain to him,
assigned me a seat by his son and heir.
The liegemen were lusty; my life-days never
such merry men over mead in hall
have I heard under heaven! The high-born queen,
people's peace-bringer, passed through the hall
cheered the young clansmen, clasps of gold
ere she sought her seat, to sundry gave.
Oft to the heroes Hrothgar's daughter,
to earls in turn, the ale-cup tendered,—
she whom I heard these hall-companions
Freawaru name, when fretted gold
she proffered the warriors. Promised is she,
gold-decked maid, to the glad son of Froda.
Sage this seems to the Scylding's-friend,
kingdom's-keeper: he counts it wise
the woman to wed so and ward off feud,
store of slaughter. But seldom ever
when men are slain, does the murder-spear sink
but briefest while, though the bride be fair![1]

  "Nor haply will like it the Heathobard lord,
and as little each of his liegemen all,

---

[1] Beowulf gives his uncle the king not mere gossip of his journey, but a statesmanlike forecast of the outcome of certain policies at the Danish court. Talk of interpolation here is absurd. As both Beowulf and Hygelac know,—and the folk for whom the *Beowulf* was put together also knew,—Froda was king of the Heathobards (probably the Langobards, once near neighbors of Angle and Saxon tribes on the continent), and had fallen in fight with the Danes. Hrothgar will set aside this feud by giving his daughter as " peace-weaver " and wife to the young king Ingeld, son of the slain Froda. But Beowulf, on general principles and from his observation of the particular case, foretells trouble.

when a thane of the Danes, in that doughty
throng,
goes with the lady along their hall,
and on him the old-time heirlooms glisten
hard and ring-decked, Heathobard's treasure,
weapons that once they wielded fair
until they lost at the linden-play [2]
liegeman leal and their lives as well.
Then, over the ale, on this heirloom gazing,
some ash-wielder old who has all in mind
that spear-death of men,[3]—he is stern of mood,
heavy at heart,—in the hero young
tests the temper and tries the soul
and war-hate wakens, with words like these:—
*Canst thou not, comrade, ken that sword*
*which to the fray thy father carried*
*in his final feud, 'neath the fighting-mask,*
*dearest of blades, when the Danish slew him*
*and wielded the war-place on Withergild's fall,*
*after havoc of heroes, those hardy Scyldings?*
*Now, the son of a certain slaughtering Dane,*
*proud of his treasure, paces this hall,*
*joys in the killing, and carries the jewel[4]*
*that rightfully ought to be owned by thee!*
Thus he urges and eggs him all the time
with keenest words, till occasion offers
that Freawaru's thane, for his father's deed,
after bite of brand in his blood must slumber,
losing his life; but that liegeman flies
living away, for the land he kens.
And thus be broken on both their sides
oaths of the earls, when Ingeld's breast
wells with war-hate, and wife-love now
after the care-billows cooler grows.

[2] Play of shields, battle. A Danish warrior cuts down Froda in the fight,
and takes his sword and armor, leaving them to a son. This son is selected
to accompany his mistress, the young princess Freawaru, to her new home
when she is Ingeld's queen. Heedlessly he wears the sword of Froda in
hall. An old warrior points it out to Ingeld, and eggs him on to vengeance.
At his instigation the Dane is killed; but the murderer, afraid of results,
and knowing the land, escapes. So the old feud must break out again.
[3] That is, their disastrous battle and the slaying of their king.
[4] The sword.

"So[5] I hold not high the Heathobards' faith
due to the Danes, or their during love
and pact of peace.—But I pass from that,
turning to Grendel, O giver-of-treasure,
and saying in full how the fight resulted,
hand-fray of heroes.  When heaven's jewel
had fled o'er far fields, that fierce sprite came,
night-foe savage, to seek us out
where safe and sound we sentried the hall.
To Hondscio then was that harassing deadly,
his fall there was fated.  He first was slain,
girded warrior.  Grendel on him
turned murderous mouth, on our mighty kinsmen,
and all of the brave man's body devoured.
Yet none the earlier, empty-handed,
would the bloody-toothed murderer, mindful of bale,
outward go from the gold-decked hall:
but me he attacked in his terror of might,
with greedy hand grasped me.  A glove hung by him[6]
wide and wondrous, wound with bands;
and in artful wise it all was wrought,
by devilish craft, of dragon-skins.
Me therein, an innocent man,
the fiendish foe was fain to thrust
with many another.  He might not so,
when I all angrily upright stood.
'Twere long to relate how that land-destroyer
I paid in kind for his cruel deeds;
yet there, my prince, this people of thine
got fame by my fighting.  He fled away,
and a little space his life preserved;
but there staid behind him his stronger hand
left in Heorot; heartsick thence
on the floor of the ocean that outcast fell.
Me for this struggle the Scyldings'-friend
paid in plenty with plates of gold,
with many a treasure, when morn had come

[5] Beowulf returns to his forecast.  Things might well go somewhat as follows, he says; sketches a little tragic story; and with this prophecy by illustration returns to the tale of his adventure.
[6] Not an actual glove, but a sort of bag.

and we all at the banquet-board sat down.
Then was song and glee. The gray-haired Scylding,
much tested, told of the times of yore.
Whiles the hero his harp bestirred,
wood-of-delight; now lays he chanted
of sooth and sadness, or said aright
legends of wonder, the wide-hearted king;
or for years of his youth he would yearn at times,
for strength of old struggles, now stricken with age,
hoary hero: his heart surged full
when, wise with winters, he wailed their flight.
Thus in the hall the whole of that day
at ease we feasted, till fell o'er earth
another night. Anon full ready
in greed of vengeance, Grendel's mother
set forth all doleful. Dead was her son
through war-hate of Weders; now, woman monstrous,
with fury fell a foeman she slew,
avenged her offspring. From Æschere old,
loyal councillor, life was gone;
nor might they e'en, when morning broke,
those Danish people, their death-done comrade
burn with brands, on balefire lay
the man they mourned. Under mountain stream
she had carried the corpse with cruel hands.
For Hrothgar that was the heaviest sorrow
of all that had laden the lord of his folk.
The leader then, by thy life, besought me
(sad was his soul) in the sea-waves' coil
to play the hero and hazard my being
for glory of prowess: my guerdon he pledged.
I then in the waters—'tis widely known—
that sea-floor-guardian savage found.
Hand-to-hand there a while we struggled;
billows welled blood; in the briny hall
her head I hewed with a hardy blade
from Grendel's mother,—and gained my life,
though not without danger. My doom was not yet.
Then the haven-of-heroes, Healfdene's son,
gave me in guerdon great gifts of price.

### XXXI

" So held this king to the customs old,
that I wanted for nought in the wage I gained,
the meed of my might; he made me gifts,
Healfdene's heir, for my own disposal.
Now to thee, my prince, I proffer them all,
gladly give them.  Thy grace alone
can find me favor.  Few indeed
have I of kinsmen, save, Hygelac, thee ! "
Then he bade them bear him the boar-head
    standard,
the battle-helm high, and breastplate gray,
the splendid sword; then spake in form:—
" Me this war-gear the wise old prince,
Hrothgar, gave, and his hest he added,
that its story be straightway said to thee.—
A while it was held by Heorogar king,
for long time lord of the land of Scyldings;
yet not to his son the sovran left it,
to daring Heoroweard,—dear as he was to him,
his harness of battle.—Well hold thou it all ! "
    And I heard that soon passed o'er the path of
        this treasure,
all apple-fallow, four good steeds,
each like the others; arms and horses
he gave to the king.  So should kinsmen be,
not weave one another the net of wiles,
or with deep-hid treachery death contrive
for neighbor and comrade.  His nephew was ever
by hardy Hygelac held full dear,
and each kept watch o'er the other's weal.
I heard, too, the necklace to Hygd he presented,
wonder-wrought treasure, which Wealhtheow gave
    him,
sovran's daughter: three steeds he added,
slender and saddle-gay.  Since such gift
the gem gleamed bright on the breast of the queen.
    Thus showed his strain the son of Ecgtheow
as a man remarked for mighty deeds

and acts of honor. At ale he slew not
comrade or kin; nor cruel his mood,
though of sons of earth his strength was greatest,
a glorious gift that God had sent
the splendid leader. Long was he spurned,
and worthless by Geatish warriors held;
him at mead the master-of-clans
failed full oft to favor at all.
Slack and shiftless the strong men deemed him,
profitless prince; but payment came,
to the warrior honored, for all his woes.—

Then the bulwark-of-earls[1] bade bring within,
hardy chieftain, Hrethel's heirloom
garnished with gold: no Geat e'er knew
in shape of a sword a statelier prize.
The brand he laid in Beowulf's lap;
and of hides assigned him seven thousand,[2]
with house and high-seat. They held in common
land alike by their line of birth,
inheritance, home: but higher the king
because of his rule o'er the realm itself.

Now further it fell with the flight of years,
with harryings horrid, that Hygelac perished,[3]
and Heardred, too, by hewing of swords
under the shield-wall slaughtered lay,
when him at the van of his victor-folk
sought hardy heroes, Heatho-Scilfings,
in arms o'erwhelming Hereric's nephew.
Then Beowulf came as king this broad
realm to wield; and he ruled it well
fifty winters,[4] a wise old prince,
warding his land, until One began

[1] Hygelac.
[2] This is generally assumed to mean hides, though the text simply says
"seven thousand." A hide in England meant about 120 acres, though "the
size of the acre varied."
[3] On the historical raid into Frankish territory between 512 and 520 A. D.
The subsequent course of events, as gathered from hints of this epic, is
partly told in Scandinavian legend.
[4] The chronology of the epic, as scholars have worked it out, would make
Beowulf well over ninety years of age when he fights the dragon. But the
fifty years of his reign need not be taken as historical fact.

in the dark of night, a Dragon, to rage.
In the grave on the hill a hoard it guarded,
in the stone-barrow steep. A strait path reached it,
unknown to mortals. Some man, however,
came by chance that cave within
to the heathen hoard.[5] In hand he took
a golden goblet, nor gave he it back,
stole with it away, while the watcher slept,
by thievish wiles: for the warden's wrath
prince and people must pay betimes!


### XXXII

THAT way he went with no will of his own,
in danger of life, to the dragon's hoard,
but for pressure of peril, some prince's thane.
He fled in fear the fatal scourge,
seeking shelter, a sinful man,
and entered in. At the awful sight
tottered that guest, and terror seized him;
yet the wretched fugitive rallied anon
from fright and fear ere he fled away,
and took the cup from that treasure-hoard.
Of such besides there was store enough,
heirlooms old, the earth below,
which some earl forgotten, in ancient years,
left the last of his lofty race,
heedfully there had hidden away,
dearest treasure. For death of yore
had hurried all hence; and he alone
left to live, the last of the clan,
weeping his friends, yet wished to bide
warding the treasure, his one delight,

---

[5] The text is here hopelessly illegible, and only the general drift of the meaning can be rescued. For one thing, we have the old myth of a dragon who guards hidden treasure. But with this runs the story of some noble, last of his race, who hides all his wealth within this barrow and there chants his farewell to life's glories. After his death the dragon takes possession of the hoard and watches over it. A condemned or banished man, desperate, hides in the barrow, discovers the treasure, and while the dragon sleeps, makes off with a golden beaker or the like, and carries it for propitiation to his master. The dragon discovers the loss and exacts fearful penalty from the people round about.

though brief his respite. The barrow, new-ready,
to strand and sea-waves stood anear,
hard by the headland, hidden and closed;
there laid within it his lordly heirlooms
and heapéd hoard of heavy gold
that warden of rings. Few words he spake:
" Now hold thou, earth, since heroes may not,
what earls have owned! Lo, erst from thee
brave men brought it! But battle-death seized
and cruel killing my clansmen all,
robbed them of life and a liegeman's joys.
None have I left to lift the sword,
or to cleanse the carven cup of price,
beaker bright. My brave are gone.
And the helmet hard, all haughty with gold,
shall part from its plating. Polishers sleep
who could brighten and burnish the battle-mask;
and those weeds of war that were wont to brave
over bicker of shields the bite of steel
rust with their bearer. The ringéd mail
fares not far with famous chieftain,
at side of hero! No harp's delight,
no glee-wood's gladness! No good hawk now
flies through the hall! Nor horses fleet
stamp in the burgstead! Battle and death
the flower of my race have reft away."
Mournful of mood, thus he moaned his woe,
alone, for them all, and unblithe wept
by day and by night, till death's fell wave
o'erwhelmed his heart. His hoard-of-bliss
that old ill-doer open found,
who, blazing at twilight the barrows haunteth,
naked foe-dragon flying by night
folded in fire: the folk of earth
dread him sore. 'Tis his doom to seek
hoard in the graves, and heathen gold
to watch, many-wintered: nor wins he thereby!
  Powerful this plague-of-the-people thus
held the house of the hoard in earth
three hundred winters; till One aroused

wrath in his breast, to the ruler bearing
that costly cup, and the king implored
for bond of peace. So the barrow was plundered,
borne off was booty. His boon was granted
that wretched man; and his ruler saw
first time what was fashioned in far-off days.

When the dragon awoke, new woe was kindled.
O'er the stone he snuffed. The stark-heart found
footprint of foe who so far had gone
in his hidden craft by the creature's head.—
So may the undoomed easily flee
evils and exile, if only he gain
the grace of The Wielder!—That warden of gold
o'er the ground went seeking, greedy to find
the man who wrought him such wrong in sleep.
Savage and burning, the barrow he circled
all without; nor was any there,
none in the waste. . . . Yet war he desired,
was eager for battle. The barrow he entered,
sought the cup, and discovered soon
that some one of mortals had searched his treasure,
his lordly gold. The guardian waited
ill-enduring till evening came;
boiling with wrath was the barrow's keeper,
and fain with flame the foe to pay
for the dear cup's loss.—Now day was fled
as the worm had wished. By its wall no more
was it glad to bide, but burning flew
folded in flame: a fearful beginning
for sons of the soil; and soon it came,
in the doom of their lord, to a dreadful end.

### XXXIII

THEN the baleful fiend its fire belched out,
and bright homes burned. The blaze stood high
all landsfolk frighting. No living thing
would that loathly one leave as aloft it flew.
Wide was the dragon's warring seen,

its fiendish fury far and near,
as the grim destroyer those Geatish people
hated and hounded. To hidden lair,
to its hoard it hastened at hint of dawn.
Folk of the land it had lapped in flame,
with bale and brand. In its barrow it trusted,
its battling and bulwarks: that boast was vain!

To Beowulf then the bale was told
quickly and truly: the king's own home,
of buildings the best, in brand-waves melted,
that gift-throne of Geats. To the good old man
sad in heart, 'twas heaviest sorrow.
The sage assumed that his sovran God
he had angered, breaking ancient law,
and embittered the Lord. His breast within
with black thoughts welled, as his wont was never.
The folk's own fastness that fiery dragon
with flame had destroyed, and the stronghold all
washed by waves; but the warlike king,
prince of the Weders, plotted vengeance.
Warriors'-bulwark, he bade them work
all of iron—the earl's commander—
a war-shield wondrous: well he knew
that forest-wood against fire were worthless,
linden could aid not.—Atheling brave,
he was fated to finish this fleeting life,[1]
his days on earth, and the dragon with him,
though long it had watched o'er the wealth of the
    hoard!—
Shame he reckoned it, sharer-of-rings,
to follow the flyer-afar with a host,
a broad-flung band; nor the battle feared he,
nor deemed he dreadful the dragon's warring,
its vigor and valor: ventures desperate
he had passed a-plenty, and perils of war,
contest-crash, since, conqueror proud,
Hrothgar's hall he had wholly purged,
and in grapple had killed the kin of Grendel,

---

[1] Literally "loan-days," days loaned to man.

loathsome breed! Not least was that
of hand-to-hand fights where Hygelac fell,
when the ruler of Geats in rush of battle,
lord of his folk, in the Frisian land,
son of Hrethel, by sword-draughts died,
by brands down-beaten. Thence Beowulf fled
through strength of himself and his swimming power,
though alone, and his arms were laden with thirty
coats of mail, when he came to the sea!
Nor yet might Hetwaras[2] haughtily boast
their craft of contest, who carried against him
shields to the fight: but few escaped
from strife with the hero to seek their homes!
Then swam over ocean Ecgtheow's son
lonely and sorrowful, seeking his land,
where Hygd made him offer of hoard and realm,
rings and royal-seat, reckoning naught
the strength of her son to save their kingdom
from hostile hordes, after Hygelac's death.
No sooner for this could the stricken ones
in any wise move that atheling's mind
over young Heardred's head as lord
and ruler of all the realm to be:
yet the hero upheld him with helpful words,
aided in honor, till, older grown,
he wielded the Weder-Geats.—Wandering exiles
sought him o'er seas, the sons of Ohtere,
who had spurned the sway of the Scylfings'-helmet,
the bravest and best that broke the rings,
in Swedish land, of the sea-kings' line,
haughty hero.[3] Hence Heardred's end.
For shelter he gave them, sword-death came,
the blade's fell blow, to bairn of Hygelac;
but the son of Ongentheow sought again
house and home when Heardred fell,
leaving Beowulf lord of Geats
and gift-seat's master.—A good king he!

[2] Chattuarii, a tribe that dwelt along the Rhine, and took part in repelling the raid of (Hygelac) Chocilaicus.

[3] Onela, son of Ongentheow, who pursues his two nephews Eanmund and Eadgils to Heardred's court, where they have taken refuge after their unsuccessful rebellion. In the fighting Heardred is killed.

## XXXIV

The fall of his lord he was fain to requite
in after days; and to Eadgils he proved
friend to the friendless, and forces sent
over the sea to the son of Ohtere,
weapons and warriors: well repaid he
those care-paths cold when the king he slew.[1]
Thus safe through struggles the son of Ecgtheow
had passed a plenty, through perils dire,
with daring deeds, till this day was come
that doomed him now with the dragon to strive.

With comrades eleven the lord of Geats
swollen in rage went seeking the dragon.
He had heard whence all the harm arose
and the killing of clansmen; that cup of price
on the lap of the lord had been laid by the finder.
In the throng was this one thirteenth man,
starter of all the strife and ill,
care-laden captive; cringing thence
forced and reluctant, he led them on
till he came in ken of that cavern-hall,
the barrow delved near billowy surges,
flood of ocean. Within 'twas full
of wire-gold and jewels; a jealous warden,
warrior trusty, the treasures held,
lurked in his lair. Not light the task
of entrance for any of earth-born men!

Sat on the headland the hero king,
spake words of hail to his hearth-companions,
gold-friend of Geats. All gloomy his soul,
wavering, death-bound. Wyrd full nigh
stood ready to greet the gray-haired man,
to seize his soul-hoard, sunder apart
life and body. Not long would be
the warrior's spirit enwound with flesh.

Beowulf spake, the bairn of Ecgtheow :—
"Through store of struggles I strove in youth,

[1] That is, Beowulf supports Eadgils against Onela, who is slain by Eadgils
in revenge for the " care-paths " of exile into which Onela forced him.

mighty feuds; I mind them all.
I was seven years old when the sovran of rings,
friend-of-his-folk, from my father took me,
had me, and held me, Hrethel the king,
with food and fee, faithful in kinship.
Ne'er, while I lived there, he loathlier found me,
bairn in the burg, than his birthright sons,
Herebeald and Hæthcyn and Hygelac mine.
For the eldest of these, by unmeet chance,
by kinsman's deed, was the death-bed strewn,
when Hæthcyn killed him with horny bow,
his own dear liege laid low with an arrow,
missed the mark and his mate shot down,
one brother the other, with bloody shaft.
A feeless fight[2] and a fearful sin,
horror to Hrethel; yet, hard as it was,
unavenged must the atheling die!
Too awful it is for an agéd man
to bide and bear, that his bairn so young
rides on the gallows. A rime he makes,
sorrow-song for his son there hanging
as rapture of ravens; no rescue now
can come from the old, disabled man!
Still is he minded, as morning breaks,
of the heir gone elsewhere;[3] another he hopes not
he will bide to see his burg within
as ward for his wealth, now the one has found
doom of death that the deed incurred.
Forlorn he looks on the lodge of his son,
wine-hall waste and wind-swept chambers
reft of revel. The rider sleepeth,
the hero, far-hidden;[4] no harp resounds,
in the courts no wassail, as once was heard.

---

[2] That is, the king could claim no wergild, or man-price, from one son for the killing of the other.
[3] Usual euphemism for death.     [4] Sc. in the grave.

## XXXV

" THEN he goes to his chamber, a grief-song chants
alone for his lost.  Too large all seems,
homestead and house.  So the helmet-of-Weders
hid in his heart for Herebeald
waves of woe. No way could he take
to avenge on the slayer slaughter so foul;
nor e'en could he harass that hero at all
with loathing deed, though he loved him not.
And so for the sorrow his soul endured,
men's gladness he gave up and God's light chose.
Lands and cities he left his sons
(as the wealthy do) when he went from earth.
There was strife and struggle 'twixt Swede and Geat
o'er the width of waters; war arose,
hard battle-horror, when Hrethel died,
and Ongentheow's offspring grew
strife-keen, bold, nor brooked o'er the seas
pact of peace, but pushed their hosts
to harass in hatred by Hreosnabeorh.
Men of my folk for that feud had vengeance,
for woful war ('tis widely known),
though one of them bought it with blood of his heart,
a bargain hard: for Hæthcyn proved
fatal that fray, for the first-of-Geats.
At morn, I heard, was the murderer killed
by kinsman for kinsman,[1] with clash of sword,
when Ongentheow met Eofor there.
Wide split the war-helm: wan he fell,
hoary Scylfing; the hand that smote him
of feud was mindful, nor flinched from the death-blow.

—" For all that he[2] gave me, my gleaming sword
repaid him at war,—such power I wielded,—
for lordly treasure: with land he entrusted me,
homestead and house.  He had no need

---

[1] Eofor for Wulf.—The immediate provocation for Eofor in killing " the
hoary Scylfing," Ongentheow, is that the latter has just struck Wulf down;
but the king, Hæthcyn, is also avenged by the blow.  See the detailed description below.
[2] Hygelac.

from Swedish realm, or from Spear-Dane folk,
or from men of the Gifths, to get him help,—
some warrior worse for wage to buy!
Ever I fought in the front of all,
sole to the fore; and so shall I fight
while I bide in life and this blade shall last
that early and late hath loyal proved
since for my doughtiness Dæghrefn fell,
slain by my hand, the Hugas' champion.
Nor fared he thence to the Frisian king
with the booty back, and breast-adornments;
but, slain in struggle, that standard-bearer
fell, atheling brave. Not with blade was he slain,
but his bones were broken by brawny gripe,
his heart-waves stilled.—The sword-edge now,
hard blade and my hand, for the hoard shall strive."

Beowulf spake, and a battle-vow made,
his last of all: "I have lived through many
wars in my youth; now once again,
old folk-defender, feud will I seek,
do doughty deeds, if the dark destroyer
forth from his cavern come to fight me!"
Then hailed he the helmeted heroes all,
for the last time greeting his liegemen dear,
comrades of war: "I should carry no weapon,
no sword to the serpent, if sure I knew
how, with such enemy, else my vows
I could gain as I did in Grendel's day.
But fire in this fight I must fear me now,
and poisonous breath; so I bring with me
breastplate and board.[3] From the barrow's keeper
no footbreadth flee I. One fight shall end
our war by the wall, as Wyrd allots,
all mankind's master. My mood is bold
but forbears to boast o'er this battling-flyer.
—Now abide by the barrow, ye breastplate-mailed,
ye heroes in harness, which of us twain
better from battle-rush bear his wounds.
Wait ye the finish. The fight is not yours,

[3] Shield.

nor meet for any but me alone
to measure might with this monster here
and play the hero.   Hardily I
shall win that wealth, or war shall seize,
cruel killing, your king and lord!"
    Up stood then with shield the sturdy champion,
stayed by the strength of his single manhood,
and hardy 'neath helmet his harness bore
under cleft of the cliffs: no coward's path!
Soon spied by the wall that warrior chief,
survivor of many a victory-field
where foemen fought with furious clashings,
an arch of stone; and within, a stream
that broke from the barrow.   The brooklet's wave
was hot with fire.   The hoard that way
he never could hope unharmed to near,
or endure those deeps,[4] for the dragon's flame.
Then let from his breast, for he burst with rage,
the Weder-Geat prince a word outgo;
stormed the stark-heart; stern went ringing
and clear his cry 'neath the cliff-rocks gray.
The hoard-guard heard a human voice;
his rage was enkindled.   No respite now
for pact of peace!   The poison-breath
of that foul worm first came forth from the cave,
hot reek-of-fight: the rocks resounded.
Stout by the stone-way his shield he raised,
lord of the Geats, against the loathed-one;
while with courage keen that coiléd foe
came seeking strife.   The sturdy king
had drawn his sword, not dull of edge,
heirloom old; and each of the two
felt fear of his foe, though fierce their mood.
Stoutly stood with his shield high-raised
the warrior king, as the worm now coiled
together amain: the mailed-one waited.
Now, spire by spire, fast sped and glided
that blazing serpent.   The shield protected,
soul and body a shorter while

[4] The hollow passage.

for the hero-king than his heart desired,
could his will have wielded the welcome respite
but once in his life! But Wyrd denied it,
and victory's honors.—His arm he lifted,
lord of the Geats, the grim foe smote
with atheling's heirloom. Its edge was turned,
brown blade, on the bone, and bit more feebly
than its noble master had need of then
in his baleful stress.—Then the barrow's keeper
waxed full wild for that weighty blow,
cast deadly flames; wide drove and far
those vicious fires. No victor's glory
the Geats' lord boasted; his brand had failed,
naked in battle, as never it should,
excellent iron!—'Twas no easy path
that Ecgtheow's honored heir must tread
over the plain to the place of the foe;
for against his will he must win a home
elsewhere far, as must all men, leaving
this lapsing life!—Not long it was
ere those champions grimly closed again.
The hoard-guard was heartened; high heaved his
        breast
once more; and by peril was pressed again,
enfolded in flames, the folk-commander!
Nor yet about him his band of comrades,
sons of athelings, arméd stood
with warlike front: to the woods they bent them,
their lives to save. But the soul of one
with care was cumbered. Kinship true
can never be marred in a noble mind!

## XXXVI

WIGLAF his name was, Weohstan's son,
linden-thane loved, the lord of Scylfings,
Ælfhere's kinsman. His king he now saw
with heat under helmet hard oppressed.
He minded the prizes his prince had given him,

wealthy seat of the Wægmunding line,
and folk-rights that his father owned.
Not long he lingered. The linden yellow,
his shield, he seized; the old sword he drew:—
as heirloom of Eanmund earth-dwellers knew it,
who was slain by the sword-edge, son of Ohtere,
friendless exile, erst in fray
killed by Weohstan, who won for his kin
brown-bright helmet, breastplate ringed,
old sword of Eotens, Onela's gift,
weeds of war of the warrior-thane,
battle-gear brave: though a brother's child
had been felled, the feud was unfelt by Onela.[1]
For winters this war-gear Weohstan kept,
breastplate and board, till his bairn had grown
earlship to earn as the old sire did:
then he gave him, mid Geats, the gear of battle,
portion huge, when he passed from life,
fared agéd forth. For the first time now
with his leader-lord the liegeman young
was bidden to share the shock of battle.
Neither softened his soul, nor the sire's bequest
weakened in war.[2] So the worm found out
when once in fight the foes had met!
Wiglaf spake,—and his words were sage;
sad in spirit, he said to his comrades:—
"I remember the time, when mead we took,
what promise we made to this prince of ours
in the banquet-hall, to our breaker-of-rings,
for gear of combat to give him requital,
for hard-sword and helmet, if hap should bring
stress of this sort! Himself who chose us
from all his army to aid him now,
urged us to glory, and gave these treasures,
because he counted us keen with the spear

[1] That is, although Eanmund was brother's son to Onela, the slaying of
the former by Weohstan is not felt as cause of feud, and is rewarded by
gift of the slain man's weapons.
[2] Both Wiglaf and the sword did their duty.—The following is one of
the classic passages for illustrating the *comitatus* as the most conspicuous
Germanic institution, and its underlying sense of duty, based partly on
the idea of loyalty and partly on the practical basis of benefits received
and repaid.

and hardy 'neath helm, though this hero-work
our leader hoped unhelped and alone
to finish for us,—folk-defender
who hath got him glory greater than all men
for daring deeds!  Now the day is come
that our noble master has need of the might
of warriors stout.  Let us stride along
the hero to help while the heat is about him
glowing and grim!  For God is my witness
I am far more fain the fire should seize
along with my lord these limbs of mine![3]
Unsuiting it seems our shields to bear
homeward hence, save here we essay
to fell the foe and defend the life
of the Weders' lord.  I wot 'twere shame
on the law of our land if alone the king
out of Geatish warriors woe endured
and sank in the struggle!  My sword and helmet,
breastplate and board, for us both shall serve!"
Through slaughter-reek strode he to succor his
      chieftain,
his battle-helm bore, and brief words spake:—
" Beowulf dearest, do all bravely,
as in youthful days of yore thou vowedst
that while life should last thou wouldst let no wise
thy glory droop!  Now, great in deeds,
atheling steadfast, with all thy strength
shield thy life!  I will stand to help thee."
    At the words the worm came once again,
murderous monster mad with rage,
with fire-billows flaming, its foes to seek,
the hated men.  In heat-waves burned
that board[4] to the boss, and the breastplate failed
to shelter at all the spear-thane young.
Yet quickly under his kinsman's shield
went eager the earl, since his own was now
all burned by the blaze.  The bold king again
had mind of his glory: with might his glaive

---

[3] Sc. " than to bide safely here,"—a common figure of incomplete comparison.    [4] Wiglaf's wooden shield.

was driven into the dragon's head,—
blow nerved by hate. But Nægling[5] was shivered,
broken in battle was Beowulf's sword,
old and gray. 'Twas granted him not
that ever the edge of iron at all
could help him at strife: too strong was his hand,
so the tale is told, and he tried too far
with strength of stroke all swords he wielded,
though sturdy their steel: they steaded him nought.
Then for the third time thought on its feud
that folk-destroyer, fire-dread dragon,
and rushed on the hero, where room allowed,
battle-grim, burning; its bitter teeth
closed on his neck, and covered him
with waves of blood from his breast that welled.

## XXXVII

'TWAS now, men say, in his sovran's need
that the earl made known his noble strain,
craft and keenness and courage enduring.
Heedless of harm, though his hand was burned,
hardy-hearted, he helped his kinsman.
A little lower the loathsome beast
he smote with sword; his steel drove in
bright and burnished; that blaze began
to lose and lessen. At last the king
wielded his wits again, war-knife drew,
a biting blade by his breastplate hanging,
and the Weders'-helm smote that worm asunder,
felled the foe, flung forth its life.

So had they killed it, kinsmen both,
athelings twain: thus an earl should be
in danger's day!—Of deeds of valor
this conqueror's-hour of the king was last,
of his work in the world. The wound began,
which that dragon-of-earth had erst inflicted,
to swell and smart; and soon he found

[5] Gering would translate "kinsman of the nail," as both are made of iron.

in his breast was boiling, baleful and deep,
pain of poison.  The prince walked on,
wise in his thought, to the wall of rock;
then sat, and stared at the structure of giants,
where arch of stone and steadfast column
upheld forever that hall in earth.
Yet here must the hand of the henchman peerless
lave with water his winsome lord,
the king and conqueror covered with blood,
with struggle spent, and unspan his helmet.
Beowulf spake in spite of his hurt,
his mortal wound; full well he knew
his portion now was past and gone
of earthly bliss, and all had fled
of his file of days, and death was near:
" I would fain bestow on son of mine
this gear of war, were given me now
that any heir should after me come
of my proper blood.  This people I ruled
fifty winters.  No folk-king was there,
none at all, of the neighboring clans
who war would wage me with ' warriors'-friends '[1]
and threat me with horrors.  At home I bided
what fate might come, and I cared for mine own;
feuds I sought not, nor falsely swore
ever on oath.  For all these things,
though fatally wounded, fain am I!
From the Ruler-of-Man no wrath shall seize me,
when life from my frame must flee away,
for killing of kinsmen!  Now quickly go
and gaze on that hoard 'neath the hoary rock,
Wiglaf loved, now the worm lies low,
sleeps, heart-sore, of his spoil bereaved.
And fare in haste.  I would fain behold
the gorgeous heirlooms, golden store,
have joy in the jewels and gems, lay down
softlier for sight of this splendid hoard
my life and the lordship I long have held."

[1] That is, swords.

### XXXVIII

I HAVE heard that swiftly the son of Weohstan
at wish and word of his wounded king,—
war-sick warrior,—woven mail-coat,
battle-sark, bore 'neath the barrow's roof.
Then the clansman keen, of conquest proud,
passing the seat,[1] saw store of jewels
and glistening gold the ground along;
by the wall were marvels, and many a vessel
in the den of the dragon, the dawn-flier old:
unburnished bowls of bygone men
reft of richness; rusty helms
of the olden age; and arm-rings many
wondrously woven.—Such wealth of gold,
booty from barrow, can burden with pride
each human wight: let him hide it who will!—
His glance too fell on a gold-wove banner
high o'er the hoard, of handiwork noblest,
brilliantly broidered; so bright its gleam,
all the earth-floor he easily saw
and viewed all these vessels. No vestige now
was seen of the serpent: the sword had ta'en him.

Then, I heard, the hill of its hoard was reft,
old work of giants, by one alone;
he burdened his bosom with beakers and plate
at his own good will, and the ensign took,
brightest of beacons.—The blade of his lord
—its edge was iron—had injured deep
one that guarded the golden hoard
many a year and its murder-fire
spread hot round the barrow in horror-billows
at midnight hour, till it met its doom.
Hasted the herald, the hoard so spurred him
his track to retrace; he was troubled by doubt,
high-souled hero, if haply he'd find
alive, where he left him, the lord of Weders,
weakening fast by the wall of the cave.
So he carried the load. His lord and king

[1] Where Beowulf lay.

he found all bleeding, famous chief,
at the lapse of life. The liegeman again
plashed him with water, till point of word
broke through the breast-hoard. Beowulf spake,
sage and sad, as he stared at the gold:—
"For the gold and treasure, to God my thanks,
to the Wielder-of-Wonders, with words I say,
for what I behold, to Heaven's Lord,
for the grace that I give such gifts to my folk
or ever the day of my death be run!
Now I've bartered here for booty of treasure
the last of my life, so look ye well
to the needs of my land! No longer I tarry.
A barrow bid ye the battle-famed raise
for my ashes. 'Twill shine by the shore of the flood,
to folk of mine memorial fair
on Hronës Headland high uplifted,
that ocean-wanderers oft may hail
Beowulf's Barrow, as back from far
they drive their keels o'er the darkling wave."
    From his neck he unclasped the collar of gold,
valorous king, to his vassal gave it
with bright-gold helmet, breastplate, and ring,
to the youthful thane: bade him use them in joy.
    "Thou art end and remnant of all our race,
the Wægmunding name. For Wyrd hath swept them,
all my line, to the land of doom,
earls in their glory: I after them go."
    This word was the last which the wise old man
harbored in heart ere hot death-waves
of balefire he chose. From his bosom fled
his soul to seek the saints' reward.

### XXXIX

IT was heavy hap for that hero young
on his lord beloved to look and find him
lying on earth with life at end,
sorrowful sight. But the slayer too,

awful earth-dragon, empty of breath,
lay felled in fight, nor, fain of its treasure,
could the writhing monster rule it more.
For edges of iron had ended its days,
hard and battle-sharp, hammers' leaving;[1]
and that flier-afar had fallen to ground
hushed by its hurt, its hoard all near,
no longer lusty aloft to whirl
at midnight, making its merriment seen,
proud of its prizes: prone it sank
by the handiwork of the hero-king.
Forsooth among folk but few achieve,
—though sturdy and strong, as stories tell me,
and never so daring in deed of valor,—
the perilous breath of a poison-foe
to brave, and to rush on the ring-board hall,
whenever his watch the warden keeps
bold in the barrow.  Beowulf paid
the price of death for that precious hoard;
and each of the foes had found the end
of this fleeting life.

                  Befell erelong
that the laggards in war the wood had left,
trothbreakers, cowards, ten together,
fearing before to flourish a spear
in the sore distress of their sovran lord.
Now in their shame their shields they carried,
armor of fight, where the old man lay;
and they gazed on Wiglaf.  Wearied he sat
at his sovran's shoulder, shieldsman good,
to wake him with water.[2]  Nowise it availed.
Though well he wished it, in world no more
could he barrier life for that leader-of-battles
nor baffle the will of all-wielding God.
Doom of the Lord was law o'er the deeds
of every man, as it is to-day.
Grim was the answer, easy to get,
from the youth for those that had yielded to fear!

---

[1] What had been left or made by the hammer; well-forged.
[2] Trying to revive him.

Wiglaf spake, the son of Weohstan,—
mournful he looked on those men unloved:—
"Who sooth will speak, can say indeed
that the ruler who gave you golden rings
and the harness of war in which ye stand
—for he at ale-bench often-times
bestowed on hall-folk helm and breastplate,
lord to liegemen, the likeliest gear
which near of far he could find to give,—
threw away and wasted these weeds of battle,
on men who failed when the foemen came!
Not at all could the king of his comrades-in-arms
venture to vaunt, though the Victory-Wielder,
God, gave him grace that he got revenge
sole with his sword in stress and need.
To rescue his life, 'twas little that I
could serve him in struggle; yet shift I made
(hopeless it seemed) to help my kinsman.
Its strength ever waned, when with weapon I struck
that fatal foe, and the fire less strongly
flowed from its head.—Too few the heroes
in throe of contest that thronged to our king!
Now gift of treasure and girding of sword,
joy of the house and home-delight
shall fail your folk; his freehold-land
every clansman within your kin
shall lose and leave, when lords highborn
hear afar of that flight of yours,
a fameless deed. Yea, death is better
for liegemen all than a life of shame!"


## XL

THAT battle-toil bade he at burg to announce,
at the fort on the cliff, where, full of sorrow,
all the morning earls had sat,
daring shieldsmen, in doubt of twain:
would they wail as dead, or welcome home,
their lord belovéd? Little[1] kept back

[1] Nothing.

of the tidings new, but told them all,
the herald that up the headland rode.—
"Now the willing-giver to Weder folk
in death-bed lies, the Lord of Geats
on the slaughter-bed sleeps by the serpent's deed!
And beside him is stretched that slayer-of-men
with knife-wounds sick:[2] no sword availed
on the awesome thing in any wise
to work a wound.  There Wiglaf sitteth,
Weohstan's bairn, by Beowulf's side,
the living earl by the other dead,
and heavy of heart a head-watch[3] keeps
o'er friend and foe.—Now our folk may look
for waging of war when once unhidden
to Frisian and Frank the fall of the king
is spread afar.—The strife began
when hot on the Hugas[4] Hygelac fell
and fared with his fleet to the Frisian land.
Him there the Hetwaras humbled in war,
plied with such prowess their power o'erwhelming
that the bold-in-battle bowed beneath it
and fell in fight.  To his friends no wise
could that earl give treasure!  And ever since
the Merowings' favor has failed us wholly.
Nor aught expect I of peace and faith
from Swedish folk.  'Twas spread afar
how Ongentheow reft at Ravenswood
Hæthcyn Hrethling of hope and life,
when the folk of Geats for the first time sought
in wanton pride the Warlike-Scylfings.
Soon the sage old sire[5] of Ohtere,
ancient and awful, gave answering blow;
the sea-king[6] he slew, and his spouse redeemed,
his good wife rescued, though robbed of her gold,
mother of Ohtere and Onela.
Then he followed his foes, who fled before him
sore beset and stole their way,
bereft of a ruler, to Ravenswood.

---

[2] Dead.    [3] Death-watch, guard of honor, "lyke-wake."
[4] A name for the Franks.    [5] Ongentheow.    [6] Hæthcyn.

With his host he besieged there what swords had left,
the weary and wounded; woes he threatened
the whole night through to that hard-pressed throng:
some with the morrow his sword should kill,
some should go to the gallows-tree
for rapture of ravens.  But rescue came
with dawn of day for those desperate men
when they heard the horn of Hygelac sound,
tones of his trumpet; the trusty king
had followed their trail with faithful band.


### XLI

" THE bloody swath of Swedes and Geats
and the storm of their strife, were seen afar,
how folk against folk the fight had wakened.
The ancient king with his atheling band
sought his citadel, sorrowing much:
Ongentheow earl went up to his burg.
He had tested Hygelac's hardihood,
the proud one's prowess, would prove it no longer,
defied no more those fighting-wanderers
nor hoped from the seamen to save his hoard,
his bairn and his bride: so he bent him again,
old, to his earth-walls.  Yet after him came
with slaughter for Swedes the standards of Hygelac
o'er peaceful plains in pride advancing,
till Hrethelings fought in the fencéd town.[1]
Then Ongentheow with edge of sword,
the hoary-bearded, was held at bay,
and the folk-king there was forced to suffer
Eofor's anger.  In ire, at the king
Wulf Wonreding with weapon struck;
and the chieftain's blood, for that blow, in streams
flowed 'neath his hair.  No fear felt he,
stout old Scylfing, but straightway repaid
in better bargain that bitter stroke

---

[1] The line may mean: till Hrethelings stormed on the hedgéd shields, -i. e.
the shield-wall or hedge of defensive war.—Hrethelings, of course, are Geats.

and faced his foe with fell intent.
Nor swift enough was the son of Wonred
answer to render the agéd chief;
too soon on his head the helm was cloven;
blood-bedecked he bowed to earth,
and fell adown; not doomed was he yet,
and well he waxed, though the wound was sore.
Then the hardy Hygelac-thane,[2]
when his brother fell, with broad brand smote,
giants' sword crashing through giants'-helm
across the shield-wall: sank the king,
his folk's old herdsman, fatally hurt.
There were many to bind the brother's wounds
and lift him, fast as fate allowed
his people to wield the place-of-war.
But Eofor took from Ongentheow,
earl from other, the iron-breastplate,
hard sword hilted, and helmet too,
and the hoar-chief's harness to Hygelac carried,
who took the trappings, and truly promised
rich fee 'mid folk,—and fulfilled it so.
For that grim strife gave the Geatish lord,
Hrethel's offspring, when home he came,
to Eofor and Wulf a wealth of treasure,
Each of them had a hundred thousand[3]
in land and linked rings; nor at less price reckoned
mid-earth men such mighty deeds!
And to Eofor he gave his only daughter
in pledge of grace, the pride of his home.

" Such is the feud, the foeman's rage,
death-hate of men: so I deem it sure
that the Swedish folk will seek us home
for this fall of their friends, the fighting-Scylfings,
when once they learn that our warrior leader
lifeless lies, who land and hoard
ever defended from all his foes,
furthered his folk's weal, finished his course

---

[2] Eofor, brother to Wulf Wonreding.
[3] Sc. " value in " hides and the weight of the gold.

a hardy hero.—Now haste is best,
that we go to gaze on our Geatish lord,
and bear the bountiful breaker-of-rings
to the funeral pyre.  No fragments merely
shall burn with the warrior.  Wealth of jewels,
gold untold and gained in terror,
treasure at last with his life obtained,
all of that booty the brands shall take,
fire shall eat it.  No earl must carry
memorial jewel.  No maiden fair
shall wreathe her neck with noble ring:
nay, sad in spirit and shorn of her gold,
oft shall she pass o'er paths of exile
now our lord all laughter has laid aside,
all mirth and revel.  Many a spear
morning-cold shall be clasped amain,
lifted aloft; nor shall lilt of harp
those warriors wake; but the wan-hued raven,
fain o'er the fallen, his feast shall praise
and boast to the eagle how bravely he ate
when he and the wolf were wasting the slain."

So he told his sorrowful tidings,
and little [4] he lied, the loyal man
of word or of work.  The warriors rose;
sad, they climbed to the Cliff-of-Eagles,
went, welling with tears, the wonder to view.
Found on the sand there, stretched at rest,
their lifeless lord, who had lavished rings
of old upon them.  Ending-day
had dawned on the doughty-one; death had seized
in woful slaughter the Weders' king.
There saw they, besides, the strangest being,
loathsome, lying their leader near,
prone on the field.  The fiery dragon,
fearful fiend, with flame was scorched.
Reckoned by feet, it was fifty measures
in length as it lay.  Aloft erewhile
it had revelled by night, and anon come back,

[4] Not at all.

seeking its den; now in death's sure clutch
it had come to the end of its earth-hall joys.
By it there stood the stoups and jars;
dishes lay there, and dear-decked swords
eaten with rust, as, on earth's lap resting,
a thousand winters they waited there.
For all that heritage huge, that gold
of bygone men, was bound by a spell,[5]
so the treasure-hall could be touched by none
of human kind,—save that Heaven's King,
God himself, might give whom he would,
Helper of Heroes, the hoard to open,—
even such a man as seemed to him meet.

### XLII

A PERILOUS path, it proved, he [1] trod
who heinously hid, that hall within,
wealth under wall! Its watcher had killed
one of a few,[2] and the feud was avenged
in woful fashion. Wondrous seems it,
what manner a man of might and valor
oft ends his life, when the earl no longer
in mead-hall may live with loving friends.
So Beowulf, when that barrow's warden
he sought, and the struggle; himself knew not
in what wise he should wend from the world at
  last.
For[3] princes potent, who placed the gold,
with a curse to doomsday covered it deep,
so that marked with sin the man should be,
hedged with horrors, in hell-bonds fast,
racked with plagues, who should rob their hoard.

[5] Laid on it when it was put in the barrow. This spell, or in our days the "curse," either prevented discovery or brought dire ills on the finder and taker.

[1] Probably the fugitive is meant who discovered the hoard. Ten Brink and Gering assume that the dragon is meant. "Hid" may well mean here "took while in hiding."

[2] That is, "one and a few others." But Beowulf seems to be indicated.

[3] Ten Brink points out the strongly heathen character of this part of the epic. Beowulf's end came, so the old tradition ran, from his unwitting interference with spell-bound treasure.

Yet no greed for gold, but the grace of heaven,
ever the king had kept in view.[4]
　Wiglaf spake, the son of Weohstan:—
" At the mandate of one, oft warriors many
sorrow must suffer; and so must we.
The people's-shepherd showed not aught
of care for our counsel, king belovèd!
That guardian of gold he should grapple not, urged we,
but let him lie where he long had been
in his earth-hall waiting the end of the world,
the hest of heaven.—This hoard is ours,
but grievously gotten; too grim the fate
which thither carried our king and lord.
I was within there, and all I viewed,
the chambered treasure, when chance allowed me
(and my path was made in no pleasant wise)
under the earth-wall. Eager, I seized
such heap from the hoard as hands could bear
and hurriedly carried it hither back
to my liege and lord. Alive was he still,
still wielding his wits. The wise old man
spake much in his sorrow, and sent you greetings
and bade that ye build, when he breathed no more,
on the place of his balefire a barrow high,
memorial mighty. Of men was he
worthiest warrior wide earth o'er
the while he had joy of his jewels and burg.
Let us set out in haste now, the second time
to see and search this store of treasure,
these wall-hid wonders,—the way I show you,—
where, gathered near, ye may gaze your fill
at broad-gold and rings. Let the bier, soon made,
be all in order when out we come,
our king and captain to carry thither
—man beloved—where long he shall bide
safe in the shelter of sovran God."
Then the bairn of Weohstan bade command,
hardy chief, to heroes many

---

[4] A hard saying, variously interpreted. In any case, it is the somewhat clumsy effort of the Christian poet to tone down the heathenism of his material by an edifying observation.

that owned their homesteads, hither to bring
firewood from far—o'er the folk they ruled—
for the famed-one's funeral. "Fire shall devour
and wan flames feed on the fearless warrior
who oft stood stout in the iron-shower,
when, sped from the string, a storm of arrows
shot o'er the shield-wall: the shaft held firm,
featly feathered, followed the barb."
And now the sage young son of Weohstan
seven chose of the chieftain's thanes,
the best he found that band within,
and went with these warriors, one of eight,
under hostile roof. In hand one bore
a lighted torch and led the way.
No lots they cast for keeping the hoard
when once the warriors saw it in hall,
altogether without a guardian,
lying there lost. And little they mourned
when they had hastily haled it out,
dear-bought treasure! The dragon they cast,
the worm, o'er the wall for the wave to take,
and surges swallowed that shepherd of gems.
Then the woven gold on a wain was laden—
countless quite!—and the king was borne,
hoary hero, to Hronës-Ness.

## XLIII

THEN fashioned for him the folk of Geats
firm on the earth a funeral-pile,
and hung it with helmets and harness of war
and breastplates bright, as the boon he asked;
and they laid amid it the mighty chieftain,
heroes mourning their master dear.
Then on the hill that hugest of balefires
the warriors wakened. Wood-smoke rose
black over blaze, and blent was the roar
of flame with weeping (the wind was still),
till the fire had broken the frame of bones,

hot at the heart.   In heavy mood
their misery moaned they, their master's death.
Wailing her woe, the widow[1] old,
her hair upbound, for Beowulf's death
sung in her sorrow, and said full oft
she dreaded the doleful days to come,
deaths enow, and doom of battle,
and shame.—The smoke by the sky was devoured.

   The folk of the Weders fashioned there
on the headland a barrow broad and high,
by ocean-farers far descried:
in ten days' time their toil had raised it,
the battle-brave's beacon.   Round brands of the pyre
a wall they built, the worthiest ever
that wit could prompt in their wisest men.
They placed in the barrow that precious booty,
the rounds and the rings they had reft erewhile,
hardy heroes, from hoard in cave,—
trusting the ground with treasure of earls,
gold in the earth, where ever it lies
useless to men as of yore it was.

   Then about that barrow the battle-keen rode,
atheling-born, a band of twelve,
lament to make, to mourn their king,
chant their dirge, and their chieftain honor.
They praised his earlship, his acts of prowess
worthily witnessed: and well it is
that men their master-friend mightily laud,
heartily love, when hence he goes
from life in the body forlorn away.


   Thus made their mourning the men of Geatland,
for their hero's passing his hearth-companions:
quoth that of all the kings of earth,
of men he was mildest and most belovéd,
to his kin the kindest, keenest for praise.

---

[1] Nothing is said of Beowulf's wife in the poem, but Bugge surmises that Beowulf finally accepted Hygd's offer of kingdom and hoard, and, as was usual, took her into the bargain.

# THE SONG OF ROLAND

TRANSLATED BY
JOHN O'HAGAN

# INTRODUCTORY NOTE

In the year 778 A.D., Charles the Great, King of the Franks, returned from a military expedition into Spain, whither he had been led by opportunities offered through dissensions among the Saracens who then dominated that country. On the 15th of August, while his army was marching through the passes of the Pyrenees, his rear-guard was attacked and annihilated by the Basque inhabitants of the mountains, in the valley of Roncesvaux. About this disaster many popular songs, it is supposed, soon sprang up; and the chief hero whom they celebrated was Hrodland, Count of the Marches of Brittany.

There are indications that the earliest of these songs arose among the Breton followers of Hrodland or Roland; but they spread to Maine, to Anjou, to Normandy, until the theme became national. By the latter part of the eleventh century, when the form of the "Song of Roland" which we possess was probably composed, the historical germ of the story had almost disappeared under the mass of legendary accretion. Charlemagne, who was a man of thirty-six at the time of the actual Roncesvaux incident, has become in the poem an old man with a flowing white beard, credited with endless conquests; the Basques have disappeared, and the Saracens have taken their place; the defeat is accounted for by the invention of the treachery of Ganelon; the expedition of 777-778 has become a campaign of seven years; Roland is made the nephew of Charlemagne, leader of the twelve peers, and is provided with a faithful friend Oliver, and a betrothed, Alda.

The poem is the first of the great French heroic poems known as "chansons de geste." It is written in stanzas of various length, bound together by the vowel-rhyme known as assonance. It is not possible to reproduce effectively this device in English, and the author of the present translation has adopted what is perhaps the nearest equivalent—the romantic measure of Coleridge and Scott.

Simple almost to bareness in style, without subtlety or high imagination, the Song of Roland is yet not without grandeur; and its patriotic ardor gives it a place as the earliest of the truly national poems of the modern world.

# THE SONG OF ROLAND

## PART I
## THE TREASON OF GANELON

SARAGOSSA. THE COUNCIL OF KING MARSIL

### I

THE king our Emperor Carlemaine,
  Hath been for seven full years in Spain.
  From highland to sea hath he won the land;
City was none might his arm withstand;
Keep and castle alike went down—
Save Saragossa, the mountain town.
The King Marsilius holds the place,
Who loveth not God, nor seeks His grace:
He prays to Apollin, and serves Mahound;
But he saved him not from the fate he found.

### II

In Saragossa King Marsil made
His council-seat in the orchard shade,
On a stair of marble of azure hue.
There his courtiers round him drew;
While there stood, the king before,
Twenty thousand men and more.
Thus to his dukes and his counts he said,
"Hear ye, my lords, we are sore bested.
The Emperor Karl of gentle France
Hither hath come for our dire mischance.
Nor host to meet him in battle line,
Nor power to shatter his power, is mine."

Speak, my sages; your counsel lend:
My doom of shame and death forefend."
But of all the heathens none spake word
Save Blancandrin, Val Fonde's lord.

### III

Blancandrin was a heathen wise,
Knightly and valiant of enterprise,
Sage in counsel his lord to aid;
And he said to the king, " Be not dismayed:
Proffer to Karl, the haughty and high,
Lowly friendship and fealty;
Ample largess lay at his feet,
Bear and lion and greyhound fleet.
Seven hundred camels his tribute be,
A thousand hawks that have moulted free.
Let full four hundred mules be told,
Laden with silver enow and gold
For fifty waggons to bear away;
So shall his soldiers receive their pay.
Say, too long hath he warred in Spain,—
Let him turn to France—to his Aix—again.
At Saint Michael's feast you will thither speed,
Bend your heart to the Christian creed,
And his liegeman be in duty and deed.
Hostages he may demand
Ten or twenty at your hand.
We will send him the sons whom our wives have
        nursed;
Were death to follow, mine own the first.
Better by far that they there should die
Than be driven all from our land to fly,
Flung to dishonor and beggary.

### IV

" Yea," said Blancandrin, " by this right hand,
And my floating beard by the free wind fanned,

Ye shall see the host of the Franks disband
And hie them back into France their land;
Each to his home as beseemeth well,
And Karl unto Aix—to his own Chapelle.
He will hold high feast on Saint Michael's day
And the time of your tryst shall pass away.
Tale nor tidings of us shall be;
Fiery and sudden, I know, is he:
He will smite off the heads of our hostages all:
Better, I say, that their heads should fall
Than we the fair land of Spain forego,
And our lives be laden with shame and woe."
" Yea," said the heathens, " it may be so."


### V

King Marsil's council is over that day,
And he called to him Clarin of Balaguet,
Estramarin, and Eudropin his peer,
Bade Garlon and Priamon both draw near,
Machiner and his uncle Maheu—with these
Joïmer and Malbien from overseas,
Blancandrin for spokesman,—of all his men
He hath summoned there the most felon ten.
" Go ye to Carlemaine," spake their liege,—
" At Cordres city he sits in siege,—
While olive branches in hand ye press,
Token of peace and of lowliness.
Win him to make fair treaty with me,
Silver and gold shall your guerdon be,
Land and lordship in ample fee."
" Nay," said the heathens, " enough have we."


### VI

So did King Marsil his council end.
" Lords," he said, " on my errand wend;
While olive branches in hand ye bring,
Say from me unto Karl the king,

For sake of his God let him pity show;
And ere ever a month shall come and go,
With a thousand faithful of my race,
I will follow swiftly upon his trace,
Freely receive his Christian law,
And his liegemen be in love and awe.
Hostages asks he? it shall be done."
Blancandrin answered, " Your peace is won."


### VII

Then King Marsil bade be dight
Ten fair mules of snowy white,
Erst from the King of Sicily brought
Their trappings with silver and gold inwrought —
Gold the bridle, and silver the selle.
On these are the messengers mounted well;
And they ride with olive boughs in hand,
To seek the Lord of the Frankish land.
Well let him watch; he shall be trepanned.


## At Cordres.  Carlemaine's Council

### VIII

King Karl is jocund and gay of mood,
He hath Cordres city at last subdued;
Its shattered walls and turrets fell
By Catapult and mangonel;
Not a heathen did there remain
But confessed him Christian or else was slain.
The Emperor sits in an orchard wide,
Roland and Olivier by his side:
Samson the duke, and Anseis proud;
Geoffrey of Anjou, whose arm was vowed
The royal gonfalon to rear;
Gerein, and his fellow in arms, Gerier;
With them many a gallant lance,

Full fifteen thousand of gentle France.
The cavaliers sit upon carpets white,
Playing at tables for their delight:
The older and sager sit at the chess,
The bachelors fence with a light address.
Seated underneath a pine,
Close beside an eglantine,
Upon a throne of beaten gold,
The lord of ample France behold;
White his hair and beard were seen,
Fair of body, and proud of mien,
Who sought him needed not ask, I ween.
The ten alight before his feet,
And him in all observance greet.


## IX

Blancandrin first his errand gave,
And he said to the king, " May God you save,
The God of glory, to whom you bend!
Marsil, our king, doth his greeting send.
Much hath he mused on the law of grace,
Much of his wealth at your feet will place—
Bears and lions, and dogs of chase,
Seven hundred camels that bend the knee,
A thousand hawks that have moulted free,
Four hundred mules, with silver and gold
Which fifty wains might scantly hold,
So shall you have of the red bezants
To pay the soldiers of gentle France.
Overlong have you dwelt in Spain,—
To Aix, your city, return again.
The lord I serve will thither come,
Accept the law of Christendom,
With claspèd hands your liegeman be,
And hold his realm of you in fee."
The Emperor raised his hands on high,
Bent and bethought him silently.

### X

The Emperor bent his head full low;
Never hasty of speech I trow;
Leisurely came his words, and slow,
Lofty his look as he raised his head:
" Thou hast spoken well," at length he said.
" King Marsil was ever my deadly foe,
And of all these words, so fair in show,
How may I the fulfilment know? "
" Hostages will you? " the heathen cried,
" Ten or twenty, or more beside.
I will send my son, were his death at hand,
With the best and noblest of all our land;
And when you sit in your palace halls,
And the feast of St. Michael of Peril falls,
Unto the waters will come our king,
Which God commanded for you to spring;
There in the laver of Christ be laved."
" Yea! " said Karl, " he may yet be saved."

### XI

Fair and bright did the evening fall:
The ten white mules were stabled in stall;
On the sward was a fair pavilion dressed,
To give to the Saracens cheer of the best;
Servitors twelve at their bidding bide,
And they rest all night until morning tide.
The Emperor rose with the day-dawn clear,
Failed not Matins and Mass to hear,
Then betook him beneath a pine,
Summoned his barons by word and sign:
As his Franks advise will his choice incline.

### XII

Under a pine is the Emperor gone,
And his barons to council come forth anon:

Archbishop Turpin, Duke Ogier bold
With his nephew Henry was Richard the old,
Gascony's gallant Count Acelin,
Tybalt of Rheims, and Milo his kin,
Gerein and his brother in arms, Gerier,
Count Roland and his faithful fere,
The gentle and valiant Olivier:
More than a thousand Franks of France
And Ganelon came, of woful chance;
By him was the deed of treason done.
So was the fatal consult begun.

### XIII

"Lords my barons," the Emperor said,
"King Marsil to me hath his envoys sped.
He proffers treasure surpassing bounds,
Bears and lions, and leashèd hounds;
Seven hundred camels that bend the knee;
A thousand hawks that have moulted free;
Four hundred mules with Arab gold,
Which fifty wains might scantly hold.
But he saith to France must I wend my way:
He will follow to Aix with brief delay,
Bend his heart unto Christ's belief,
And hold his marches of me in fief;
Yet I know not what in his heart may lie."
"Beware! beware!" was the Franks' outcry.

### XIV

Scarce his speech did the Emperor close,
When in high displeasure Count Roland rose,
Fronted his uncle upon the spot,
And said, "This Marsil, believe him not:
Seven full years have we warred in Spain;
Commibles and Noples for you have I ta'en,
Tudela and Sebilie, cities twain;
Valtierra I won, and the land of Pine,

And Balaguet fell to this arm of mine.
King Marsil hath ever a traitor been:
He sent of his heathens, at first fifteen.
Bearing each one on olive bough,
Speaking the self-same words as now.
Into council with your Franks you went,
Lightly they flattered your heart's intent;
Two of your barons to him you sent,—
They were Basan and Basil, the brother knights:
He smote off their heads on Haltoia's heights.
War, I say!—end as you well began,
Unto Saragossa lead on your van;
Were the siege to last your lifetime through,
Avenge the nobles this felon slew."


### XV

The Emperor bent him and mused within,
Twisted his beard upon lip and chin,
Answered his nephew nor good nor ill;
And the Franks, save Ganelon, all were still:
Hastily to his feet he sprang,
Haughtily his words outrang:—
" By me or others be not misled,—
Look to your own good ends," he said.
" Since now King Marsil his faith assures,
That, with hands together clasped in yours,
He will henceforth your vassal be,
Receive the Christian law as we,
And hold his realm of you in fee,
Whoso would treaty like this deny,
Recks not, sire, by what death we die:
Good never came from counsel of pride,—
List to the wise, and let madmen bide."


### XVI

Then his form Duke Naimes upreared,
White of hair and hoary of beard.

Better vassal in court was none.
"You have hearkened," he said, "unto Ganelon.
Well hath Count Ganelon made reply;
Wise are his words, if you bide thereby.
King Marsil is beaten and broken in war;
You have captured his castles anear and far,
With your engines shattered his walls amain,
His cities burned, his soldiers slain:
Respite and ruth if he now implore,
Sin it were to molest him more.
Let his hostages vouch for the faith he plights,
And send him one of your Christian knights.
'Twere time this war to an ending came."
"Well saith the duke!" the Franks exclaim.

### XVII

"Lords my barons, who then were best
In Saragossa to do our hest?"
"I," said Naimes, "of your royal grace,
Yield me in token your glove and mace."
"Nay—my sagest of men art thou:
By my beard upon lip and chin I vow
Thou shalt never depart so far from me:
Sit thee down till I summon thee.

### XVIII

"Lords my barons, whom send we, then,
To Saragossa, the Saracen den?"
"I," said Roland, "will blithely go."
"Nay," said Olivier; nay, not so.
All too fiery of mood thou art;
Thou wouldst play, I fear me, a perilous part.
I go myself, if the king but will."
"I command," said Karl, "that ye both be still.
Neither shall be on this errand bound,
Nor one of the twelve—my peers around;

So by my blanching beard I swear."
The Franks are abashed and silent there.

### XIX

Turpin of Rheims from amid the ranks
Said: " Look, my liege, on your faithful Franks:
Seven full years have they held this land,
With pain and peril on every hand.
To me be the mace and the glove consigned;
I will go this Saracen lord to find,
And freely forth will I speak my mind."
The Emperor answered in angry plight,
" Sit thee down on that carpet white;
Speak not till I thy speech invite.

### XX

" My cavaliers," he began anew,
" Choose of my marches a baron true,
Before King Marsil my hest to do."
" Be it, then," said Roland, " my stepsire Gan,
In vain ye seek for a meeter man."
The Franks exclaim, " He is worth the trust,
So it please the king it is right and just."
Count Ganelon then was with anguish wrung,
His mantle of fur from his neck he flung,
Stood all stark in his silken vest,
And his grey eyes gleamed with a fierce unrest.
Fair of body and large of limb,
All in wonderment gazed on him.
" Thou madman," thus he to Roland cried,
" What may this rage against me betide?
I am thy stepsire, as all men know,
And thou doom'st me on hest like this to go;
But so God my safe return bestow,
I promise to work thee scathe and strife
Long as thou breathest the breath of life."

"Pride and folly!" said Roland, then.
"Am I known to wreck of the threats of men?
But this is work for the sagest head.
So it please the king, I will go instead."


### XXI

"In *my* stead?—never, of mine accord.
Thou art not my vassal nor I thy lord.
Since Karl commands me his hest to fill,
Unto Saragossa ride forth I will;
Yet I fear me to wreak some deed of ill,
Thereby to slake this passion's might."
Roland listened, and laughed outright.


### XXII

At Roland's laughter Count Ganelon's pain
Was as though his bosom were cleft in twain.
He turned to his stepson as one distraught:
"I do not love thee," he said, "in aught;
Thou hast false judgment against me wrought.
O righteous Emperor, here I stand
To execute your high command.


### XXIII

"Unto Saragossa I needs must go;—
Who goeth may never return, I know;—
Yet withal, your sister is spouse of mine,
And our son—no fairer of mortal line—
Baldwin bids to be goodly knight;
I leave him my honors and fiefs of right.
Guard him—no more shall he greet my sight."
Saith Karl, "Thou art over tender of heart.
Since I command it, thou shalt depart.

### XXIV

"Fair Sir Gan," the Emperor spake,
" This my message to Marsil take:
He shall make confession of Christ's belief,
And I yield him, full half of Spain in fief;
In the other half shall Count Roland reign.
If he choose not the terms I now ordain,
I will march unto Saragossa's gate,
Besiege and capture the city straight,
Take and bind him both hands and feet,
Lead him to Aix, to my royal seat,
There to be tried and judged and slain,
Dying a death of disgrace and pain.
I have sealed the scroll of my command.
Deliver it into the heathen's hand.

### XXV

" Gan," said the Emperor, " draw thou near:
Take my glove and my bâton here;
On thee did the choice of thy fellows fall."
" Sire, 't was Roland who wrought it all.
I shall not love him while life may last,
Nor Olivier his comrade fast,
Nor the peers who cherish and prize him so,—
Gage of defiance to all I throw."
Saith Karl, " Thine anger hath too much sway.
Since I ordain it, thou must obey."
" I go, but warranty none have I
That I may not like Basil and Basan die."

### XXVI

The Emperor reached him his right-hand glove;
Gan for his office had scanty love;
As he bent him forward, it fell to ground:
" God, what is this? " said the Franks around;

"Evil will come of this quest we fear."
"My lords," said Ganelon, "ye shall hear."


### XXVII

"Sire," he said, "let me wend my way;
Since go I must, what boots delay?"
Said the king, "In Jesus' name and mine!"
And his right hand sained him with holy sign.
Then he to Ganelon's grasp did yield
His royal mace and missive sealed.


### XXVIII

Home to his hostel is Ganelon gone,
His choicest of harness and arms to don;
On his charger Taschebrun to mount and ride,
With his good sword Murgleis girt at side.
On his feet are fastened the spurs of gold,
And his uncle Guinemer doth his stirrup hold.
Then might ye look upon cavaliers
A-many round him who spake in tears.
"Sir," they said, "what a woful day!
Long were you ranked in the king's array,
A noble vassal as none gainsay.
For him who doomed you to journey hence
Carlemagne's self shall be scant defence;
Foul was the thought in Count Roland's mind,
When you and he are so high affined.
Sir," they said, "let us with you wend."
"Nay," said Ganelon, "God forefend.
Liefer alone to my death I go,
Than such brave bachelors perish so.
Sirs, ye return into France the fair;
Greeting from me to my lady bear,
To my friend and peer Sir Pinabel,
And to Baldwin, my son, whom ye all know well,—
Cherish him, own him your lord of right."
He hath passed on his journey and left their sight.

### The Embassy and Crime of Ganelon

#### XXIX

Ganelon rides under olives high,
And comes the Saracen envoys nigh.
Blancandrin lingers until they meet,
And in cunning converse each other greet.
The Saracen thus began their parle:
"What a man, what a wondrous man is Karl!
Apulia—Calabria—all subdued,
Unto England crossed he the salt sea rude,
Won for Saint Peter his tribute fee;
But what in our marches maketh he?"
Ganelon said, "He is great of heart,
Never man shall fill so mighty a part."

#### XXX

Said Blancandrin, "Your Franks are high of fame,
But your dukes and counts are sore to blame.
Such counsel to their lord they give,
Nor he nor others in peace may live."
Ganelon answered, "I know of none,
Save Roland, who thus to his shame hath done.
Last morn the Emperor sat in the shade,
His nephew came in his mail arrayed,—
He had plundered Carcassonne just before,
And a vermeil apple in hand he bore:
'Sire,' he said, 'to your feet I bring
The crown of every earthly king.'
Disaster is sure such pride to blast;
He setteth his life on a daily cast.
Were he slain, we all should have peace at last."

#### XXXI

"Ruthless is Roland," Blancandrin spake,
"Who every race would recreant make,

And on all possessions of men would seize;
But in whom doth he trust for feats like these?"
"The Franks! the Franks!" Count Ganelon cried;
"They love him, and never desert his side;
For he lavisheth gifts that seldom fail,
Gold and silver in countless tale,
Mules and chargers, and silks and mail,
The king himself may have spoil at call.
From hence to the East he will conquer all."


### XXXII

Thus Blancandrin and Ganelon rode,
Till each on other his faith bestowed
That Roland should be by practice slain,
And so they journeyed by path and plain,
Till in Saragossa they bridle drew,
There alighted beneath a yew.
In a pine-tree's shadow a throne was set;
Alexandrian silk was the coverlet:
There the monarch of Spain they found,
With twenty thousand Saracens round,
Yet from them came nor breath nor sound;
All for the tidings they strained to hear,
As they saw Blancandrin and Ganelon near.


### XXXIII

Blancandrin stepped before Marsil's throne,
Ganelon's hand was in his own.
"Mahound you save," to the king he said,
"And Apollin, whose holy law we dread!
Fairly your errand to Karl was done;
But other answer made he none,
Save that his hands to Heaven he raised,
Save that a space his God he praised;
He sends a baron of his court,
Knight of France, and of high report,

Of him your tidings of peace receive."
"Let him speak," said Marsil, "we yield him leave."

### XXXIV

Gan had bethought him, and mused with art;
Well was he skilled to play his part;
And he said to Marsil, "May God you save,
The God of glory, whose grace we crave!
Thus saith the noble Carlemaine:
You shall make in Christ confession plain.
And he gives you in fief full half of Spain;
The other half shall be Roland's share
(Right haughty partner, he yields you there);
And should you slight the terms I bear,
He will come and gird Saragossa round,
You shall be taken by force and bound,
Led unto Aix, to his royal seat,
There to perish by judgment meet,
Dying a villainous death of shame."
Over King Marsil a horror came;
He grasped his javelin, plumed with gold,
In act to smite, were he not controlled.

### XXXV

King Marsil's cheek the hue hath left,
And his right hand grasped his weapon's heft.
When Ganelon saw it, his sword he drew
Finger lengths from the scabbard two.
"Sword," he said, "thou art clear and bright;
I have borne thee long in my fellows' sight,
Mine emperor never shall say of me,
That I perished afar, in a strange countrie,
Ere thou in the blood of their best wert dyed."
"Dispart the mellay," the heathens cried.

### XXXVI

The noblest Saracens thronged amain,
Seated the king on his throne again,
And the Algalif said, "'Twas a sorry prank,
Raising your weapon to slay the Frank.
It was yours to hearken in silence there."
"Sir," said Gan, "I may meetly bear,
But for all the wealth of your land arrayed,
For all the gold that God hath made,
Would I not live and leave unsaid,
What Karl, the mightiest king below,
Sends, through me, to his mortal foe."
His mantle of fur, that was round him twined,
With silk of Alexandria lined,
Down at Blancandrin's feet he cast,
But still he held by his good sword fast,
Grasping the hilt by its golden ball.
"A noble knight," say the heathens all.

### XXXVII

Ganelon came to the king once more.
"Your anger," he said, "misserves you sore.
As the princely Carlemaine saith, I say,
You shall the Christian law obey.
And half of Spain you shall hold in fee,
The other half shall Count Roland's be,
(And a haughty partner 't is yours to see).
Reject the treaty I here propose,
Round Saragossa his lines will close;
You shall be bound in fetters strong,
Led to his city of Aix along.
Nor steed nor palfrey shall you bestride,
Nor mule nor jennet be yours to ride;
On a sorry sumpter you shall be cast,
And your head by doom stricken off at last.
So is the Emperor's mandate traced,"—
And the scroll in the heathen's hand he placed.

### XXXVIII

Discolored with ire was King Marsil's hue;
The seal he brake and to earth he threw,
Read of the scroll the tenor clear.
"So Karl the Emperor writes me here.
Bids me remember his wrath and pain
For sake of Basan and Basil slain,
Whose necks I smote on Haltoia's hill;
Yet, if my life I would ransom still,
Mine uncle the Algalif must I send,
Or love between us were else at end."
Then outspake Jurfalez, Marsil's son:
"This is but madness of Ganelon.
For crime so deadly his life shall pay;
Justice be mine on his head this day."
Ganelon heard him, and waved his blade,
While his back against a pine he stayed.

### XXXIX

Into his orchard King Marsil stepped.
His nobles round him their station kept:
There was Jurfalez, his son and heir,
Blancandrin of the hoary hair,
The Algalif, truest of all his kin.
Said Blancandrin, "Summon the Christian in;
His troth he pledged me upon our side."
"Go," said Marsil, "be thou his guide."
Blancandrin led him, hand-in-hand,
Before King Marsil''s face to stand.
Then was the villainous treason planned.

### XL

"Fair Sir Ganelon," spake the king,
"I did a rash and despighteous thing,
Raising against thee mine arm to smite.
Richly will I the wrong requite.

See these sables whose worth were told
At full five hundred pounds of gold:
Thine shall they be ere the coming day."
"I may not," said Gan, "your grace gainsay.
God in His pleasure will you repay."


## XLI

"Trust me I love thee, Sir Gan, and fain
Would I hear thee discourse of Carlemaine.
He is old, methinks, exceedingly old;
And full two hundred years hath told;
With toil his body spent and worn,
So many blows on his buckler borne,
So many a haughty king laid low,
When will he weary of warring so?"
"Such is not Carlemaine," Gan replied;
"Man never knew him, nor stood beside,
But will say how noble a lord is he,
Princely and valiant in high degree.
Never could words of mine express
His honor, his bounty, his gentleness,
'Twas God who graced him with gifts so high.
Ere I leave his vassalage I will die."


## XLII

The heathen said, "I marvel sore
Of Carlemaine, so old and hoar,
Who counts I ween two hundred years,
Hath borne such strokes of blades and spears,
So many lands hath overrun,
So many mighty kings undone,
When will he tire of war and strife?"
"Not while his nephew breathes in life.
Beneath the cope of heaven this day
Such vassal leads not king's array.
Gallant and sage is Olivier,

And all the twelve, to Karl so dear,
With twenty thousand Franks in van,
He feareth not the face of man."


### XLIII

"Strange," said Marsil, "seems to me,
Karl, so white with eld is he,
Twice a hundred years, men say,
Since his birth have passed away.
All his wars in many lands,
All the strokes of trenchant brands,
All the kings despoiled and slain,—
When will he from war refrain?"
"Not till Roland breathes no more,
For from hence to eastern shore,
Where is chief with him may vie?
Olivier his comrades by,
And the peers, of Karl the pride,
Twenty thousand Franks beside,
Vanguard of his host, and flower:
Karl may mock at mortal power."


### XLIV

"I tell thee, Sir Gan, that a power is mine;
Fairer did never in armor shine,
Four hundred thousand cavaliers,
With the Franks of Karl to measure spears."
"Fling such folly," said Gan, "away;
Sorely your heathen would rue the day.
Proffer the Emperor ample prize,
A sight to dazzle the Frankish eyes;
Send him hostages full of score,
So returns he to France once more.
But his rear will tarry behind the host;
There, I trow, will be Roland's post—
There will Sir Olivier remain.

Hearken to me, and the counts lie slain;
The pride of Karl shall be crushed that day,
And his wars be ended with you for aye."


### XLV

" Speak, then, and tell me, Sir Ganelon,
How may Roland to death be done?"
" Through Cizra's pass will the Emperor wind,
But his rear will linger in march behind;
Roland and Olivier there shall be,
With twenty thousand in company.
Muster your battle against them then,
A hundred thousand heathen men.
Till worn and spent be the Frankish bands,
Though your bravest perish beneath their hands.
For another battle your powers be massed,
Roland will sink, overcome at last.
There were a feat of arms indeed,
And your life from peril thenceforth be freed.


### XLVI

" For whoso Roland to death shall bring,
From Karl his good right aim will wring,
The marvellous host will melt away,
No more shall he muster a like array,
And the mighty land will in peace repose."
King Marsil heard him to the close;
Then kissed him on the neck, and bade
His royal treasures be displayed.


### XLVII

What said they more? Why tell the rest?
Said Marsil, " Fastest bound is best;
Come, swear me here to Roland's fall."
" Your will," said Gan, " be mine in all."

He swore on the relics in the hilt
Of his sword Murgleis, and crowned his guilt.


### XLVIII

A stool was there of ivory wrought.
King Marsil bade a book be brought,
Wherein was all the law contained
Mahound and Termagaunt ordained.
The Saracen hath sworn thereby,
If Roland in the rear-guard lie,
With all his men-at-arms to go,
And combat till the count lay low.
Sir Gan repeated, " Be it so."


### XLIX

King Marsil's foster-father came,
A heathen, Valdabrun by name.
He spake to Gan with laughter clear.
" My sword, that never found its peer,—
A thousand pieces would not buy
The riches in the hilt that lie,—
To you I give in guerdon free;
Your aid in Roland's fall to see,
Let but the rear-guard be his place."
" I trust," said Gan, " to do you grace."
Then each kissed other on the face.


### L

Next broke with jocund laughter in,
Another heathen, Climorin.
To Gan he said, " Accept my helm,
The best and trustiest in the realm,
Conditioned that your aid we claim
To bring the marchman unto shame."
" Be it," said Ganelon, " as you list."
And then on cheek and mouth they kissed.

### LI

Now Bramimonde, King Marsil's queen,
To Ganelon came with gentle mien.
"I love thee well, Sir Count," she spake,
"For my lord the king and his nobles' sake.
See these clasps for a lady's wrist,
Of gold, and jacinth, and amethyst,
That all the jewels of Rome outshine;
Never your Emperor owned so fine;
These by the queen to your spouse are sent."
The gems within his boot he pent.

### LII

Then did the king on his treasurer call,
"My gifts for Karl, are they ready all?"
"Yea, sire, seven hundred camels' load
Of gold and silver well bestowed,
And twenty hostages thereby,
The noblest underneath the sky."

### LIII

On Ganelon's shoulder King Marsil leant.
"Thou art sage," he said, "and of gallant bent;
But by all thy holiest law deems dear,
Let not thy thought from our purpose veer.
Ten mules' burthen I give to thee
Of gold, the finest of Araby;
Nor ever year henceforth shall pass
But it brings thee riches in equal mass.
Take the keys of my city gates,
Take the treasure that Karl awaits—
Render them all; but oh, decide
That Roland in the rear-guard bide;
So may I find him by pass or height,
As I swear to meet him in mortal fight."

Cried Gan, " Meseemeth too long we stay,"
Sprang on his charger and rode away.


### LIV

The Emperor homeward hath turned his face,
To Gailne city he marched apace,
(By Roland erst in ruins strown—
Deserted thence it lay and lone,
Until a hundred years had flown).
Here waits he, word of Gan to gain
With tribute of the land of Spain;
And here, at earliest break of day,
Came Gan where the encampment lay.


### LV

The Emperor rose with the day dawn clear,
Failed not Matins and Mass to hear,
Sate at his tent on the fair green sward,
Roland and Olivier nigh their lord,
Duke Naimes and all his peers of fame.
Gan the felon, the perjured, came—
False was the treacherous tale he gave,—
And these his words, " May God you save!
I bear you Saragossa's keys,
Vast the treasure I bring with these,
And twenty hostages; guard them well,
The noble Marsil bids me tell—
Not on him shall your anger fall,
If I fetch not the Algalif here withal;
For mine eyes beheld, beneath their ken,
Three hundred thousand armèd men,
With sword and casque and coat of mail,
Put forth with him on the sea to sail,
All for hate of the Christian creed,
Which they would neither hold nor heed.
They had not floated a league but four,

When a tempest down on their galleys bore.
Drowned they lie to be seen no more.
If the Algalif were but living wight,
He had stood this morn before your sight.
Sire, for the Saracen king I say,
Ere ever a month shall pass away,
On into France he will follow free,
Bend to our Christian law the knee,
Homage swear for his Spanish land,
And hold the realm at your command."
" Now praise to God," the Emperor said,
" And thanks, my Ganelon, well you sped."
A thousand clarions then resound,
The sumpter-mules are girt on ground,
For France, for France the Franks are bound.


LVI

Karl the Great hath wasted Spain,
Her cities sacked, her castles ta'en;
But now " My wars are done," he cried,
" And home to gentle France we ride."
Count Roland plants his standard high
Upon a peak against the sky;
The Franks around encamping lie.
Alas! the heathen host the while,
Through valley deep and dark defile,
Are riding on the Chistians' track,
All armed in steel from breast to back;
Their lances poised, their helmets laced,
Their falchions glittering from the waist,
Their bucklers from the shoulder swung,
And so they ride the steeps among,
Till, in a forest on the height,
They rest to wait the morning light,
Four hundred thousand crouching there.
O God! the Franks are unaware.

### LVII

The day declined, night darkling crept,
And Karl, the mighty Emperor, slept.
He dreamt a dream: he seemed to stand
In Cizra's pass, with lance in hand.
Count Ganelon came athwart, and lo,
He wrenched the aspen spear him fro,
Brandished and shook it aloft with might,
Till it brake in pieces before his sight;
High towards heaven the splinters flew;
Karl awoke not, he dreamed anew


### LVIII

In his second dream he seemed to dwell
In his palace of Aix, at his own Chapelle.
A bear seized grimly his right arm on,
And bit the flesh to the very bone.
Anon a leopard from Arden wood,
Fiercely flew at him where he stood.
When lo! from his hall, with leap and bound,
Sprang to the rescue a gallant hound.
First from the bear the ear he tore,
Then on the leopard his fangs he bore.
The Franks exclaim, "'Tis a stirring fray,
But who the victor none may say."
Karl awoke not—he slept alway.


### LIX

The night wore by, the day dawn glowed,
Proudly the Emperor rose and rode,
Keenly and oft his host he scanned.
"Lords, my barons, survey this land,
See the passes so straight and steep:
To whom shall I trust the rear to keep?"
"To my stepson Roland:" Count Gan replied.
"Knight like him have you none beside."

The Emperor heard him with moody brow.
" A living demon," he said, " art thou;
Some mortal rage hath thy soul possessed.
To head my vanguard, who then were best?"
"Ogier," he answered, " the gallant Dane,
Braver baron will none remain."

### LX

Roland, when thus the choice he saw,
Spake, full knightly, by knightly law:
" Sir Stepsire, well may I hold thee dear,
That thou hast named me to guard the rear;
Karl shall lose not, if I take heed,
Charger, or palfrey, or mule or steed,
Hackney or sumpter that groom may lead;
The reason else our swords shall tell."
" It is sooth," said Gan, " and I know it well."

### LXI

Fiercely once more Count Roland turned
To speak the scorn that in him burned.
" Ha! deem'st thou, dastard, of dastard race,
That I shall drop the glove in place,
As in sight of Karl thou didst the mace?"

### LXII

Then of his uncle he made demand:
" Yield me the bow that you hold in hand;
Never of me shall the tale be told,
As of Ganelon erst, that it failed my hold."
Sadly the Emperor bowed his head,
With working finger his beard he spread,
Tears in his own despite he shed.

### LXIII

But soon Duke Naimes doth by him stand—
No better vassal in all his band.
"You have seen and heard it all, O sire,
Count Roland waxeth much in ire.
On him the choice for the rear-guard fell,
And where is baron could speed so well?
Yield him the bow that your arm hath bent,
And let good succor to him be lent."
The Emperor reached it forth, and lo!
He gave, and Roland received, the bow.

### LXIV

"Fair Sir Nephew, I tell thee free.
Half of my host will I leave with thee."
"God be my judge," was the count's reply,
"If ever I thus my race belie.
But twenty thousand with me shall rest,
Bravest of all your Franks and best;
The mountain passes in safety tread,
While I breathe in life you have nought to dread."

### LXV

Count Roland sprang to a hill-top's height,
And donned his peerless armor bright;
Laced his helm, for a baron made;
Girt Durindana, gold-hilted blade;
Around his neck he hung the shield,
With flowers emblazoned was the field;
Nor steed but Veillantif will ride;
And he grasped his lance with its pennon's pride.
White was the pennon, with rim of gold;
Low to the handle the fringes rolled.
Who are his lovers men now may see;
And the Franks exclaim, "We will follow thee."

### LXVI

Roland hath mounted his charger on;
Sir Olivier to his side hath gone;
Gerein and his fellow in arms, Gerier;
Otho the Count, and Berengier,
Samson, and with him Anseis old,
Gerard of Roussillon, the bold.
Thither the Gascon Engelier sped;
"I go," said Turpin, "I pledge my head;"
"And I with thee," Count Walter said;
"I am Roland's man, to his service bound."
So twenty thousand knights were found.

### LXVII

Roland beckoned Count Walter then.
"Take of our Franks a thousand men;
Sweep the heights and the passes clear,
That the Emperor's host may have nought to fear."
"I go," said Walter, "at your behest,"
And a thousand Franks around him pressed.
They ranged the heights and passes through,
Nor for evil tidings backward drew,
Until seven hundred swords outflew.
The Lord of Belferna's land, that day,
King Almaris met him in deadly fray.

### LXVIII

Through Roncesvalles the march began;
Ogier, the baron, led the van;
For them was neither doubt nor fear,
Since Roland rested to guard the rear,
With twenty thousand in full array:
Theirs the battle—be God their stay.
Gan knows all; in his felon heart
Scarce hath he courage to play his part.

### LXIX

High were the peaks, and the valleys deep,
The mountains wondrous dark and steep;
Sadly the Franks through the passes wound,
Full fifteen leagues did their tread resound.
To their own great land they are drawing nigh,
And they look on the fields of Gascony.
They think of their homes and their manors there,
Their gentle spouses and damsels fair.
Is none but for pity the tear lets fall;
But the anguish of Karl is beyond them all.
His sister's son at the gates of Spain
Smites on his heart, and he weeps amain.

### LXX

On the Spanish marches the twelve abide,
With twice ten thousand Franks beside.
Fear to die have they none, nor care:
But Karl returns into France the fair;
Beneath his mantle his face he hides.
Naimes, the duke, at his bridle rides.
"Say, sire, what grief doth your heart oppress?"
"To ask," he said, "brings worse distress;
I cannot but weep for heaviness.
By Gan the ruin of France is wrought.
In an angel's vision, last night, methought
He wrested forth from my hand the spear:
'Twas he gave Roland to guard the rear.
God! should I lose him, my nephew dear,
Whom I left on a foreign soil behind,
His peer on earth I shall never find!"

### LXXI

Karl the Great cannot choose but weep,
For him hath his host compassion deep;

And for Roland, a marvellous boding dread.
It was Gan, the felon, this treason bred;
He hath heathen gifts of silver and gold,
Costly raiment, and silken fold,
Horses and camels, and mules and steeds.—
But lo! King Marsil the mandate speeds,
To his dukes, his counts, and his vassals all,
To each almasour and amiral.
And so, before three suns had set,
Four hundred thousand in muster met.
Through Saragossa the tabors sound;
On the loftiest turret they raise Mahound:
Before him the Pagans bend and pray,
Then mount and fiercely ride away,
Across Cerdagna, by vale and height,
Till stream the banners of France in sight,
Where the peers of Carlemaine proudly stand,
And the shock of battle is hard at hand.

## LXXII

Up to King Marsil his nephew rode,
With a mule for steed, and a staff for goad:
Free and joyous his accents fell,
" Fair Sir King, I have served you well.
So let my toils and my perils tell.
I have fought and vanquished for you in field.
One good boon for my service yield,—
Be it mine on Roland to strike the blow;
At point of lance will I lay him low;
And so Mohammed to aid me deign,
Free will I sweep the soil of Spain,
From the gorge of Aspra to Dourestan,
Till Karl grows weary such wars to plan.
Then for your life have you won repose."
King Marsil on him his glove bestows.

### LXXIII

His nephew, while the glove he pressed,
Proudly once more the king addressed.
" Sire, you have crowned my dearest vow;
Name me eleven of your barons now,
In battle against the twelve to bide."
Falsaron first to the call replied;
Brother to Marsil, the king, was he;
"Fair Sir nephew, I go with thee;
In mortal combat we front, to-day,
The rear-guard of the grand array.
Foredoomed to die by our spears are they."

### LXXIV

King Corsablis the next drew nigh,
Miscreant Monarch of Barbary;
Yet he spake like vassal staunch and bold—
Blench would he not for all God's gold.
The third, Malprimis, of Brigal's breed,
More fleet of foot than the fleetest steed,
Before King Marsil he raised his cry,
" On unto Roncesvalles I:
In mine encounter shall Roland die."

### LXXV

An Emir of Balaguet came in place,
Proud of body, and fair of face;
Since first he sprang on steed to ride,
To wear his harness was all his pride;
For feats of prowess great laud he won;
Were he Christian, nobler baron none.
To Marsil came he, and cried aloud,
" Unto Roncesvalles mine arm is vowed;
May I meet with Roland and Olivier,
Or the twelve together, their doom is near.
The Franks shall perish in scathe and scorn;

Karl the Great, who is old and worn,
Weary shall grow his hosts to lead,
And the land of Spain be for ever freed."
King Marsil's thanks were his gracious meed.


### LXXVI

A Mauritanian Almasour
(Breathed not in Spain such a felon Moor)
Stepped unto Marsil, with braggart boast:
"Unto Roncesvalles I lead my host,
Full twenty thousand, with lance and shield.
Let me meet with Roland upon the field,
Lifelong tears for him Karl shall yield."


### LXXVII

Turgis, Count of Tortosa came.
Lord of the city, he bears its name.
Scathe to the Christian to him is best,
And in Marsil's presence he joined the rest.
To the king he said, "Be fearless found;
Peter of Rome cannot mate Mahound.
If we serve him truly, we win this day;
Unto Roncesvalles I ride straightway.
No power shall Roland from slaughter save:
See the length of my peerless glaive,
That with Durindana to cross I go,
And who the victor, ye then shall know.
Sorrow and shame old Karl shall share,
Crown on earth never more shall wear."


### LXXVIII

Lord of Valtierra was Escremis;
Saracen he, and the region his;
He cried to Marsil, amid the throng,
"Unto Roncesvalles I spur along,

The pride of Roland in dust to tread,
Nor shall he carry from thence his head;
Nor Olivier who leads the band.
And of all the twelve is the doom at hand.
The Franks shall perish, and France be lorn,
And Karl of his bravest vassals shorn."


### LXXIX

Estorgan next to Marsil hied,
With Estramarin his mate beside.
Hireling traitors and felons they.
Aloud cried Marsil, " My lords, away
Unto Roncesvalles, the pass to gain,
Of my people's captains ye shall be twain."
" Sire, full welcome to us the call,
On Roland and Olivier we fall.
None the twelve from their death shall screen,
The swords we carry are bright and keen;
We will dye them red with the hot blood's vent,
The Franks shall perish and Karl lament.
We will yield all France as your tribute meet.
Come, that the vision your eyes may greet;
The Emperor's self shall be at your feet."


### LXXX

With speed came Margaris—lord was he
Of the land of Sibilie to the sea;
Beloved of dames for his beauty's sake,
Was none but joy in his look would take,
The goodliest knight of heathenesse,—
And he cried to the king over all the press,
" Sire, let nothing your heart dismay;
I will Roland in Roncesvalles slay,
Nor thence shall Olivier scathless come,
The peers await but their martyrdom.
The Emir of Primis bestowed this blade;
Look on its hilt, with gold inlaid:

It shall crimsoned be with the red blood's trace:
Death to the Franks, and to France disgrace!
Karl the old, with his beard so white,
Shall have pain and sorrow both day and night;
France shall be ours ere a year go by;
At Saint Denys' bourg shall our leaguer lie."
King Marsil bent him reverently.

### LXXXI

Chernubles is there, from the valley black,
His long hair makes on the earth its track;
A load, when it lists him, he bears in play,
Which four mules' burthen would well outweigh.
Men say, in the land where he was born
Nor shineth sun, nor springeth corn,
Nor falleth rain, nor droppeth dew;
The very stones are of sable hue.
'Tis the home of demons, as some assert.
And he cried, " My good sword have I girt,
In Roncesvalles to dye it red.
Let Roland but in my pathway tread,
Trust ye to me that I strike him dead,
His Durindana beat down with mine.
The Franks shall perish and France decline."
Thus were mustered King Marsil's peers,
With a hundred thousand heathen spears.
In haste to press to the battle on,
In a pine-tree forest their arms they don.

### LXXXII

They don their hauberks of Saracen mould,
Wrought for the most with a triple fold;
In Saragossa their helms were made;
Steel of Vienne was each girded blade;
Valentia lances and targets bright,
Pennons of azure and red and white.
They leave their sumpters and mules aside,

Leap on their chargers and serried ride.
Bright was the sunshine and fair the day;
Their arms resplendent gave back the ray.
Then sound a thousand clarions clear,
Till the Franks the mighty clangor hear,
"Sir Comrade," said Olivier, "I trow
There is battle at hand with the Saracen foe."
"God grant," said Roland, "it may be so.
Here our post for our king we hold;
For his lord the vassal bears heat and cold,
Toil and peril endures for him,
Risks in his service both life and limb.
For mighty blows let our arms be strung,
Lest songs of scorn be against us sung.
With the Christian is good, with the heathen ill:
No dastard part shall ye see me fill."

## PART II

# THE PRELUDE OF THE GREAT BATTLE

### LXXXIII

OLIVIER clomb to a mountain height,
  Glanced through the valley that stretched to
    right;
He saw advancing the Saracen men,
And thus to Roland he spake agen:
"What sights and sounds from the Spanish side,
White gleaming hauberks and helms in pride?
In deadliest wrath our Franks shall be!
Ganelon wrought this perfidy;
It was he who doomed us to hold the rear."
"Hush," said Roland; "O Olivier,
No word be said of my stepsire here."

### LXXXIV

Sir Olivier to the peak hath clomb,
Looks far on the realm of Spain therefrom;
He sees the Saracen power arrayed,—
Helmets gleaming with gold inlaid,
Shields and hauberks in serried row,
Spears with pennons that from them flow.
He may not reckon the mighty mass,
So far their numbers his thought surpass.

[The stanzas of the translation not found in the Oxford MS., but taken from
the stanzas inserted from other versions by M. Gautier, are, as regards Part II.
the following: Stanzas 113, 114, 115, 118, 119, 120, 122, 123, 126, 127, 139, 143, 144
145, 146, 163.]

All in bewilderment and dismay,
Down from the mountain he takes his way,
Comes to the Franks the tale to say.

### LXXXV

"I have seen the paynim," said Olivier.
"Never on earth did such host appear:
A hundred thousand with targets bright,
With helmets laced and hauberks white,
Erect and shining their lances tall;
Such battle as waits you did ne'er befall.
My Lords of France, be God your stay,
That you be not vanquished in field to-day."
"Accursed," say the Franks, "be they who fly
None shall blench from the fear to die."

## ROLAND'S PRIDE

### LXXXVI

"In mighty strength are the heathen crew,"
Olivier said, "and our Franks are few;
My comrade, Roland, sound on your horn;
Karl will hear and his host return."
"I were mad," said Roland, "to do such deed;
Lost in France were my glory's meed.
My Durindana shall smite full hard,
And her hilt be red to the golden guard.
The heathen felons shall find their fate;
Their death, I swear, in the pass they wait."

### LXXXVII

"O Roland, sound on your ivory horn,
To the ear of Karl shall the blast be borne:
He will bid his legions backward bend,
And all his barons their aid will lend."

"Now God forbid it, for very shame,
That for me my kindred were stained with blame,
Or that gentle France to such vileness fell:
This good sword that hath served me well,
My Durindana such strokes shall deal,
That with blood encrimsoned shall be the steel.
By their evil star are the felons led;
They shall all be numbered among the dead."

### LXXXVIII

"Roland, Roland, yet wind one blast!
Karl will hear ere the gorge be passed,
And the Franks return on their path full fast."
"I will not sound on mine ivory horn:
It shall never be spoken of me in scorn,
That for heathen felons one blast I blew;
I may not dishonor my lineage true.
But I will strike, ere this fight be o'er,
A thousand strokes and seven hundred more,
And my Durindana shall drip with gore.
Our Franks will bear them like vassals brave
The Saracens flock but to find a grave."

### LXXXIX

"I deem of neither reproach nor stain.
I have seen the Saracen host of Spain,
Over plain and valley and mountain spread,
And the regions hidden beneath their tread.
Countless the swarm of the foe, and we
A marvellous little company."
Roland answered him, "All the more
My spirit within me burns therefore.
God and his angels of heaven defend
That France through me from her glory bend.
Death were better than fame laid low.
Our Emperor loveth a downright blow."

### XC

Roland is daring and Olivier wise,
Both of marvellous high emprise;
On their chargers mounted, and girt in mail,
To the death in battle they will not quail.
Brave are the counts, and their words are high,
And the Pagans are fiercely riding nigh.
"See, Roland, see them, how close they are,
The Saracen foemen, and Karl how far!
Thou didst disdain on thy horn to blow.
Were the king but here we were spared this woe.
Look up through Aspra's dread defile,
Where standeth our doomed rear-guard the while;
They will do their last brave feat this day,
No more to mingle in mortal fray."
"Hush!" said Roland, "the craven tale—
Foul fall who carries a heart so pale;
Foot to foot shall we hold the place,
And rain our buffets and blows apace."

### XCI

When Roland felt that the battle came,
Lion or leopard to him were tame;
He shouted aloud to his Franks, and then
Called to his gentle compeer agen.
"My friend, my comrade, my Olivier,
The Emperor left us his bravest here;
Twice ten thousand he set apart,
And he knew among them no dastard heart.
For his lord the vassal must bear the stress
Of the winter's cold and the sun's excess—
Peril his flesh and his blood thereby:
Strike thou with thy good lance-point and I,
With Durindana, the matchless glaive
Which the king himself to my keeping gave,
That he who wears it when I lie cold
May say 't was the sword of a vassal bold."

### XCII

Archbishop Turpin, above the rest,
Spurred his steed to a jutting crest.
His sermon thus to the Franks he spake:—
"Lords, we are here for our monarch's sake;
Hold we for him, though our death should come;
Fight for the succor of Christendom.
The battle approaches—ye know it well,
For ye see the ranks of the infidel.
Cry *mea culpa,* and lowly kneel;
I will assoil you, your souls to heal.
In death ye are holy martyrs crowned."
The Franks alighted, and knelt on ground;
In God's high name the host he blessed,
And for penance gave them—to smite their best.

### XCIII

The Franks arose from bended knee,
Assoiled, and from their sins set free;
The archbishop blessed them fervently:
Then each one sprang on his bounding barb,
Armed and laced in knightly garb,
Apparelled all for the battle line.
At last said Roland, "Companion mine,
Too well the treason is now displayed,
How Ganelon hath our band betrayed.
To him the gifts and the treasures fell;
But our Emperor will avenge us well.
King Marsil deemeth us bought and sold;
The price shall be with our good swords told."

### XCIV

Roland rideth the passes through,
On Veillantif, his charger true;
Girt in his harness that shone full fair,
And baron-like his lance he bare.

The steel erect in the sunshine gleamed,
With the snow-white pennon that from it streamed;
The golden fringes beat on his hand.
Joyous of visage was he, and bland,
Exceeding beautiful of frame;
And his warriors hailed him with glad acclaim.
Proudly he looked on the heathen ranks,
Humbly and sweetly upon his Franks.
Courteously spake he, in words of grace—
"Ride, my barons, at gentle pace.
The Saracens here to their slaughter toil:
Reap we, to-day, a glorious spoil,
Never fell to Monarch of France the like."
At his word, the hosts are in act to strike.


### XCV

Said Olivier, "Idle is speech, I trow;
Thou didst disdain on thy horn to blow.
Succor of Karl is far apart;
Our strait he knows not, the noble heart:
Not to him nor his host be blame;
Therefore, barons, in God's good name,
Press ye onward, and strike your best,
Make your stand on this field to rest;
Think but of blows, both to give and take,
Never the watchword of Karl forsake."
Then from the Franks resounded high—
"*Montjoie!*"  Whoever had heard that cry
Would hold remembrance of chivalry.
Then ride they—how proudly, O God, they ride!—
With rowels dashed in their coursers' side.
Fearless, too, are their paynim foes.
Frank and Saracen, thus they close.

## The Mellay

### XCVI

King Marsil's nephew, Aelroth his name,
Vaunting in front of the battle came,
Words of scorn on our Franks he cast:
"Felon Franks, ye are met at last,
By your chosen guardian betrayed and sold,
By your king left madly the pass to hold.
This day shall France of her fame be shorn,
And from Karl the mighty his right arm torn."
Roland heard him in wrath and pain!—
He spurred his steed, he slacked the rein,
Drave at the heathen with might and main,
Shattered his shield and his hauberk broke,
Right to the breast-bone went the stroke;
Pierced him, spine and marrow through,
And the felon's soul from his body flew.
A moment reeled he upon his horse,
Then all heavily dropped the corse;
Wrenched was his neck as on earth he fell,
Yet would Roland scorn with scorn repel.
"Thou dastard! never hath Karl been mad,
Nor love for treason or traitors had.
To guard the passes he left us here,
Like a noble king and chevalier.
Nor shall France this day her fame forego.
Strike in, my barons; the foremost blow
Dealt in the fight doth to us belong:
We have the right and these dogs the wrong."

### XCVII

A duke was there, named Falsaron,
Of the land of Dathan and Abiron;
Brother to Marsil, the king, was he;
More miscreant felon ye might not see.
Huge of forehead, his eyes between,

A span of a full half-foot, I ween.
Bitter sorrow was his, to mark
His nephew before him lie slain and stark.
Hastily came he from forth the press,
Raising the war-cry of heathenesse.
Braggart words from his lips were tost:
" This day the honour of France is lost."
Hotly Sir Olivier's anger stirs;
He pricked his steed with golden spurs,
Fairly dealt him a baron's blow,
And hurled him dead from the saddle-bow.
Buckler and mail were reft and rent,
And the pennon's flaps to his heart's blood
    went.
He saw the miscreant stretched on earth:
" Caitiff, thy threats are of little worth.
On, Franks! the felons before us fall;
*Montjoie!* " 'Tis the Emperor's battle-call.


## XCVIII

A king was there of a strange countrie,
King Corsablis of Barbary;
Before the Saracen van he cried,
" Right well may we in this battle bide;
Puny the host of the Franks I deem,
And those that front us, of vile esteem.
Not one by succor of Karl shall fly;
The day hath dawned that shall see them die."
Archbishop Turpin hath heard him well;
No mortal hates he with hate so fell:
He pricked with spurs of the fine gold wrought,
And in deadly passage the heathen sought;
Shield and corselet were pierced and riven,
And the lance's point through his body driven;
To and fro, at the mighty thrust,
He reeled, and then fell stark in dust.
Turpin looked on him, stretched on ground.
" Loud thou liest, thou heathen hound!

King Karl is ever our pride and stay;
Nor one of the Franks shall blench this day,
But your comrades here on the field shall lie;
I bring you tidings: ye all shall die.
Strike, Franks! remember your chivalry;
First blows are ours, high God be praised!"
Once more the cry, *"Montjoie!"* he raised.

### XCIX

Gerein to Malprimis of Brigal sped,
Whose good shield stood him no whit in stead;
Its knob of crystal was cleft in twain,
And one half fell on the battle plain.
Right through the hauberk, and through the skin,
He drave the lance to the flesh within;
Prone and sudden the heathen fell,
And Satan carried his soul to hell.

### C

Anon, his comrade in arms, Gerier,
Spurred at the Emir with levelled spear;
Severed his shield and his mail apart,—
The lance went through them, to pierce his heart.
Dead on the field at the blow he lay.
Olivier said, "'Tis a stirring fray."

### CI

At the Almasour's shield Duke Samson rode—
With blazon of flowers and gold it glowed;
But nor shield nor cuirass availed to save,
When through heart and lungs the lance he drave.
Dead lies he, weep him who list or no.
The Archbishop said, "'Tis a baron's blow."

## CII

Anseis cast his bridle free;
At Turgis, Tortosa's lord, rode he:
Above the centre his shield he smote,
Brake his mail with its double coat,
Speeding the lance with a stroke so true,
That the iron traversed his body through.
So lay he lifeless, at point of spear.
Said Roland, " Struck like a cavalier."

## CIII

Engelier, Gascon of Bordeaux,
On his courser's mane let the bridle flow;
Smote Escremis, from Valtierra sprung,
Shattered the shield from his neck that swung;
On through his hauberk's vental pressed,
And betwixt his shoulders pierced his breast.
Forth from the saddle he cast him dead.
" So shall ye perish all," he said.

## CIV

The heathen Estorgan was Otho's aim:
Right in front of his shield he came;
Rent its colors of red and white,
Pierced the joints of his harness bright,
Flung him dead from his bridle rein.
Said Otho, " Thus shall ye all be slain."

## CV

Berengier smote Estramarin,
Planting his lance his heart within,
Through shivered shield and hauberk torn.
The Saracen to earth was borne

Amid a thousand of his train.
Thus ten of the heathen twelve are slain;
But two are left alive I wis—
Chernubles and Count Margaris.


### CVI

Count Margaris was a valiant knight,
Stalwart of body, and lithe and light:
He spurred his steed unto Olivier,
Brake his shield at the golden sphere,
Pushed the lance till it touched his side;
God of his grace made it harmless glide.
Margaris rideth unhurt withal,
Sounding his trumpet, his men to call.


### CVII

Mingled and marvellous grows the fray,
And in Roland's heart is no dismay.
He fought with lance while his good lance stood;
Fifteen encounters have strained its wood.
At the last it brake; then he grasped in hand
His Durindana, his naked brand.
He smote Chernubles' helm upon,
Where, in the centre, carbuncles shone:
Down through his coif and his fell of hair,
Betwixt his eyes came the falchion bare,
Down through his plated harness fine,
Down through the Saracen's chest and chine,
Down through the saddle with gold inlaid,
Till sank in the living horse the blade,
Severed the spine where no joint was found,
And horse and rider lay dead on ground.
"Caitiff, thou camest in evil hour;
To save thee passeth Mohammed's power.
Never to miscreants like to thee
Shall come the guerdon of victory."

### CVIII

Count Roland rideth the battle through,
With Durindana, to cleave and hew;
Havoc fell of the foe he made,
Saracen corse upon corse was laid,
The field all flowed with the bright blood shed;
Roland, to corselet and arm, was red—
Red his steed to the neck and flank.
Nor is Olivier niggard of blows as frank;
Nor to one of the peers be blame this day,
For the Franks are fiery to smite and slay.
"Well fought," said Turpin, "our barons true!"
And he raised the war-cry, *"Montjoie!"* anew.

### CIX

Through the storm of battle rides Olivier,
His weapon, the butt of his broken spear,
Down upon Malseron's shield he beat,
Where flowers and gold emblazoned meet,
Dashing his eyes from forth his head:
Low at his feet were the brains bespread,
And the heathen lies with seven hundred dead!
Estorgus and Turgin next he slew,
Till the shaft he wielded in splinters flew.
"Comrade!" said Roland, "what makest thou?
Is it time to fight with a truncheon now?
Steel and iron such strife may claim;
Where is thy sword, Hauteclere by name,
With its crystal pommel and golden guard?"
"Of time to draw it I stood debarred,
Such stress was on me of smiting hard."

### CX

Then drew Sir Olivier forth his blade,
As had his comrade Roland prayed.
He proved it in knightly wise straightway,
On the heathen Justin of Val Ferrée.

At a stroke he severed his head in two,
Cleft him body and harness through;
Down through the gold-incrusted selle,
To the horse's chine, the falchion fell:
Dead on the sward lay man and steed.
Said Roland, " My brother, henceforth, indeed!
The Emperor loves us for such brave blows!"
Around them the cry of " *Montjoie!* " arose.

### CXI

Gerein his Sorel rides; Gerier
Is mounted on his own Pass-deer:
The reins they slacken, and prick full well
Against the Saracen Timozel.
One smites his cuirass, and one his shield,
Break in his body the spears they wield;
They cast him dead on the fallow mould.
I know not, nor yet to mine ear was told,
Which of the twain was more swift and bold.
Then Espreveris, Borel's son,
By Engelier unto death was done.
Archbishop Turpin slew Siglorel,
The wizard, who erst had been in hell,
By Jupiter thither in magic led.
" Well have we 'scaped," the archbishop said:
" Crushed is the caitiff," Count Roland replies,
" Olivier, brother, such strokes I prize!"

### CXII

Furious waxeth the fight, and strange;
Frank and heathen their blows exchange;
While these defend, and those assail,
And their lances broken and bloody fail.
Ensign and pennon are rent and cleft,
And the Franks of their fairest youth bereft,
Who will look on mother or spouse no more,
Or the host that waiteth the gorge before.

Karl the Mighty may weep and wail;
What skilleth sorrow, if succour fail?
An evil service was Gan's that day,
When to Saragossa he bent his way,
His faith and kindred to betray.
But a doom thereafter awaited him—
Amerced in Aix, of life and limb,
With thirty of his kin beside,
To whom was hope of grace denied.

### CXIII

King Almaris with his band, the while,
Wound through a marvellous strait defile,
Where doth Count Walter the heights maintain
And the passes that lie at the gates of Spain.
"Gan, the traitor, hath made of us,"
Said Walter, "a bargain full dolorous."

### CXIV

King Almaris to the mount hath clomb,
With sixty thousand of heathendom.
In deadly wrath on the Franks they fall,
And with furious onset smite them all:
Routed, scattered, or slain they lie.
Then rose the wrath of Count Walter high;
His sword he drew, his helm he laced,
Slowly in front of the line he paced,
And with evil greeting his foeman faced.

### CXV

Right on his foemen doth Walter ride,
And the heathen assail him on every side;
Broken down was his shield of might,
Bruised and pierced was his hauberk white;

Four lances at once did his body wound:
No longer bore he—four times he swooned;
He turned perforce from the field aside,
Slowly adown the mount he hied,
And aloud to Roland for succour cried.

## CXVI

Wild and fierce is the battle still:
Roland and Olivier fight their fill;
The Archbishop dealeth a thousand blows
Nor knoweth one of the peers repose;
The Franks are fighting commingled all,
And the foe in hundreds and thousands fall;
Choice have they none but to flee or die,
Leaving their lives despighteously.
Yet the Franks are reft of their chivalry,
Who will see nor parent nor kindred fond,
Nor Karl who waits them the pass beyond.

## CXVII

Now a wondrous storm o'er France hath passed,
With thunder-stroke and whirlwind's blast;
Rain unmeasured, and hail, there came,
Sharp and sudden the lightning's flame;
And an earthquake ran—the sooth I say,
From Besançon city to Wissant Bay;
From Saint Michael's Mount to thy shrine, Cologne,
House unrifted was there none.
And a darkness spread in the noontide high—
No light, save gleams from the cloven sky.
On all who saw came a mighty fear.
They said, "The end of the world is near."
Alas, they spake but with idle breath,—
'Tis the great lament for Roland's death.

### CXVIII

Dread are the omens and fierce the storm,
Over France the signs and wonders swarm:
From noonday on to the vesper hour,
Night and darkness alone have power;
Nor sun nor moon one ray doth shed,
Who sees it ranks him among the dead.
Well may they suffer such pain and woe,
When Roland, captain of all, lies low.
Never on earth hath his fellow been,
To slay the heathen or realms to win.

### CXIX

Stern and stubborn is the fight;
Staunch are the Franks with the sword to smite;
Nor is there one but whose blade is red,
" *Montjoie!* " is ever their war-cry dread.
Through the land they ride in hot pursuit,
And the heathens feel 'tis a fierce dispute.

### CXX

In wrath and anguish, the heathen race
Turn in flight from the field their face;
The Franks as hotly behind them strain.
Then might ye look on a cumbered plain:
Saracens stretched on the green grass bare,
Helms and hauberks that shone full fair,
Standards riven and arms undone:
So by the Franks was the battle won.
The foremost battle that then befell—
O God, what sorrow remains to tell!

### CXXI

With heart and prowess the Franks have stood;
Slain was the heathen multitude;
Of a hundred thousand survive not two:
The archbishop crieth, "O staunch and true!
Written it is in the Frankish geste,
That our Emperor's vassals shall bear them best."
To seek their dead through the field they press,
And their eyes drop tears of tenderness:
Their hearts are turned to their kindred dear.
Marsil the while with his host is near.

### CXXII

Distraught was Roland with wrath and pain;
Distraught were the twelve of Carlemaine—
With deadly strokes the Franks have striven,
And the Saracen horde to the slaughter given;
Of a hundred thousand escaped but one—
King Margaris fled from the field alone;
But no disgrace in his flight he bore—
Wounded was he by lances four.
To the side of Spain did he take his way,
To tell King Marsil what chanced that day.

### CXXIII

Alone King Margaris left the field,
With broken spear and piercèd shield,
Scarce half a foot from the knob remained,
And his brand of steel with blood was stained;
On his body were four lance wounds to see:
Were he Christian, what a baron he!
He sped to Marsil his tale to tell;
Swift at the feet of the king he fell:
"Ride, sire, on to the field forthright,
You will find the Franks in an evil plight;

Full half and more of their host lies slain,
And sore enfeebled who yet remain;
Nor arms have they in their utmost need:
To crush them now were an easy deed,"
Marsil listened with heart aflame.
Onward in search of the Franks he came.


### CXXIV

King Marsil on through the valley sped,
With the mighty host he has marshallèd.
Twice ten battalions the king arrayed:
Helmets shone, with their gems displayed,
Bucklers and braided hauberks bound,
Seven thousand trumpets the onset sound;
Dread was the clangor afar to hear.
Said Roland, "My brother, my Olivier,
Gan the traitor our death hath sworn,
Nor may his treason be now forborne.
To our Emperor vengeance may well belong,—
To us the battle fierce and strong;
Never hath mortal beheld the like.
With my Durindana I trust to strike;
And thou, my comrade, with thy Hauteclere:
We have borne them gallantly otherwhere.
So many fields 'twas ours to gain,
They shall sing against us no scornful strain."


### CXXV

As the Franks the heathen power descried,
Filling the champaign from side to side,
Loud unto Roland they made their call,
And to Olivier and their captains all,
Spake the archbishop as him became:
"O barons, think not one thought of shame;
Fly not, for sake of our God I pray.
That on you be chaunted no evil lay.
Better by far on the field to die;

For in sooth I deem that our end is nigh.
But in holy Paradise ye shall meet,
And with the innocents be your seat."
The Franks exult his words to hear,
And the cry " *Montjoie;* " resoundeth clear.


### CXXVI

King Marsil on the hill-top bides,
While Grandonie with his legion rides.
He nails his flag with three nails of gold:
" Ride ye onwards, my barons bold."
Then loud a thousand clarions rang.
And the Franks exclaimed as they heard the clang—
" O God, our Father, what cometh on !
Woe that we ever saw Ganelon:
Foully, by treason, he us betrayed."
Gallantly then the archbishop said,
" Soldiers and lieges of God are ye,
And in Paradise shall your guerdon be.
To lie on its holy flowerets fair,
Dastard never shall enter there."
Say the Franks, " We will win it every one."
The archbishop bestoweth his benison.
Proudly mounted they at his word,
And, like lions chafed, at the heathen spurred.


### CXXVII

Thus doth King Marsil divide his men:
He keeps around him battalions ten.
As the Franks the other ten descry,
" What dark disaster," they said, " is nigh?
What doom shall now our peers betide?"
Archbishop Turpin full well replied.
" My cavaliers, of God the friends,
Your crown of glory to-day He sends,
To rest on the flowers of Paradise,
That never were won by cowardice."

The Franks made answer, "No cravens we,
Nor shall we gainsay God's decree;
Against the enemy yet we hold,—
Few may we be, but staunch and bold."
Their spurs against the foe they set,
Frank and paynim—once more they met.


### CXXVIII

A heathen of Saragossa came.
Full half the city was his to claim.
It was Climorin: hollow of heart was he,
He had plighted with Gan in perfidy,
What time each other on mouth they kissed,
And he gave him his helm and amethyst.
He would bring fair France from her glory down
And from the Emperor wrest his crown.
He sate upon Barbamouche, his steed,
Than hawk or swallow more swift in speed.
Pricked with the spur, and the rein let flow,
To strike at the Gascon of Bordeaux,
Whom shield nor cuirass availed to save.
Within his harness the point he drave,
The sharp steel on through his body passed,
Dead on the field was the Gascon cast.
Said Climorin, "Easy to lay them low:
Strike in, my pagans, give blow for blow."
For their champion slain, the Franks cry woe.


### CXXIX

Sir Roland called unto Olivier,
"Sir Comrade, dead lieth Engelier;
Braver knight had we none than he."
"God grant," he answered, "revenge to me."
His spurs of gold to his horse he laid,
Grasping Hauteclere with his bloody blade.
Climorin smote he, with stroke so fell,
Slain at the blow was the infidel.

Whose soul the Enemy bore away.
Then turned he, Alphaien, the duke, to slay;
From Escababi the head he shore,
And Arabs seven to the earth he bore.
Saith Roland, " My comrade is much in wrath;
Won great laud by my side he hath;
Us such prowess to Karl endears.
Fight on, fight ever, my cavaliers."


### CXXX

Then came the Saracen Valdabrun,
Of whom King Marsil was foster-son.
Four hundred galleys he owned at sea,
And of all the mariners lord was he.
Jerusalem erst he had falsely won,
Profaned the temple of Solomon,
Slaying the patriarch at the fount.
'Twas he who in plight unto Gan the count,
His sword with a thousand coins bestowed.
Gramimond named he the steed he rode,
Swifter than ever was falcon's flight;
Well did he prick with the sharp spurs bright,
To strike Duke Samson, the fearless knight.
Buckler and cuirass at once he rent,
And his pennon's flaps through his body sent;
Dead he cast him, with levelled spear.
" Strike, ye heathens; their doom is near."
The Franks cry woe for their cavalier.


### CXXXI

When Roland was ware of Samson slain,
Well may you weet of his bitter pain.
With bloody spur he his steed impelled,
While Durindana aloft he held,
The sword more costly than purest gold;
And he smote, with passion uncontrolled,

On the heathen's helm, with its jewelled crown,—
Through head, and cuirass, and body down,
And the saddle embossed with gold, till sank
The griding steel in the charger's flank;
Blame or praise him, the twain he slew.
"A fearful stroke!" said the heathen crew.
"I shall never love you," Count Roland cried.
"With you are falsehood and evil pride."

### CXXXII

From Afric's shore, of Afric's brood,
Malquiant, son of King Malcus stood;
Wrought of the beaten gold, his vest
Flamed to the sun over all the rest.
Saut-perdu hath he named his horse,
Fleeter than ever was steed in course;
He smote Anseis upon the shield,
Cleft its vermeil and azure field,
Severed the joints of his hauberk good,
In his body planted both steel and wood.
Dead he lieth, his day is o'er,
And the Franks the loss of their peer deplore.

### CXXXIII

Turpin rideth the press among;
Never such priest the Mass had sung,
Nor who hath such feats of his body done.
"God send thee," he said, "His malison!
For the knight thou slewest my heart is sore."
He sets the spur to his steed once more,
Smites the shield in Toledo made,
And the heathen low on the sward is laid.

### CXXXIV

Forth came the Saracen Grandonie,
Bestriding his charger Marmorie;

He was son unto Cappadocia's king,
And his steed was fleeter than bird on wing.
He let the rein on his neck decline,
And spurred him hard against Count Gerein,
Shattered the vermeil shield he bore,
And his armor of proof all open tore;
In went the pennon, so fierce the shock,
And he cast him, dead, on a lofty rock;
Then he slew his comrade in arms, Gerier,
Guy of Saint Anton and Berengier.
Next lay the great Duke Astor prone.
The Lord of Valence upon the Rhone.
Among the heathen great joy he cast.
Say the Franks, lamenting, " We perish fast."

### CXXXV

Count Roland graspeth his bloody sword:
Well hath he heard how the Franks deplored;
His heart is burning within his breast.
" God's malediction upon thee rest!
Right dearly shalt thou this blood repay."
His war-horse springs to the spur straightway,
And they come together—go down who may.

### CXXXVI

A gallant captain was Grandonie,
Great in arms and in chivalry.
Never, till then, had he Roland seen,
But well he knew him by form and mien,
By the stately bearing and glance of pride,
And a fear was on him he might not hide.
Fain would he fly, but it skills not here;
Roland smote him with stroke so sheer,
That it cleft the nasal his helm beneath,
Slitting nostril and mouth and teeth,
Cleft his body and mail of plate,
And the gilded saddle whereon he sate,

Deep the back of the charger through:
Beyond all succor the twain he slew.
From the Spanish ranks a wail arose,
And the Franks exult in their champion's blows.


### CXXXVII

The battle is wondrous yet, and dire,
And the Franks are cleaving in deadly ire;
Wrists and ribs and chines afresh,
And vestures, in to the living flesh;
On the green grass streaming the bright blood ran,
"O mighty country, Mahound thee ban!
For thy sons are strong over might of man."
And one and all unto Marsil cried,
"Hither, O king, to our succor ride."


### CXXXVIII

Marvellous yet is the fight around,
The Franks are thrusting with spears embrowned;
And great the carnage there to ken,
Slain and wounded and bleeding men,
Flung, each by other, on back or face.
Hold no more can the heathen race.
They turn and fly from the field apace;
The Franks as hotly pursue in chase.


### CXXXIX

Knightly the deeds by Roland done,
Respite or rest for his Franks is none;
Hard they ride on the heathen rear,
At trot or gallop in full career.
With crimson blood are their bodies stained,
And their brands of steel are snapped or strained;
And when the weapons their hands forsake,
Then unto trumpet and horn they take.

Serried they charge, in power and pride;
And the Saracens cry—"May ill betide
The hour we came on this fatal track!"
So on our host do they turn the back,
The Christians cleaving them as they fled,
Till to Marsil stretcheth the line of dead.

### CXL

King Marsil looks on his legions strown,
He bids the clarion blast be blown,
With all his host he onward speeds:
Abîme the heathen his vanguard leads.
No felon worse in the host than he,
Black of hue as a shrivelled pea;
He believes not in Holy Mary's Son;
Full many an evil deed hath done.
Treason and murder he prizeth more
Than all the gold of Galicia's shore;
Men never knew him to laugh nor jest,
But brave and daring among the best—
Endeared to the felon king therefor;
And the dragon flag of his race he bore.
The archbishop loathed him—full well he might,—
And as he saw him he yearned to smite,
To himself he speaketh, low and quick,
"This heathen seems much a heretic;
I go to slay him, or else to die,
For I love not dastards or dastardy."

### CXLI

The archbishop began the fight once more;
He rode the steed he had won of yore,
When in Denmark Grossaille the king he slew.
Fleet the charger, and fair to view:
His feet were small and fashioned fine,
Long the flank, and high the chine,

Chest and croup full amply spread,
With taper ear and tawny head,
And snow-white tail and yellow mane:
To seek his peer on earth were vain.
The archbishop spurred him in fiery haste,
And, on the moment Abîme he faced,
Came down on the wondrous shield the blow,
The shield with amethysts all aglow,
Carbuncle and topaz, each priceless stone;
'T was once the Emir Galafir's own;
A demon gave it in Metas vale;
But when Turpin smote it might nought avail—
From side to side did his weapon trace,
And he flung him dead in an open space.
Say the Franks, "Such deeds beseem the brave.
Well the archbishop his cross can save."

### CXLII

Count Roland Olivier bespake:
"Sir comrade, dost thou my thought partake?
A braver breathes not this day on earth
Than our archbishop in knightly worth.
How nobly smites he with lance and blade!"
Saith Olivier, "Yea, let us yield him aid;"
And the Franks once more the fight essayed.
Stern and deadly resound the blows.
For the Christians, alas, 't is a tale of woes!

### CXLIII

The Franks of France of their arms are reft,
Three hundred blades alone are left.
The glittering helms they smite and shred,
And cleave asunder full many a head;
Through riven helm and hauberk rent,
Maim head and foot and lineament.

"Disfigured are we," the heathens cry.
"Who guards him not hath but choice to die."
Right unto Marsil their way they take.
"Help, O king, for your people's sake!"
King Marsil heard their cry at hand,
"Mahound destroy thee, O mighty land;
Thy race came hither to crush mine own.
What cities wasted and overthrown,
Doth Karl of the hoary head possess!
Rome and Apulia his power confess,
Constantinople and Saxony;
Yet better die by the Franks than flee.
On, Saracens! recreant heart be none;
If Roland live, we are all foredone."


### CXLIV

Then with the lance did the heathens smite
On shield and gleaming helmet bright;
Of steel and iron arose the clang,
Towards heaven the flames and sparkles sprang;
Brains and blood on the champaign flowed;
But on Roland's heart is a dreary load,
To see his vassals lie cold in death;
His gentle France he remembereth,
And his uncle, the good King Carlemaine;
And the spirit within him groans for pain.


### CXLV

Count Roland entered within the prease,
And smote full deadly without surcease;
While Durindana aloft he held,
Hauberk and helm he pierced and quelled,
Intrenching body and hand and head.
The Saracens lie by the hundred dead,
And the heathen host is discomfited.

### CXLVI

Valiantly Olivier, otherwhere,
Brandished on high his sword Hauteclere—
Save Durindana, of swords the best.
To the battle proudly he him addressed.
His arms with the crimson blood were dyed.
" God, what a vassal ! " Count Roland cried.
" O gentle baron, so true and leal,
This day shall set on our love the seal !
The Emperor cometh to find us dead,
For ever parted and severèd.
France never looked on such woful day;
Nor breathes a Frank but for us will pray,—
From the cloister cells shall the orisons rise,
And our souls find rest in Paradise."
Olivier heard him, amid the throng,
Spurred his steed to his side along.
Saith each to other, " Be near me still;
We will die together, if God so will."

### CXLVII

Roland and Olivier then are seen
To lash and hew with their falchions keen;
With his lance the archbishop thrusts and slays,
And the numbers slain we may well appraise;
In charter and writ is the tale expressed—
Beyond four thousand, saith the geste.
In four encounters they sped them well:
Dire and grievous the fifth befell.
The cavaliers of the Franks are slain
All but sixty, who yet remain;
God preserved them, that ere they die,
They may sell their lives full hardily.

## The Horn

### CXLVIII

As Roland gazed on his slaughtered men,
He bespake his gentle compeer agen:
"Ah, dear companion, may God thee shield!
Behold, our bravest lie dead on field!
Well may we weep for France the fair,
Of her noble barons despoiled and bare.
Had he been with us, our king and friend!
Speak, my brother, thy counsel lend,—
How unto Karl shall we tidings send?"
Olivier answered, "I wist not how.
Liefer death than be recreant now."

### CXLIX

"I will sound," said Roland, "upon my horn,
Karl, as he passeth the gorge, to warn.
The Franks, I know, will return apace."
Said Olivier, "Nay, it were foul disgrace
On your noble kindred to wreak such wrong;
They would bear the stain their lifetime long.
Erewhile I sought it, and sued in vain;
But to sound thy horn thou wouldst not deign.
Not now shall mine assent be won,
Nor shall I say it is knightly done.
Lo! both your arms are streaming red."
"In sooth," said Roland, "good strokes I sped."

### CL

Said Roland, "Our battle goes hard, I fear;
I will sound my horn that Karl may hear."
"'T were a deed unknightly," said Olivier;
"Thou didst disdain when I sought and prayed:
Saved had we been with our Karl to aid;

Unto him and his host no blame shall be:
By this my beard, might I hope to see
My gentle sister Alda's face,
Thou shouldst never hold her in thine embrace."


### CLI

" Ah, why on me doth thine anger fall?"
" Roland, 't is thou who hast wrought it all.
Valor and madness are scarce allied,—
Better discretion than daring pride.
All of thy folly our Franks lie slain,
Nor shall render service to Karl again,
As I implored thee, if thou hadst done,
The king had come and the field were won;
Marsil captive, or slain, I trow.
Thy daring, Roland, hath wrought our woe.
No service more unto Karl we pay,
That first of men till the judgment day;
Thou shalt die, and France dishonored be
Ended our loyal company—
A woful parting this eve shall see."


### CLII

Archbishop Turpin their strife hath heard,
His steed with the spurs of gold he spurred,
And thus rebuked them, riding near:
" Sir Roland, and thou, Sir Olivier,
Contend not, in God's great name, I crave.
Not now availeth the horn to save;
And yet behoves you to wind its call,—
Karl will come to avenge our fall,
Nor hence the foemen in joyance wend.
The Franks will all from their steeds descend;
When they find us slain and martyred here,
They will raise our bodies on mule and bier,
And, while in pity aloud they weep,
Lay us in hallowed earth to sleep;

Nor wolf nor boar on our limbs shall feed."
Said Roland, " Yea, 't is a goodly rede."


### CLIII

Then to his lips the horn he drew,
And full and lustily he blew.
The mountain peaks soared high around;
Thirty leagues was borne the sound.
Karl hath heard it, and all his band.
" Our men have battle," he said, " on hand."
Ganelon rose in front and cried,
" If another spake, I would say he lied."


### CLIV

With deadly travail, in stress and pain,
Count Roland sounded the mighty strain.
Forth from his mouth the bright blood sprang,
And his temples burst for the very pang.
On and onward was borne the blast,
Till Karl hath heard as the gorge he passed,
And Naimes and all his men of war.
" It is Roland's horn," said the Emperor,
" And, save in battle, he had not blown."
" Battle," said Ganelon, " is there none.
Old are you grown—all white and hoar;
Such words bespeak you a child once more.
Have you, then, forgotten Roland's pride,
Which I marvel God should so long abide,
How he captured Noples without your hest?
Forth from the city the heathen pressed,
To your vassal Roland they battle gave,—
He slew them all with the trenchant glaive,
Then turned the waters upon the plain,
That trace of blood might none remain.
He would sound all day for a single hare:

'T is a jest with him and his fellows there;
For who would battle against him dare?
Ride onward—wherefore this chill delay?
Your mighty land is yet far away."


CLV

On Roland's mouth is the bloody stain,
Burst asunder his temple's vein;
His horn he soundeth in anguish drear;
King Karl and the Franks around him hear.
Said Karl, " That horn is long of breath."
Said Naimes, " 'T is Roland who travaileth.
There is battle yonder by mine avow.
He who betrayed him deceives you now.
Arm, sire; ring forth your rallying cry,
And stand your noble household by;
For you hear your Roland in jeopardy."


CLVI

The king commands to sound the alarm.
To the trumpet the Franks alight and arm;
With casque and corselet and gilded brand,
Buckler and stalwart lance in hand,
Pennons of crimson and white and blue,
The barons leap on their steeds anew,
And onward spur the passes through;
Nor is there one but to other saith,
" Could we reach but Roland before his death,
Blows would we strike for him grim and great."
Ah! what availeth!—'t is all too late.


CLVII

The evening passed into brightening dawn.
Against the sun their harness shone;

From helm and hauberk glanced the rays,
And their painted bucklers seemed all ablaze.
The Emperor rode in wrath apart.
The Franks were moody and sad of heart;
Was none but dropped the bitter tear,
For they thought of Roland with deadly fear.——
Then bade the Emperor take and bind
Count Gan, and had him in scorn consigned
To Besgun, chief of his kitchen train.
"Hold me this felon," he said, "in chain."
Then full a hundred round him pressed,
Of the kitchen varlets the worst and best;
His beard upon lip and chin they tore,
Cuffs of the fist each dealt him four,
Roundly they beat him with rods and staves;
Then around his neck those kitchen knaves
Flung a fetterlock fast and strong,
As ye lead a bear in a chain along;
On a beast of burthen the count they cast,
Till they yield him back to Karl at last.

### CLVIII

Dark, vast, and high the summits soar,
The waters down through the valleys pour.
The trumpets sound in front and rear,
And to Roland's horn make answer clear.
The Emperor rideth in wrathful mood,
The Franks in grievous solicitude;
Nor one among them can stint to weep,
Beseeching God that He Roland keep,
Till they stand beside him upon the field,
To the death together their arms to wield.
Ah, timeless succor, and all in vain!
Too long they tarried, too late they strain.

### CLIX

Onward King Karl in his anger goes;
Down on his harness his white beard flows.
The barons of France spur hard behind;
But on all there presseth one grief of mind—
That they stand not beside Count Roland then,
As he fronts the power of the Saracen.
Were he hurt in fight, who would then survive?
Yet three score barons around him strive.
And what a sixty! Nor chief nor king
Had ever such gallant following.

### CLX

Roland looketh to hill and plain,
He sees the lines of his warriors slain,
And he weeps like a noble cavalier,
" Barons of France, God hold you dear,
And take you to Paradise's bowers,
Where your souls may lie on the holy flowers;
Braver vassals on earth were none,
So many kingdoms for Karl ye won;
Years a-many your ranks I led,
And for end like this were ye nurturèd.
Land of France, thou art soothly fair;
To-day thou liest bereaved and bare;
It was all for me your lives you gave,
And I was helpless to shield or save.
May the great God save you who cannot lie.
Olivier, brother, I stand thee by;
I die of grief, if I 'scape unslain:
In, brother, in to the fight again."

### CLXI

Once more pressed Roland within the fight,
His Durindana he grasped with might;

Faldron of Pui did he cleave in two,
And twenty-four of their bravest slew.
Never was man on such vengeance bound;
And, as flee the roe-deer before the hound,
So in face of Roland the heathen flee.
Saith Turpin, "Right well this liketh me.
Such prowess a cavalier befits,
Who harness wears, and on charger sits;
In battle shall he be strong and great,
Or I prize him not at four deniers' rate;
Let him else be monk in a cloister cell,
His daily prayers for our souls to tell."
Cries Roland, " Smite them, and do not spare."
Down once more on the foe they bear,
But the Christian ranks grow thinned and rare.

CLXII

Who knoweth ransom is none for him,
Maketh in battle resistance grim;
The Franks like wrathful lions strike,
But King Marsil beareth him baron-like;
He bestrideth his charger, Gaignon hight,
And he pricketh him hard, Sir Beuve to smite,
The Lord of Beaune and of Dijon town,
Through shield and cuirass, he struck him down:
Dead past succor of man he lay.
Ivon and Ivor did Marsil slay;
Gerard of Roussillon beside.
Not far was Roland, and loud he cried,
" Be thou forever in God's disgrace,
Who hast slain my fellows before my face,
Before we part thou shalt blows essay,
And learn the name of my sword to-day.
Down, at the word, came the trenchant brand,
And from Marsil severed his good right hand:
With another stroke, the head he won
Of the fair-haired Jurfalez, Marsil's son.
"Help us, Mahound!" say the heathen train,

"May our gods avenge us on Carlemaine!
Such daring felons he hither sent,
Who will hold the field till their lives be spent."
"Let us flee and save us," cry one and all,
Unto flight a hundred thousand fall,
Nor can aught the fugitives recall.

### CLXIII

But what availeth? though Marsil fly,
His uncle, the Algalif, still is nigh;
Lord of Carthagena is he,
Of Alferna's shore and Garmalie,
And of Ethiopia, accursed land:
The black battalions at his command,
With nostrils huge and flattened ears,
Outnumber fifty thousand spears;
And on they ride in haste and ire,
Shouting their heathen war-cry dire.
"At last," said Roland, "the hour is come,
Here receive we our martyrdom;
Yet strike with your burnished brands—accursed
Who sells not his life right dearly first;
In life or death be your thought the same,
That gentle France be not brought to shame.
When the Emperor hither his steps hath bent,
And he sees the Saracens' chastisement,
Fifteen of their dead against our one,
He will breathe on our souls his benison."

### DEATH OF OLIVIER

### CLXIV

WHEN Roland saw the abhorrèd race,
Than blackest ink more black in face,
Who have nothing white but the teeth alone,
"Now," he said, "it is truly shown,

That the hour of our death is close at hand.
Fight, my Franks, 't is my last command."
Said Olivier, " Shame is the laggard's due."
And at his word they engage anew.


## CLXV

When the heathen saw that the Franks were few,
Heart and strength from the sight they drew;
They said, " The Emperor hath the worse."
The Algalif sat on a sorrel horse;
He pricked with spurs of the gold refined,
Smote Olivier in the back behind.
On through his harness the lance he pressed,
Till the steel came out at the baron's breast.
" Thou hast it !" the Algalif, vaunting, cried,
" Ye were sent by Karl in an evil tide.
Of his wrongs against us he shall not boast;
In thee alone I avenge our host."


## CLXVI

Olivier felt the deadly wound,
Yet he grasped Hauteclere, with its steel embrowned;
He smote on the Algalif's crest of gold,—
Gem and flowers to the earth were rolled;
Clave his head to the teeth below,
And struck him dead with the single blow.
" All evil, caitiff, thy soul pursue.
Full well our Emperor's loss I knew;
But for thee—thou goest not hence to boast
To wife or dame on thy natal coast,
Of one denier from the Emperor won,
Or of scathe to me or to others done."
Then Roland's aid he called upon.

### CLXVII

Olivier knoweth him hurt to death;
The more to vengeance he hasteneth;
Knightly as ever his arms he bore,
Staves of lances and shields he shore;
Sides and shoulders and hands and feet,—
Whose eyes soever the sight would greet,
How the Saracens all disfigured lie,
Corpse upon corpse, each other by,
Would think upon gallant deeds; nor yet
Doth he the war-cry of Karl forget—
" Montjoie! " he shouted, shrill and clear;
Then called he Roland, his friend and peer,
" Sir, my comrade, anear me ride;
This day of dolor shall us divide."

### CLXVIII

Roland looked Olivier in the face,—
Ghastly paleness was there to trace;
Forth from his wound did the bright blood flow,
And rain in showers to the earth below.
"O God!" said Roland, "is this the end
Of all thy prowess, my gentle friend?
Nor know I whither to bear me now:
On earth shall never be such as thou.
Ah, gentle France, thou art overthrown,
Reft of thy bravest, despoiled and lone;
The Emperor's loss is full indeed!"
At the word he fainted upon his steed.

### CLXIX

See Roland there on his charger swooned,
Olivier smitten with his death wound.
His eyes from bleeding are dimmed and dark,
Nor mortal, near or far, can mark;

And when his comrade beside him pressed,
Fiercely he smote on his golden crest;
Down to the nasal the helm he shred,
But passed no further, nor pierced his head.
Roland marvelled at such a blow,
And thus bespake him soft and low:
"Hast thou done it, my comrade, wittingly?
Roland who loves thee so dear, am I,
Thou hast no quarrel with me to seek?"
Olivier answered, "I hear thee speak,
But I see thee not. God seeth thee.
Have I struck thee, brother? Forgive it me."
"I am not hurt, O Olivier;
And in sight of God, I forgive thee here."
Then each to other his head has laid,
And in love like this was their parting made.

### CLXX

Olivier feeleth his throe begin;
His eyes are turning his head within,
Sight and hearing alike are gone.
He alights and couches the earth upon;
His *Mea Culpa* aloud he cries,
And his hands in prayer unto God arise,
That he grant him Paradise to share,
That he bless King Karl and France the fair,
His brother Roland o'er all mankind;
Then sank his heart, and his head declined,
Stretched at length on the earth he lay,—
So passed Sir Olivier away.
Roland was left to weep alone:
Man so woful hath ne'er been known.

### CLXXI

When Roland saw that life had fled,
And with face to earth his comrade dead.

He thus bewept him, soft and still:
" Ah, friend, thy prowess wrought thee ill!
So many days and years gone by
We lived together, thou and I:
And thou hast never done me wrong,
Nor I to thee, our lifetime long.
Since thou art dead, to live is pain."
He swooned on Veillantif again,
Yet may not unto earth be cast,
His golden stirrups held him fast.

CLXXII

When passed away had Roland's swoon,
With sense restored, he saw full soon
What ruin lay beneath his view.
His Franks have perished all save two—
The archbishop and Walter of Hum alone.
From the mountain-side hath Walter flown,
Where he met in battle the bands of Spain,
And the heathen won and his men were slain
In his own despite to the vale he came;
Called unto Roland, his aid to claim.
" Ah, count! brave gentleman, gallant peer!
Where art thou?  With thee I know not fear.
I am Walter, who vanquished Maelgut of yore,
Nephew to Drouin, the old and hoar.
For knightly deeds I was once thy friend.
I fought the Saracen to the end;
My lance is shivered, my shield is cleft,
Of my broken mail are but fragments left.
I bear in my body eight thrusts of spear;
I die, but I sold my life right dear."
Count Roland heard as he spake the word,
Pricked his steed, and anear him spurred.

### CLXXIII

"Walter," said Roland, "thou hadst affray
With the Saracen foe on the heights to-day.
Thou wert wont a valorous knight to be:
A thousand horsemen gave I thee;
Render them back, for my need is sore."
"Alas, thou seest them never more!
Stretched they lie on the dolorous ground,
Where myriad Saracen swarms we found,—
Armenians, Turks, and the giant brood
Of Balisa, famous for hardihood,
Bestriding their Arab coursers fleet,
Such host in battle 't was ours to meet;
Nor vaunting thence shall the heathen go,—
Full sixty thousand on earth lie low.
With our brands of steel we avenged us well,
But every Frank by the foeman fell.
My hauberk plates are riven wide,
And I bear such wounds in flank and side,
That from every part the bright blood flows,
And feebler ever my body grows.
I am dying fast, I am well aware:
Thy liegeman I, and claim thy care.
If I fled perforce, thou wilt forgive,
And yield me succor while thou dost live."
Roland sweated with wrath and pain,
Tore the skirts of his vest in twain,
Bound Walter's every bleeding vein.

### CLXXIV

In Roland's sorrow his wrath arose,
Hotly he struck at the heathen foes,
Nor left he one of a score alive;
Walter slew six, the archbishop five.
The heathens cry, "What a felon three!
Look to it, lords, that they shall not flee.

Dastard is he who confronts them not;
Craven, who lets them depart this spot."
Their cries and shoutings begin once more,
And from every side on the Franks they pour.

## CLXXV

Count Roland in sooth is a noble peer;
Count Walter, a valorous cavalier;
The archbishop, in battle proved and tried,
Each struck as if knight there were none beside.
From their steeds a thousand Saracens leap,
Yet forty thousand their saddles keep;
I trow they dare not approach them near,
But they hurl against them lance and spear,
Pike and javelin, shaft and dart.
Walter is slain as the missiles part;
The archbishop's shield in pieces shred,
Riven his helm, and pierced his head;
His corselet of steel they rent and tore,
Wounded his body with lances four;
His steed beneath him dropped withal:
What woe to see the archbishop fall!

## CLXXVI

When Turpin felt him flung to ground,
And four lance wounds within him found,
He swiftly rose, the dauntless man,
To Roland looked, and nigh him ran.
Spake but, "I am not overthrown—
Brave warrior yields with life alone."
He drew Almace's burnished steel,
A thousand ruthless blows to deal.
In after time, the Emperor said
He found four hundred round him spread,—
Some wounded, others cleft in twain;
Some lying headless on the plain.

So Giles the saint, who saw it, tells,
For whom High God wrought miracles.
In Laon cell the scroll he wrote;
He little weets who knows it not.


## CLXXVII

Count Roland combateth nobly yet,
His body burning and bathed in sweat;
In his brow a mighty pain, since first,
When his horn he sounded, his temple burst;
But he yearns of Karl's approach to know,
And lifts his horn once more—but oh,
How faint and feeble a note to blow!
The Emperor listened, and stood full still.
" My lords," he said, " we are faring ill.
This day is Roland my nephew's last;
Like dying man he winds that blast.
On! Who would aid, for life must press.
Sound every trump our ranks possess."
Peal sixty thousand clarions high,
The hills re-echo, the vales reply.
It is now no jest for the heathen band.
" Karl! " they cry, " it is Karl at hand! "


## CLXXVIII

They said, " 'Tis the Emperor's advance,
We hear the trumpets resound of France.
If he assail us, hope in vain;
If Roland live, 'tis war again,
And we lose for aye the land of Spain."
Four hundred in arms together drew,
The bravest of the heathen crew;
With serried power they on him press,
And dire in sooth is the count's distress.

### CLXXIX

When Roland saw his coming foes,
All proud and stern his spirit rose;
Alive he shall never be brought to yield:
Veillantif spurred he across the field,
With golden spurs he pricked him well,
To break the ranks of the infidel;
Archbishop Turpin by his side.
"Let us flee, and save us," the heathen cried;
"These are the trumpets of France we hear—
It is Karl, the mighty Emperor, near."

### CLXXX

Count Roland never hath loved the base,
Nor the proud of heart, nor the dastard race,—
Nor knight, but if he were vassal good,—
And he spake to Turpin, as there he stood;
"On foot are you, on horseback I;
For your love I halt, and stand you by.
Together for good and ill we hold;
I will not leave you for man of mould.
We will pay the heathen their onset back,
Nor shall Durindana of blows be slack."
"Base," said Turpin, "who spares to smite:
When the Emperor comes, he will all requite."

### CLXXXI

The heathens said, "We were born to shame.
This day for our disaster came:
Our lords and leaders in battle lost,
And Karl at hand with his marshalled host;
We hear the trumpets of France ring out,
And the cry 'Montjoie!' their rallying shout.
Roland's pride is of such a height,

Not to be vanquished by mortal wight;
Hurl we our missiles, and hold aloof."
And the word they spake, they put in proof,—
They flung, with all their strength and craft,
Javelin, barb, and plumèd shaft.
Roland's buckler was torn and frayed,
His cuirass broken and disarrayed,
Yet entrance none to his flesh they made.
From thirty wounds Veillantif bled,
Beneath his rider they cast him, dead;
Then from the field have the heathen flown:
Roland remaineth, on foot, alone.

### THE LAST BENEDICTION OF THE ARCHBISHOP

#### CLXXXII

THE heathens fly in rage and dread;
To the land of Spain have their footsteps sped;
Nor can Count Roland make pursuit—
Slain is his steed, and he rests afoot;
To succor Turpin he turned in haste,
The golden helm from his head unlaced,
Ungirt the corselet from his breast,
In stripes divided his silken vest;
The archbishop's wounds hath he staunched and
bound,
His arms around him softly wound;
On the green sward gently his body laid,
And, with tender greeting, thus him prayed:
"For a little space, let me take farewell;
Our dear companions, who round us fell,
I go to seek; if I haply find,
I will place them at thy feet reclined."
"Go," said Turpin; "the field is thine—
To God the glory, 't is thine and mine."

## CLXXXIII

Alone seeks Roland the field of fight,
He searcheth vale, he searcheth height.
Ivon and Ivor he found, laid low,
And the Gascon Engelier of Bordeaux,
Gerein and his fellow in arms, Gerier;
Otho he found, and Berengier;
Samson the duke, and Anseis bold,
Gerard of Roussillon, the old.
Their bodies, one after one, he bore,
And laid them Turpin's feet before.
The archbishop saw them stretched arow,
Nor can he hinder the tears that flow;
In benediction his hands he spread:
"Alas! for your doom, my lords," he said,
"That God in mercy your souls may give,
On the flowers of Paradise to live;
Mine own death comes, with anguish sore
That I see mine Emperor never more."

## CLXXXIV

Once more to the field doth Roland wend,
Till he findeth Olivier his friend;
The lifeless form to his heart he strained,
Bore him back with what strength remained,
On a buckler laid him, beside the rest,
The archbishop assoiled them all, and blessed.
Their dole and pity anew find vent,
And Roland maketh his fond lament:
"My Olivier, my chosen one,
Thou wert the noble Duke Renier's son,
Lord of the March unto Rivier vale.
To shiver lance and shatter mail,
The brave in council to guide and cheer,
To smite the miscreant foe with fear,—
Was never on earth such cavalier."

### CLXXXV

Dead around him his peers to see,
And the man he loved so tenderly,
Fast the tears of Count Roland ran,
His visage discolored became, and wan,
He swooned for sorrow beyond control.
"Alas," said Turpin, "how great thy dole!"

### CLXXXVI

To look on Roland swooning there,
Surpassed all sorrow he ever bare;
He stretched his hand, the horn he took,—
Through Roncesvalles there flowed a brook,—
A draught to Roland he thought to bring;
But his steps were feeble and tottering,
Spent his strength, from waste of blood,—
He struggled on for scarce a rood,
When sank his heart, and drooped his frame,
And his mortal anguish on him came.

### CLXXXVII

Roland revived from his swoon again;
On his feet he rose, but in deadly pain;
He looked on high, and he looked below,
Till, a space his other companions fro,
He beheld the baron, stretched on sward,
The archbishop, vicar of God our Lord.
*Mea Culpa* was Turpin's cry,
While he raised his hands to heaven on high,
Imploring Paradise to gain.
So died the soldier of Carlemaine,—
With word or weapon, to preach or fight,
A champion ever of Christian right,
And a deadly foe of the infidel.
God's benediction within him dwell!

### CLXXXVIII

When Roland saw him stark on earth
(His very vitals were bursting forth,
And his brain was oozing from out his head),
He took the fair white hands outspread,
Crossed and clasped them upon his breast,
And thus his plaint to the dead addressed,—
So did his country's law ordain:—
" Ah, gentleman of noble strain,
I trust thee unto God the True,
Whose service never man shall do
With more devoted heart and mind:
To guard the faith, to win mankind,
From the apostles' days till now,
Such prophet never rose as thou.
Nor pain or torment thy soul await,
But of Paradise the open gate."

## The Death of Roland

### CLXXXIX

Roland feeleth his death is near,
His brain is oozing by either ear.
For his peers he prayed—God keep them well;
Invoked the angel Gabriel.
That none reproach him, his horn he clasped;
His other hand Durindana grasped;
Then, far as quarrel from crossbow sent,
Across the march of Spain he went,
Where, on a mound, two trees between,
Four flights of marble steps were seen;
Backward he fell, on the field to lie;
And he swooned anon, for the end was nigh.

## CXC

High were the mountains and high the trees,
Bright shone the marble terraces;
On the green grass Roland hath swooned away.
A Saracen spied him where he lay:
Stretched with the rest he had feigned him dead,
His face and body with blood bespread.
To his feet he sprang, and in haste he hied,—
He was fair and strong and of courage tried,
In pride and wrath he was overbold,—
And on Roland, body and arms, laid hold.
"The nephew of Karl is overthrown!
To Araby bear I this sword, mine own."
He stooped to grasp it, but as he drew,
Roland returned to his sense anew.

## CXCI

He saw the Saracen seize his sword;
His eyes he oped, and he spake one word—
"Thou art not one of our band, I trow,"
And he clutched the horn he would ne'er forego;
On the golden crest he smote him full,
Shattering steel and bone and skull,
Forth from his head his eyes he beat,
And cast him lifeless before his feet.
"Miscreant, makest thou then so free,
As, right or wrong, to lay hold on me?
Who hears it will deem thee a madman born;
Behold the mouth of mine ivory horn
Broken for thee, and the gems and gold
Around its rim to earth are rolled."

## CXCII

Roland feeleth his eyesight reft,
Yet he stands erect with what strength is left;

From his bloodless cheek is the hue dispelled,
But his Durindana all bare he held.
In front a dark brown rock arose—
He smote upon it ten grievous blows.
Grated the steel as it struck the flint,
Yet it brake not, nor bore its edge one dint.
"Mary, Mother, be thou mine aid!
Ah, Durindana, my ill-starred blade,
I may no longer thy guardian be!
What fields of battle I won with thee!
What realms and regions 't was ours to gain,
Now the lordship of Carlemaine!
Never shalt thou possessor know
Who would turn from face of mortal foe;
A gallant vassal so long thee bore,
Such as France the free shall know no more."


### CXCIII

He smote anew on the marble stair.
It grated, but breach nor notch was there.
When Roland found that it would not break,
Thus began he his plaint to make.
"Ah, Durindana, how fair and bright
Thou sparklest, flaming against the light!
When Karl in Maurienne valley lay,
God sent his angel from heaven to say—
'This sword shall a valorous captain's be,'
And he girt it, the gentle king, on me.
With it I vanquished Poitou and Maine,
Provence I conquered and Aquitaine;
I conquered Normandy the free,
Anjou, and the marches of Brittany;
Romagna I won, and Lombardy,
Bavaria, Flanders from side to side,
And Burgundy, and Poland wide;
Constantinople affiance vowed,
And the Saxon soil to his bidding bowed;
Scotia, and Wales, and Ireland's plain,

Of England made he his own domain.
What mighty regions I won of old,
For the hoary-headed Karl to hold!
But there presses on me a grievous pain,
Lest thou in heathen hands remain.
O God our Father, keep France from stain!"

## CXCIV

His strokes once more on the brown rock fell,
And the steel was bent past words to tell;
Yet it brake not, nor was notched the grain,
Erect it leaped to the sky again.
When he failed at the last to break his blade,
His lamentation he inly made.
" Oh, fair and holy, my peerless sword,
What relics lie in thy pommel stored!
Tooth of Saint Peter, Saint Basil's blood,
Hair of Saint Denis beside them strewed,
Fragment of holy Mary's vest.
'Twere shame that thou with the heathen rest;
Thee should the hand of a Christian serve
One who would never in battle swerve.
What regions won I with thee of yore,
The empire now of Karl the hoar!
Rich and mighty is he therefore."

## CXCV

That death was on him he knew full well;
Down from his head to his heart it fell.
On the grass beneath a pine-tree's shade,
With face to earth, his form he laid,
Beneath him placed he his horn and sword,
And turned his face to the heathen horde.
Thus hath he done the sooth to show,
That Karl and his warriors all may know,
That the gentle count a conqueror died.
*Mea Culpa* full oft he cried;

And, for all his sins, unto God above,
In sign of penance, he raised his glove.


### CXCVI

Roland feeleth his hour at hand;
On a knoll he lies towards the Spanish land.
With one hand beats he upon his breast:
"In thy sight, O God, be my sins confessed.
From my hour of birth, both the great and small,
Down to this day, I repent of all."
As his glove he raises to God on high,
Angels of heaven descend him nigh.


### CXCVII

Beneath a pine was his resting-place,
To the land of Spain hath he turned his face,
On his memory rose full many a thought—
Of the lands he won and the fields he fought;
Of his gentle France, of his kin and line;
Of his nursing father, King Karl benign;—
He may not the tear and sob control,
Nor yet forgets he his parting soul.
To God's compassion he makes his cry:
"O Father true, who canst not lie,
Who didst Lazarus raise unto life agen,
And Daniel shield in the lions' den;
Shield my soul from its peril, due
For the sins I sinned my lifetime through."
He did his right-hand glove uplift—
Saint Gabriel took from his hand the gift;
Then drooped his head upon his breast,
And with claspèd hands he went to rest.
God from on high sent down to him
One of his angel Cherubim—
Saint Michael of Peril of the sea,
Saint Gabriel in company—
From heaven they came for that soul of price,
And they bore it with them to Paradise.

## PART III
# THE REPRISALS

### The Chastisement of the Saracens

#### CXCVIII

DEAD is Roland; his soul with God.
    While to Roncesvalles the Emperor rode,
    Where neither path nor track he found,
Nor open space nor rood of ground,
But was strewn with Frank or heathen slain,
"Where art thou, Roland?" he cried in pain:
"The Archbishop where, and Olivier,
Gerein and his brother in arms, Gerier?
Count Otho where, and Berengier,
Ivon and Ivor, so dear to me;
And Engelier of Gascony;
Samson the duke, and Anseis the bold;
Gerard, of Roussillon, the old;
My peers, the twelve whom I left behind?"
In vain!— No answer may he find.
"O God," he cried, "what grief is mine
That I was not in front of this battle line!"
For very wrath his beard he tore,
His knights and barons weeping sore;
Aswoon full fifty thousand fall;
Duke Naimes hath pity and dole for all.

#### CXCIX

Nor knight nor baron was there to see
But wept full fast, and bitterly;
For son and brother their tears descend,
For lord and liege, for kin and friend;

Aswoon all numberless they fell,
But Naimes did gallantly and well.
He spake the first to the Emperor—
" Look onward, sire, two leagues before,
See the dust from the ways arise,—
There the strength of the heathen lies.
Ride on; avenge you for this dark day."
" O God," said Karl, " they are far away!
Yet for right and honor, the sooth ye say.
Fair France's flower they have torn from me."
To Otun and Gebouin beckoned he,
To Tybalt of Rheims, and Milo the count.
" Guard the battle-field, vale, and mount—
Leave the dead as ye see them lie;
Watch, that nor lion nor beast come nigh,
Nor on them varlet or squire lay hand;
None shall touch them, 'tis my command,
Till with God's good grace we return again."
They answered lowly, in loving strain,
" Great lord, fair sire, we will do your hest,"
And a thousand warriors with them rest.

CC

The Emperor bade his clarions ring,
Marched with his host the noble king.
They came at last on the heathens' trace,
And all together pursued in chase;
But the king of the falling eve was ware:
He alighted down in a meadow fair,
Knelt on the earth unto God to pray
That he make the sun in his course delay,
Retard the night, and prolong the day.
Then his wonted angel who with him spake,
Swiftly to Karl did answer make,
" Ride on! Light shall not thee forego;
God seeth the flower of France laid low;
Thy vengeance wreak on the felon crew."
The Emperor sprang to his steed anew.

### CCI

God wrought for Karl a miracle:
In his place in heaven the sun stood still.
The heathens fled, the Franks pursued,
And in Val Tenèbres beside them stood;
Towards Saragossa the rout they drave,
And deadly were the strokes they gave.
They barred against them path and road;
In front the water of Ebro flowed:
Strong was the current, deep and large,
Was neither shallop, nor boat, nor barge.
With a cry to their idol Termagaunt,
The heathens plunge, but with scanty vaunt.
Encumbered with their armor's weight,
Sank the most to the bottom, straight;
Others floated adown the stream;
And the luckiest drank their fill, I deem:
All were in marvellous anguish drowned.
Cry the Franks, " In Roland your fate ye found."

### CCII

As he sees the doom of the heathen host,
Slain are some and drowned the most,
(Great spoil have won the Christian knights),
The gentle king from his steed alights,
And kneels, his thanks unto God to pour:
The sun had set as he rose once more.
" It is time to rest," the Emperor cried,
"And to Roncesvalles 't were late to ride.
Our steeds are weary and spent with pain;
Strip them of saddle and bridle-rein,
Free let them browse on the verdant mead."
" Sire," say the Franks, " it were well indeed."

### CCIII

The Emperor hath his quarters ta'en,
And the Franks alight in the vacant plain;

The saddles from their steeds they strip,
And the bridle-reins from their heads they slip;
They set them free on the green grass fair,
Nor can they render them other care.
On the ground the weary warriors slept;
Watch nor vigil that night they kept.


### CCIV

In the mead the Emperor made his bed,
With his mighty spear beside his head,
Nor will he doff his arms to-night,
But lies in his broidered hauberk white.
Laced is his helm, with gold inlaid,
Girt on Joyeuse, the peerless blade,
Which changes thirty times a day
The brightness of its varying ray.
Nor may the lance unspoken be
Which pierced our Saviour on the tree;
Karl hath its point—so God him graced—
Within his golden hilt enchased.
And for this honor and boon of heaven,
The name Joyeuse to the sword was given;
The Franks may hold it in memory.
Thence came *"Montjoie,"* their battle-cry,
And thence no race with them may vie.


### CCV

Clear was the night, and the fair moon shone,
But grief weighed heavy King Karl upon;
He thought of Roland and Olivier,
Of his Franks and every gallant peer,
Whom he left to perish in Roncesvale,
Nor can he stint but to weep and wail,
Imploring God their souls to bless,—
Till, overcome with long distress,
He slumbers at last for heaviness.

The Franks are sleeping throughout the meads;
Nor rest on foot can the weary steeds—
They crop the herb as they stretch them prone.—
Much hath he learned who hath sorrow known.


### CCVI

The Emperor slumbered like man forespent,
While God his angel Gabriel sent
The couch of Carlemaine to guard.
All night the angel kept watch and ward,
And in a vision to Karl presaged
A coming battle against him waged.
'T was shown in fearful augury;
The king looked upward to the sky—
There saw he lightning, and hail, and storm,
Wind and tempest in fearful form.
A dread apparel of fire and flame,
Down at once on his host they came.
Their ashen lances the flames enfold,
And their bucklers in to the knobs of gold;
Grated the steel of helm and mail.
Yet other perils the Franks assail,
And his cavaliers are in deadly strait.
Bears and lions to rend them wait,
Wiverns, snakes and fiends of fire,
More than a thousand griffins dire;
Enfuried at the host they fly.
"Help us, Karl!" was the Franks' outcry,
Ruth and sorrow the king beset;
Fain would he aid, but was sternly let.
A lion came from the forest path,
Proud and daring, and fierce in wrath;
Forward sprang he the king to grasp,
And each seized other with deadly clasp;
But who shall conquer or who shall fall,
None knoweth. Nor woke the king withal.

### CCVII

Another vision came him o'er:
He was in France, his land, once more;
In Aix, upon his palace stair,
And held in double chain a bear.
When thirty more from Arden ran,
Each spake with voice of living man:
" Release him, sire!" aloud they call;
" Our kinsman shall not rest in thrall.
To succor him our arms are bound."
Then from the palace leaped a hound,
On the mightiest of the bears he pressed,
Upon the sward, before the rest.
The wondrous fight King Karl may see,
But knows not who shall victor be.
These did the angel to Karl display;
But the Emperor slept till dawning day.

### CCVIII

At morning-tide when day-dawn broke,
The Emperor from his slumber woke.
His holy guardian, Gabriel,
With hand uplifted sained him well.
The king aside his armor laid,
And his warriors all were disarrayed.
Then mount they, and in haste they ride,
Through lengthening path and highway wide
Until they see the doleful sight
In Roncesvalles, the field of fight.

### CCIX

Unto Roncesvalles King Karl hath sped,
And his tears are falling above the dead;
" Ride, my barons, at gentle pace,—
I will go before, a little space,

For my nephew's sake, whom I fain would find.
It was once in Aix, I recall to mind,
When we met at the yearly festal-tide,—
My cavaliers in vaunting vied
Of stricken fields and joustings proud,—
I heard my Roland declare aloud,
In foreign land would he never fall
But in front of his peers and his warriors all,
He would lie with head to the foeman's shore,
And make his end like a conqueror."
Then far as man a staff might fling,
Clomb to a rising knoll the king.


### CCX

As the king in quest of Roland speeds,
The flowers and grass throughout the meads
He sees all red with our baron's blood,
And his tears of pity break forth in flood.
He upward climbs, till, beneath two trees,
The dints upon the rock he sees.
Of Roland's corse he was then aware;
Stretched it lay on the green grass bare.
No marvel sorrow the king oppressed;
He alighted down, and in haste he pressed,
Took the body his arms between,
And fainted: dire his grief I ween.


### CCXI

As did reviving sense begin,
Naimes, the duke, and Count Acelin,
The noble Geoffrey of Anjou,
And his brother Henry nigh him drew.
They made a pine-tree's trunk his stay;
But he looked to earth where his nephew lay,
And thus all gently made his dole:
"My friend, my Roland, God guard thy soul!

Never on earth such knight hath been,
Fields of battle to fight and win.
My pride and glory, alas, are gone!"
He endured no longer; he swooned anon.

### CCXII

As Karl the king revived once more,
His hands were held by barons four.
He saw his nephew, cold and wan;
Stark his frame, but his hue was gone;
His eyes turned inward, dark and dim;
And Karl in love lamented him:
"Dear Roland, God thy spirit rest
In Paradise, amongst His blest!
In evil hour thou soughtest Spain:
No day shall dawn but sees my pain,
And me of strength and pride bereft.
No champion of mine honor left;
Without a friend beneath the sky;
And though my kindred still be nigh,
Is none like thee their ranks among."
With both his hands his beard he wrung.
The Franks bewailed in unison;
A hundred thousand wept like one.

### CCXIII

"Dear Roland, I return again
To Laon, to mine own domain;
Where men will come from many a land,
And seek Count Roland at my hand.
A bitter tale must I unfold—
'In Spanish earth he lieth cold,'
A joyless realm henceforth I hold,
And weep with daily tears untold.

### CCXIV

"Dear Roland, beautiful and brave,
All men of me will tidings crave,
When I return to La Chapelle.
Oh, what a tale is mine to tell!
That low my glorious nephew lies.
Now will the Saxon foeman rise;
Bulgar and Hun in arms will come,
Apulia's power, the might of Rome,
Palermitan and Afric bands,
And men from fierce and distant lands.
To sorrow sorrow must succeed;
My hosts to battle who shall lead,
When the mighty captain is overthrown?
Ah! France deserted now, and lone.
Come, death, before such grief I bear."
Once more his beard and hoary hair
Began he with his hands to tear;
A hundred thousand fainted there.

### CCXV.

"Dear Roland, and was this thy fate?
May Paradise thy soul await.
Who slew thee wrought fair France's bane:
I cannot live, so deep my pain.
For me my kindred lie undone;
And would to Holy Mary's Son,
Ere I at Cizra's gorge alight,
My soul may take its parting flight:
My spirit would with theirs abide;
My body rest their dust beside."
With sobs his hoary beard he tore.
"Alas!" said Naimes, "for the Emperor."

### CCXVI

"Sir Emperor," Geoffrey of Anjou said,
"Be not by sorrow so sore misled.

Let us seek our comrades throughout the plain,
Who fell by the hands of the men of Spain;
And let their bodies on biers be borne."
"Yea," said the Emperor. "Sound your horn."

### CCXVII

Now doth Count Geoffrey his bugle sound,
And the Franks from their steeds alight to ground
As they their dead companions find,
They lay them low on biers reclined;
Nor prayers of bishop or abbot ceased,
Of monk or canon, or tonsured priest.
The dead they blessed in God's great name,
Set myrrh and frankincense aflame.
Their incense to the dead they gave,
Then laid them, as beseemed the brave—
What could they more?—in honored grave.

### CCXVIII

But the king kept watch o'er Roland's bier
O'er Turpin and Sir Olivier.
He bade their bodies opened be,
Took the hearts of the barons three,
Swathed them in silken cerements light,
Laid them in urns of the marble white.
Their bodies did the Franks enfold
In skins of deer, around them rolled;
Laved them with spices and with wine,
Till the king to Milo gave his sign,
To Tybalt, Otun, and Gebouin;
Their bodies three on biers they set,
Each in its silken coverlet.
*    *    *    *    *    *    *

### CCXIX

To Saragossa did Marsil flee.
He alighted beneath an olive tree,

And sadly to his serfs he gave
His helm, his cuirass, and his glaive,
Then flung him on the herbage green;
Came nigh him Bramimonde his queen.
Shorn from his wrist was his right hand good;
He swooned for pain and waste of blood.
The queen, in anguish, wept and cried,
With twenty thousand by her side.
King Karl and gentle France they cursed;
Then on their gods their anger burst.
Unto Apollin's crypt they ran,
And with revilings thus began:
"Ah, evil-hearted god, to bring
Such dark dishonor on our king.
Thy servants ill dost thou repay."
His crown and wand they wrench away,
They bind him to a pillar fast,
And then his form to earth they cast,
His limbs with staves they bruise and break:
From Termagaunt his gem they take:
Mohammed to a trench they bear,
For dogs and boars to tread and tear.


### CCXX

Within his vaulted hall they bore
King Marsil, when his swoon was o'er;
The hall with colored writings stained.
And loud the queen in anguish plained,
The while she tore her streaming hair,
"Ah, Saragossa, reft and bare,
Thou seest thy noble king o'erthrown!
Such felony our gods have shown,
Who failed in fight his aids to be.
The Emir comes—a dastard he,
Unless he will that race essay,
Who proudly fling their lives away.
Their Emperor of the hoary beard,
In valor's desperation reared,

Will never fly for mortal foe.
Till he be slain, how deep my woe!"[1]

\*        \*        \*        \*        \*        \*        \*

## CCXXI

Fierce is the heat and thick the dust.
The Franks the flying Arabs thrust.
To Saragossa speeds their flight.
The queen ascends a turret's height.
The clerks and canons on her wait,
Of that false law God holds in hate.
Order or tonsure have they none.
And when she thus beheld undone
The Arab power, all disarrayed,
Aloud she cried, " Mahound us aid!
My king! defeated is our race,
The Emir slain in foul disgrace."
King Marsil turns him to the wall,
And weeps—his visage darkened all.
He dies for grief—in sin he dies,
His wretched soul the demon's prize.

## CCXXII

Dead lay the heathens, or turned to flight,
And Karl was victor in the fight.
Down Saragossa's wall he brake—
Defence he knew was none to make.
And as the city lay subdued,
The hoary king all proudly stood,
There rested his victorious powers.
The queen hath yielded up the towers—
Ten great towers and fifty small.
Well strives he whom God aids withal.

---

[1] Here intervenes the episode of the great battle fought between Charlemagne and Baligant, Emir of Babylon, who had come, with a mighty army,
to the succor of King Marsil his vassal.  This episode has been suspected
of being a later interpolation.  The translation is resumed at the end of
the battle, after the Emir had been slain by Charlemagne's own hand, and
when the Franks enter Saragossa in pursuit of the Saracens.

### CCXXIII

Day passed; the shades of night drew on,
And moon and stars refulgent shone.
Now Karl is Saragossa's lord,
And a thousand Franks, by the king's award,
Roam the city, to search and see
Where mosque or synagogue may be.
With axe and mallet of steel in hand,
They let nor idol nor image stand;
The shrines of sorcery down they hew,
For Karl hath faith in God the True,
And will Him righteous service do.
The bishops have the water blessed,
The heathen to the font are pressed.
If any Karl's command gainsay,
He has him hanged or burned straightway.
So a hundred thousand to Christ are won;
But Bramimonde the queen alone
Shall unto France be captive brought,
And in love be her conversion wrought.


### CCXXIV

Night passed, and came the daylight hours,
Karl garrisoned the city's towers;
He left a thousand valiant knights,
To sentinel their Emperor's rights.
Then all his Franks ascend their steeds,
While Bramimonde in bonds he leads,
To work her good his sole intent.
And so, in pride and strength, they went;
They passed Narbonne in gallant show,
And reached thy stately walls, Bordeaux.
There, on Saint Severin's altar high,
Karl placed Count Roland's horn to lie,
With mangons filled, and coins of gold,
As pilgrims to this hour behold.
Across Garonne he bent his way,

In ships within the stream that lay,
And brought his nephew unto Blaye,
With his noble comrade, Olivier,
And Turpin sage, the gallant peer.
Of the marble white their tombs were made;
In Saint Roman's shrine are the baron's laid,
Whom the Franks to God and his saints commend.
And Karl by hill and vale doth wend,
Nor stays till Aix is reached, and there
Alighteth on his marble stair.
When sits he in his palace hall,
He sends around to his judges all,
From Frisia, Saxony, Loraine,
From Burgundy and Allemaine,
From Normandy, Brittaine, Poitou:
The realm of France he searches through,
And summons every sagest man.
The plea of Ganelon then began.


### CCXXV

From Spain the Emperor made retreat,
To Aix in France, his kingly seat;
And thither, to his halls, there came,
Alda, the fair and gentle dame.
"Where is my Roland, sire," she cried,
"Who vowed to take me for his bride?"
O'er Karl the flood of sorrow swept;
He tore his beard and loud he wept.
"Dear sister, gentle friend," he said,
"Thou seekest one who lieth dead:
I plight to thee my son instead,—
Louis, who lord of my realm shall be."
"Strange," she said, "seems this to me.
God and his angels forbid that I
Should live on earth if Roland die."
Pale grew her cheek—she sank amain,
Down at the feet of Carlemaine.
So died she. God receive her soul!
The Franks bewail her in grief and dole.

### CCXXVI

So to her death went Alda fair.
The king but deemed she fainted there.
While dropped his tears of pity warm,
He took her hands and raised her form.
Upon his shoulder drooped her head,
And Karl was ware that she was dead.
When thus he saw that life was o'er,
He summoned noble ladies four.
Within a cloister was she borne;
They watched beside her until morn;
Beneath a shrine her limbs were laid;—
Such honor Karl to Alda paid.

### CCXXVII

The Emperor sitteth in Aix again,
With Gan, the felon, in iron chain,
The very palace walls beside,
By serfs unto a stake was tied.
They bound his hands with leathern thong,
Beat him with staves and cordage strong;
Nor hath he earned a better fee.
And there in pain awaits his plea.

### CCXXVIII

'Tis written in the ancient geste,
How Karl hath summoned east and west.
At La Chapelle assembled they;
High was the feast and great the day—
Saint Sylvester's, the legend ran.
The plea and judgment then began
Of Ganelon, who the treason wrought,
Now face to face with his Emperor brought.

### CCXXIX

"Lords, my barons," said Karl the king,
"On Gan be righteous reckoning:
He followed in my host to Spain;
Through him ten thousand Franks lie slain
And slain was he, my sister's son,
Whom never more ye look upon,
With Olivier the sage and bold,
And all my peers, betrayed for gold."
"Shame befall me," said Gan, "if I
Now'or ever the deed deny;
Foully he wronged me in wealth and land,
And I his death and ruin planned:
Therein, I say, was treason none."
They said, "We will advise thereon."

### CCXXX.

Count Gan to the Emperor's presence came,
Fresh of hue and lithe of frame,
With a baron's mien, were his heart but true.
On his judges round his glance he threw,
And on thirty kinsmen by his side,
And thus, with mighty voice, he cried:
"Hear me, barons, for love of God.
In the Emperor's host was I abroad—
Well I served him, and loyally,
But his nephew, Roland, hated me:
He doomed my doom of death and woe,
That I to Marsil's court should go.
My craft the danger put aside,
But Roland loudly I defied,
With Olivier, and all their crew,
As Karl, and these his barons, knew.
Vengeance, not treason, have I wrought."
"Thereon," they answered, "take we thought."

### CCXXXI

When Ganelon saw the plea begin,
He mustered thirty of his kin,
With one revered by all the rest—
Pinabel of Sorrence's crest.
Well can his tongue his cause unfold,
And a vassal brave his arms to hold.
"Thine aid," said Ganelon, "I claim;
To rescue me from death and shame."
Said Pinabel, "Rescued shalt thou be.
Let any Frank thy death decree,
And, wheresoe'er the king deems meet,
I will him body to body greet,
Give him the lie with my brand of steel."
Ganelon sank at his feet to kneel.

### CCXXXII

Come Frank and Norman to council in,
Bavarian, Saxon, and Poitevin,
With all the barons of Teuton blood;
But the men of Auvergne are mild of mood—
Their hearts are swayed unto Pinabel.
Saith each to other, "Pause we well.
Let us leave this plea, and the king implore
To set Count Ganelon free once more,
Henceforth to serve him in love and faith:
Count Roland lieth cold in death:
Not all the gold beneath the sky
Can give him back to mortal eye;
Such battle would but madness be."
They all applauded his decree,
Save Thierry—Geoffrey's brother he.

### CCXXXIII

The barons came the king before.
"Fair Sire, we all thy grace implore,

That Gan be suffered free to go,
His faith and love henceforth to show.
Oh, let him live—a noble he.
Your Roland you shall never see:
No wealth of gold may him recall."
Karl answered, " Ye are felons all."


### CCXXXIV

When Karl saw all forsake him now,
Dark grew his face and drooped his brow.
He said, " Of men most wretched I ! "
Stepped forth Thierry speedily,
Duke Geoffrey's brother, a noble knight,
Spare of body, and lithe and light,
Dark his hair and his hue withal,
Nor low of stature, nor over tall :
To Karl, in courteous wise, he said,
" Fair Sire, be not disheartenèd.
I have served you truly, and, in the name
Of my lineage, I this quarrel claim.
If Roland wronged Sir Gan in aught,
Your service had his safeguard wrought.
Ganelon bore him like caitiff base,
A perjured traitor before your face.
I adjudge him to die on the gallows tree ;
Flung to the hounds let his carcase be,
The doom of treason and felony.
Let kin of his but say I lie,
And with this girded sword will I
My plighted word in fight maintain."
" Well spoken," cry the Franks amain.


### CCXXXV

Sir Pinabel stood before Karl in place,
Vast of body and swift of pace,—
Small hope hath he whom his sword may smite.
" Sire, it is yours to decide the right.

Bid this clamor around to pause.
Thierry hath dared to adjudge the cause;
He lieth. Battle thereon I do."
And forth his right-hand glove he drew.
But the Emperor said, " In bail to me
Shall thirty of his kinsmen be;
I yield him pledges on my side:
Be they guarded well till the right be tried."
When Thierry saw the fight shall be,
To Karl his right glove reacheth he;
The Emperor gave his pledges o'er.
And set in place were benches four—
Thereon the champions take their seat,
And all is ranged in order meet,—
The preparations Ogier speeds,—
And both demand their arms and steeds.


### CCXXXVI

But yet, ere lay they lance in rest,
They make their shrift, are sained and blessed;
They hear the Mass, the Host receive,
Great gifts to church and cloister leave.
They stand before the Emperor's face;
The spurs upon their feet they lace;
Gird on their corselets, strong and light;
Close on their heads the helmets bright.
The golden hilts at belt are hung;
Their quartered shields from shoulder swung.
In hand the mighty spears they lift,
Then spring they on their chargers swift.
A hundred thousand cavaliers
The while for Thierry drop their tears;
They pity him for Roland's sake.
God knows what end the strife will take.


### CCXXXVII

At Aix is a wide and grassy plain,
Where met in battle the barons twain.

Both of valorous knighthood are,
Their chargers swift and apt for war.
They prick them hard with slackened rein;
Drive each at other with might and main.
Their bucklers are in fragments flung,
Their hauberks rent, their girths unstrung;
With saddles turned, they earthward rolled.
A hundred thousand in tears behold.


### CCXXXVIII

Both cavaliers to earth are gone,
Both rise and leap on foot anon.
Strong is Pinabel, swift and light;
Each striketh other, unhorsed they fight;
With golden-hilted swords, they deal
Fiery strokes on the helms of steel.
Trenchant and fierce is their every blow.
The Franks look on in wondrous woe.
"O God," saith Karl, "Thy judgment show."


### CCXXXIX

"Yield thee, Thierry," said Pinabel.
"In love and faith will I serve thee well,
And all my wealth to thy feet will bring,
Win Ganelon's pardon from the king."
"Never," Thierry in scorn replied,
"Shall thought so base in my bosom bide!
God betwixt us this day decide."


### CCXL

"Ah, Pinabel!" so Thierry spake,
"Thou art a baron of stalwart make,
Thy knighthood known to every peer,—
Come, let us cease this battle here.

With Karl thy concord shall be won,
But on Ganelon be justice done;
Of him henceforth let speech be none."
"No," said Pinabel; "God forefend!
My kinsman I to the last defend;
Nor will I blench for mortal face,—
Far better death than such disgrace."
Began they with their glaves anew
The gold-encrusted helms to hew;
Towards heaven the fiery sparkles flew.
They shall not be disjoined again,
Nor end the strife till one be slain.

### CCXLI

Pinabel, lord of Sorrence's keep,
Smote Thierry's helm with stroke so deep
The very fire that from it came
Hath set the prairie round in flame;
The edge of steel did his forehead trace
Adown the middle of his face;
His hauberk to the centre clave.
God deigned Thierry from death to save.

### CCXLII

When Thierry felt him wounded so,
For his bright blood flowed on the grass below,
He smote on Pinabel's helmet brown,
Cut and clave to the nasal down;
Dashed his brains from forth his head,
And, with stroke of prowess, cast him dead.
Thus, at a blow, was the battle won:
"God," say the Franks, "hath this marvel done."

### CCXLIII

When Thierry thus was conqueror,
He came the Emperor Karl before.

Full fifty barons were in his train,
Duke Naimes, and Ogier the noble Dane,
Geoffrey of Anjou and William of Blaye.
Karl clasped him in his arms straightway
With skin of sable he wiped his face;
Then cast it from him, and, in its place,
Bade him in fresh attire be drest.
His armor gently the knights divest;
On an Arab mule they make him ride:
So returns he, in joy and pride.
To the open plain of Aix they come,
Where the kin of Ganelon wait their doom.

### CCXLIV

Karl his dukes and his counts addressed:
" Say, what of those who in bondage rest—
Who came Count Ganelon's plea to aid,
And for Pinabel were bailsmen made?"
" One and all let them die the death."
And the king to Basbrun, his provost, saith
".Go, hang them all on the gallows tree.
By my beard I swear, so white to see,
If one escape, thou shalt surely die."
" Mine be the task," he made reply.
A hundred men-at-arms are there:
The thirty to their doom they bear.
The traitor shall his guilt atone,
With blood of others and his own.

### CCXLV

The men of Bavaria and Allemaine,
Norman and Breton return again,
And with all the Franks aloud they cry,
That Gan a traitor's death shall die.
They bade be brought four stallions fleet;
Bound to them Ganelon, hands and feet:

Wild and swift was each savage steed,
And a mare was standing within the mead;
Four grooms impelled the coursers on,—
A fearful ending for Ganelon.
His every nerve was stretched and torn,
And the limbs of his body apart were borne;
The bright blood, springing from every vein,
Left on the herbage green its stain.
He died a felon and recreant:
Never shall traitor his treason vaunt.

### CCXLVI

Now was the Emperor's vengeance done,
And he called to the bishops of France anon
With those of Bavaria and Allemaine.
" A noble captive is in my train.
She hath hearkened to sermon and homily,
And a true believer in Christ will be;
Baptize her so that her soul have grace."
They say, " Let ladies of noble race,
At her christening, be her sponsors vowed."
And so there gathered a mighty crowd.
At the baths of Aix was the wondrous scene—
There baptized they the Spanish queen;
Julienne they have named her name.
In faith and truth unto Christ she came.

### CCXLVII

When the Emperor's justice was satisfied,
His mighty wrath did awhile subside.
Queen Bramimonde was a Christian made,
The day passed on into night's dark shade;
As the king in his vaulted chamber lay,
Saint Gabriel came from God to say,
" Karl, thou shalt summon thine empire's host,
And march in haste to Bira's coast;

Unto Impha city relief to bring,
And succor Vivian, the Christian king.
The heathens in siege have the town essayed,
And the shattered Christians invoke thine aid."
Fain would Karl such task decline.
"God! what a life of toil is mine!"
He wept; his hoary beard he wrung.

So ends the lay Turoldus sung.

# THE DESTRUCTION
# OF DÁ DERGA'S HOSTEL

TRANSLATED BY
WHITLEY STOKES, D.C.L.

# INTRODUCTORY NOTE

THE *vast and interesting epic literature of Ireland remained practically inaccessible to English readers till within the last sixty years. In 1853, Nicholas O'Kearney published the Irish text and an English translation of "The Battle of Gabra," and since that date the volume of printed texts and English versions has steadily increased, until now there lies open to the ordinary reader a very considerable mass of material illustrating the imaginative life of medieval Ireland.*

*Of these Irish epic tales, "The Destruction of Dà Derga's Hostel" is a specimen of remarkable beauty and power. The primitive nature of the story is shown by the fact that the plot turns upon the disasters that follow on the violation of tabus, or prohibitions often with a supernatural sanction, by the monstrous nature of many of the warriors, and by the utter absence of any attempt to rationalize or explain the beliefs implied or the marvels related in it. The powers and achievements of the heroes are fantastic and extraordinary beyond description, and the natural and extra-natural constantly mingle; yet nowhere does the narrator express surprise. The technical method of the tale, too, is curiously and almost mechanically symmetrical, after the manner of savage art; and both description and narration are marked by a high degree of freshness and vividness.*

*The following translation is, with slight modification, that of Dr. Whitley Stokes, from a text constructed by him on the basis of eight manuscripts, the oldest going back to about 1100 A.D. The story itself is, without doubt, several centuries earlier, and belongs to the oldest group of extant Irish sagas.*

# THE DESTRUCTION
## OF DÁ DERGA'S HOSTEL

THERE was a famous and noble king over Erin, named
Eochaid Feidlech. Once upon a time he came over
the fairgreen of Brí Léith, and he saw at the edge
of a well a woman with a bright comb of silver adorned
with gold, washing in a silver basin wherein were four
golden birds and little, bright gems of purple carbuncle in
the rims of the basin. A mantle she had, curly and purple,
a beautiful cloak, and in the mantle silvery fringes arranged,
and a brooch of fairest gold. A kirtle she wore, long,
hooded, hard-smooth, of green silk, with red embroidery of
gold. Marvellous clasps of gold and silver in the kirtle
on her breasts and her shoulders and spaulds on every
side. The sun kept shining upon her, so that the glistening
of the gold against the sun from the green silk was manifest
to men. On her head were two golden-yellow tresses, in
each of which was a plait of four locks, with a bead at the
point of each lock. The hue of that hair seemed to them
like the flower of the iris in summer, or like red gold after
the burnishing thereof.

There she was, undoing her hair to wash it, with her
arms out through the sleeve-holes of her smock. White as
the snow of one night were the two hands, soft and even,
and red as foxglove were the two clear-beautiful cheeks.
Dark as the back of a stag-beetle the two eyebrows. Like
a shower of pearls were the teeth in her head. Blue as a
hyacinth were the eyes. Red as rowan-berries the lips.
Very high, smooth and soft-white the shoulders. Clear-
white and lengthy the fingers. Long were the hands. White
as the foam of a wave was the flank, slender, long, tender,
smooth, soft as wool. Polished and warm, sleek and white

211

were the two thighs. Round and small, hard and white the two knees. Short and white and rulestraight the two shins. Justly straight and beautiful the two heels. If a measure were put on the feet it would hardly have found them unequal, unless the flesh of the coverings should grow upon them. The bright radiance of the moon was in her noble face: the loftiness of pride in her smooth eyebrows: the light of wooing in each of her regal eyes. A dimple of delight in each of her cheeks, with a dappling (?) in them, at one time, of purple spots with redness of a calf's blood, and at another with the bright lustre of snow. Soft womanly dignity in her voice; a step steady and slow she had: a queenly gait was hers. Verily, of the world's women 'twas she was the dearest and loveliest and justest that the eyes of men had ever beheld. It seemed to King Eochaid and his followers that she was from the elfmounds. Of her was said: "Shapely are all till compared with Etáin," "Dear are all till compared with Etáin."

A longing for her straightway seized the king; so he sent forward a man of his people to detain her. The king asked tidings of her and said, while announcing himself: "Shall I have an hour of dalliance with thee?"

" 'Tis for that we have come hither under thy safeguard," quoth she.

"Query, whence art thou and whence hast thou come?" says Eochaid.

"Easy to say," quoth she. "Etáin am I, daughter of Etar, king of the cavalcade from the elfmounds. I have been here for twenty years since I was born in an elfmound. The men of the elfmound, both kings and nobles, have been wooing me; but nought was gotten from me, because ever since I was able to speak, I have loved thee and given thee a child's love for the high tales about thee and thy splendour. And though I had never seen thee, I knew thee at once from thy description: it is *thou*, then, I have reached."

"No 'seeking of an ill friend afar' shall be thine," says Eochaid. "Thou shalt have welcome, and for thee every other woman shall be left by me, and with thee alone will I live so long as thou hast honour."

"My proper bride-price to me!" she says, "and afterwards my desire."

"Thou shalt have both," says Eochaid.

Seven *cumals* [1] are given to her.

Then the king, even Eochaid Feidlech, dies, leaving one daughter named, like her mother, Etáin, and wedded to Cormac, king of Ulaid.

After the end of a time Cormac, king of Ulaid, "the man of the three gifts," forsakes Eochaid's daughter, because she was barren save for one daughter that she had borne to Cormac after the making of the pottage which her mother —the woman from the elfmounds—gave her. Then she said to her mother: "Bad is what thou hast given me: it will be a daughter that I shall bear."

"That will not be good," says her mother; "a king's pursuit will be on her."

Then Cormac weds again his wife, even Etáin, and this was his desire, that the daughter of the woman who had before been abandoned [i. e. his own daughter] should be killed. So Cormac would not leave the girl to her mother to be nursed. Then his two thralls take her to a pit, and she smiles a laughing smile at them as they were putting her into it. Then their kindly nature came to them. They carry her into the calfshed of the cowherds of Etirscél, great-grandson of Iar, king of Tara, and they fostered her till she became a good embroideress; and there was not in Ireland a king's daughter dearer than she.

A fenced house of wickerwork was made by the thralls for her, without any door, but only a window and a skylight. King Eterscél's folk espy that house and suppose that it was food that the cowherds kept there. But one of them went and looked through the skylight, and he saw in the house the dearest, beautifullest maiden! This is told to the king, and straightway he sends his people to break the house and carry her off without asking the cowherds. For the king was childless, and it had been prophesied to him by his wizards that a woman of unknown race would bear him a son.

Then said the king: "This is the woman that has been prophesied to me!"

---

[1] *I. e.*, twenty-one cows.

Now while she was there next morning she saw a Bird on the skylight coming to her, and he leaves his birdskin on the floor of the house, and went to her and possessed her, and said: "They are coming to thee from the king to wreck thy house and to bring thee to him perforce. And thou wilt be pregnant by me, and bear a son, and that son must not kill birds.[2] And 'Conaire, son of Mess Buachalla' shall be his name," for hers was Mess Buachalla, "the Cowherds' fosterchild."

And then she was brought to the king, and with her went her fosterers, and she was betrothed to the king, and he gave her seven *cumals* and to her fosterers seven other *cumals*. And afterwards they were made chieftains, so that they all became legitimate, whence are the two Fedlimthi Rechtaidi. And then she bore a son to the king, even Conaire son of Mess Buachalla, and these were her three urgent prayers to the king, to wit, the nursing of her son among three households, that is, the fosterers who had nurtured her, and the two Honeyworded Mainès, and she herself is the third; and she said that such of the men of Erin as should wish to do aught for this boy should give to those three households for the boy's protection.

So in that wise he was reared, and the men of Erin straightway knew this boy on the day he was born. And other boys were fostered with him, to wit, Fer Le and Fer Gar and Fer Rogein, three great-grandsons of Donn Désa the champion, an army-man of the army from Muc-lesi.

Now Conaire possessed three gifts, to wit, the gift of hearing and the gift of eyesight and the gift of judgment; and of those three gifts he taught one to each of his three fosterbrothers. And whatever meal was prepared for him, the four of them would go to it. Even though three meals were prepared for him each of them would go to his meal. The same raiment and armour and colour of horses had the four.

Then the king, even Eterscéle, died. A bull-feast is gathered by the men of Erin, in order to determine their future king; that is, a bull used to be killed by them and

[2] This passage indicates the existence in Ireland of totems, and of the rule that the person to whom a totem belongs must not kill the totem-animal.—W. S.

thereof one man would eat his fill and drink its broth, and a spell of truth was chanted over him in his bed. Whosoever he would see in his sleep would be king, and the sleeper would perish if he uttered a falsehood.

Four men in chariots were on the Plain of Liffey at their game, Conaire himself and his three fosterbrothers. Then his fosterers went to him that he might repair to the bull-feast. The bull-feaster, then in his sleep, at the end of the night beheld a man stark-naked, passing along the road of Tara, with a stone in his sling.

"I will go in the morning after you," quoth he.

He left his fosterbrothers at their game, and turned his chariot and his charioteer until he was in Dublin. There he saw great, white-speckled birds, of unusual size and colour and beauty. He pursues then until his horses were tired. The birds would go a spearcast before him, and would not go any further. He alighted, and takes his sling for them out of the chariot. He goes after them until he was at the sea. The birds betake themselves to the wave. He went to them and overcame them. The birds quit their birdskins, and turn upon him with spears and swords. One of them protects him, and addressed him, saying: "I am Némglan, king of thy father's birds; and thou hast been forbidden to cast at birds, for here there is no one that should not be dear to thee because of his father or mother."

"Till today," says Conaire, "I knew not this."

"Go to Tara tonight," says Némglan; "'tis fittest for thee. A bull-feast is there, and through it thou shalt be king. A man stark-naked, who shall go at the end of the night along one of the roads of Tara, having a stone and a sling—'tis he that shall be king."

So in this wise Conaire fared forth; and on each of the four roads whereby men go to Tara there were three kings awaiting him, and they had raiment for him, since it had been foretold that he would come stark-naked. Then he was seen from the road on which his fosterers were, and they put royal raiment about him, and placed him in a chariot, and he bound his pledges.

The folk of Tara said to him: "It seems to us that our

bullfeast and our spell of truth are a failure, if it be only a young, beardless lad that we have visioned therein."

"That is of no moment," quoth he. "For a young, generous king like me to be in the kingship is no disgrace, since the binding of Tara's pledges is mine by right of father and grandsire."

"Excellent! excellent!" says the host. They set the kingship of Erin upon him. And he said: "I will enquire of wise men that I myself may be wise."

Then he uttered all this as he had been taught by the man at the wave, who said this to him: "Thy reign will be subject to a restriction, but the bird-reign will be noble, and this shall be thy restriction, i. e. thy tabu.

"Thou shalt not go righthandwise round Tara and lefthandwise round Bregia.

"The evil-beasts of Cerna must not be hunted by thee.

"And thou shalt not go out every ninth night beyond Tara.

"Thou shalt not sleep in a house from which firelight is manifest outside, after sunset, and in which light is manifest from without.

"And three Reds shall not go before thee to Red's house.

"And no rapine shall be wrought in thy reign.

"And after sunset a company of one woman or one man shall not enter the house in which thou art.

"And thou shalt not settle the quarrel of thy two thralls.

Now there were in his reign great bounties, to wit, seven ships in every June in every year arriving at Inver Colptha,[3] and oakmast up to the knees in every autumn, and plenty of fish in the rivers Bush and Boyne in the June of each year, and such abundance of good will that no one slew another in Erin during his reign. And to every one in Erin his fellow's voice seemed as sweet as the strings of lutes. From mid-spring to mid-autumn no wind disturbed a cow's tail. His reign was neither thunderous nor stormy.

Now his fosterbrothers murmured at the taking from them of their father's and their grandsire's gifts, namely Theft and Robbery and Slaughter of men and Rapine. They thieved the three thefts from the same man, to wit, a swine and an ox and a cow, every year, that they might

---

[3] The mouth of the river Boyne.—W. S.

see what punishment therefor the king would inflict upon them, and what damage the theft in his reign would cause to the king.

Now every year the farmer would come to the king to complain, and the king would say to him. " Go thou and address Donn Désá's three great-grandsons, for 'tis they that have taken the beasts." Whenever he went to speak to Donn Désá's descendants they would almost kill him, and he would not return to the king lest Conaire should attend his hurt.

Since, then, pride and wilfulness possessed them, they took to marauding, surrounded by the sons of the lords of the men of Erin. Thrice fifty men had they as pupils when they (the pupils) were were-wolfing in the province of Connaught, until Maine Milscothach's swineherd saw them, and he had never seen that before. He went in flight. When they heard him they pursued him. The swineherd shouted, and the people of the two Mainès came to him, and the thrice fifty men were arrested, along with their auxiliaries, and taken to Tara. They consulted the king concerning the matter, and he said: " Let each (father) slay his son, but let my fosterlings be spared."

" Leave, leave ! " says every one: " it shall be done for thee."

" Nay indeed," quoth he; " no ' cast of life ' by me is the doom I have delivered. The men shall not be hung; but let veterans go with them that they may wreak their rapine on the men of Alba."

This they do. Thence they put to sea and met the son of the king of Britain, even Ingcél the One-eyed, grandson of Conmac: thrice fifty men and their veterans they met upon the sea.

They make an alliance, and go with Ingcél and wrought rapine with him.

This is the destruction which his own impulse gave him. That was the night that his mother and his father and his seven brothers had been bidden to the house of the king of his district. All of them were destroyed by Ingcél in a single night. Then the Irish pirates put out to sea to the land of Erin to seek a destruction as payment for that to which Ingcél had been entitled from them.

In Conaire's reign there was perfect peace in Erin, save that in Thomond there was a joining of battle between the two Carbres. Two fosterbrothers of his were they. And until Conaire came it was impossible to make peace between them. 'Twas a tabu of his to go to separate them before they had repaired to him. He went, however, although to do so was one of his tabus, and he made peace between them. He remained five nights with each of the two. That also was a tabu of his.

After settling the two quarrels, he was travelling to Tara. This is the way they took to Tara, past Usnech of Meath; and they saw the raiding from east and west, and from south and north, and they saw the warbands and the hosts, and the men stark-naked; and the land of the southern O'Neills was a cloud of fire around him.

"What is this?" asked Conaire. "Easy to say," his people answer. "Easy to know that the king's law has broken down therein, since the country has begun to burn."

"Whither shall we betake ourselves?" says Conaire.

"To the Northeast," says his people.

So then they went righthandwise round Tara, and lefthandwise round Bregia, and the evil beasts of Cerna were hunted by him. But he saw it not till the chase had ended.

They that made of the world that smoky mist of magic were elves, and they did so because Conaire's tabus had been violated.

Great fear then fell on Conaire because they had no way to wend save upon the Road of Midluachair and the Road of Cualu.

So they took their way by the coast of Ireland southward. Then said Conaire on the Road of Cualu: "whither shall we go tonight?"

"May I succeed in telling thee! my fosterling Conaire," says Mac cecht, son of Snade Teiched, the champion of Conaire, son of Eterscél. "Oftener have the men of Erin been contending for thee every night than thou hast been wandering about for a guesthouse."

"Judgment goes with good times," says Conaire. "I

had a friend in this country, if only we knew the way to his house!"

"What is his name?" asked Mac cecht.

"Dá Derga of Leinster," answered Conaire. "He came unto me to seek a gift from me, and he did not come with a refusal. I gave him a hundred kine of the drove. I gave him a hundred fatted swine. I gave him a hundred mantles made of close cloth. I gave him a hundred blue-coloured weapons of battle. I gave him ten red, gilded brooches. I gave him ten vats good and brown. I gave him ten thralls. I gave him ten querns. I gave him thrice nine hounds all-white in their silvern chains. I gave him a hundred race-horses in the herds of deer. There would be no abatement in his case though he should come again. He would make return. It is strange if he is surly to me tonight when reaching his abode."

"When I was acquainted with his house," says Mac cecht, "the road whereon thou art going towards him was the boundary of his abode. It continues till it enters his house, for through the house passes the road. There are seven doorways into the house, and seven bedrooms between every two doorways; but there is only one door-valve on it, and that valve is turned to every doorway to which the wind blows."

"With all that thou hast here," says Conaire, "thou shalt go in thy great multitude until thou alight in the midst of the house."

"If so be," answers Mac cecht, that thou goest thither, I go on that I may strike fire there ahead of thee."

When Conaire after this was journeying along the Road of Cuálu, he marked before him three horsemen riding towards the house. Three red frocks had they, and three red mantles: three red bucklers they bore, and three red spears were in their hands: three red steeds they bestrode, and three red heads of hair were on them. Red were they all, both body and hair and raiment, both steeds and men.

"Who is it that fares before us?" asked Conaire. "It was a tabu of mine for those Three to go before me—the three Reds to the house of Red. Who will follow them and tell them to come towards me in my track?"

"I will follow them," says Lé fri flaith, Conaire's son.

He goes after them, lashing his horse, and overtook them not. There was the length of a spearcast between them: but they did not gain upon him and he did not gain upon them.

He told them not to go before the king. He overtook them not; but one of the three men sang a lay to him over his shoulder:

"Lo, my son, great the news, news from a hostel . . . Lo, my son!"

They go away from him then: he could not detain them.

The boy waited for the host. He told his father what was said to him. Conaire liked it not. "After them, thou!" says Conaire, "and offer them three oxen and three bacon-pigs, and so long as they shall be in my household, no one shall be among them from fire to wall."

So the lad goes after them, and offers them that, and overtook them not. But one of the three men sang a lay to him over his shoulder:

"Lo, my son, great the news! A generous king's great ardour whets thee, burns thee. Through ancient men's enchantments a company of nine yields. Lo, my son!"

The boy turns back and repeated the lay to Conaire.

"Go after them," says Conaire, "and offer them six oxen and six bacon-pigs, and my leavings, and gifts tomorrow, and so long as they shall be in my household no one to be among them from fire to wall."

The lad then went after them, and overtook them not; but one of the three men answered and said:

"Lo, my son, great the news. Weary are the steeds we ride. We ride the steeds of Donn Tetscorach from the elfmounds. Though we are alive we are dead. Great are the signs; destruction of life: sating of ravens: feeding of crows, strife of slaughter: wetting of sword-edge, shields with broken bosses in hours after sundown. Lo, my son!"

Then they go from him.

"I see that thou hast not detained the men," says Conaire.

"Indeed it is not I that betrayed it," says Lé fri flaith.

He recited the last answer that they gave him. Conaire

and his retainers were not blithe thereat: and afterwards evil forebodings of terror were on them.

"All my tabus have seized me tonight," says Conaire, "since those Three Reds are the banished folks."[4]

They went forward to the house and took their seats therein, and fastened their red steeds to the door of the house.

That is the Forefaring of the Three Reds in the *Bruden Dá Derga*.

This is the way that Conaire took with his troops, to Dublin.

'Tis then the man of the black, cropt hair, with his one hand and one eye and one foot, overtook them. Rough cropt hair upon him. Though a sackful of wild apples were flung on his crown, not an apple would fall on the ground, but each of them would stick on his hair. Though his snout were flung on a branch they would remain together. Long and thick as an outer yoke was each of his two shins. Each of his buttocks was the size of a cheese on a withe. A forked pole of iron black-pointed was in his hand. A swine, black-bristled, singed, was on his back, squealing continually, and a woman big-mouthed, huge, dark, sorry, hideous, was behind him. Though her snout were flung on a branch, the branch would support it. Her lower lip would reach her knee.

He starts forward to meet Conaire, and made him welcome. "Welcome to thee, O master Conaire! Long hath thy coming hither been known."

"Who gives the welcome?" asks Conaire.

"Fer Caille here, with his black swine for thee to consume that thou be not fasting tonight, for 'tis thou art the best king that has come into the world!"

"What is thy wife's name?" says Conaire.

"Cichuil," he answers.

"Any other night," says Conaire, "that pleases you, I will come to you,—and leave us alone to night."

"Nay," say the churl, "for we will go to thee to the place wherein thou wilt be tonight, O fair little master Conaire!"

---

[4] They had been banished from the elfmounds, and for them to precede Conaire was to violate one of his tabus.—W. S.

So he goes towards the house, with his great, big-mouthed wife behind him, and his swine short-bristled, black, singed, squealing continually, on his back. That was one of Conaire's tabus, and that plunder should be taken in Ireland during his reign was another tabu of his.

Now plunder was taken by the sons of Donn Désa, and five hundred there were in the body of their marauders, besides what underlings were with them. This, too, was a tabu of Conaire's. There was a good warrior in the north country, "Wain over withered sticks," this was his name. Why he was so called was because he used to go over his opponent even as a wain would go over withered sticks. Now plunder was taken by him, and there were five hundred in the body of their marauders alone, besides underlings.

There was after that a troop of still haughtier heroes, namely, the seven sons of Ailill and Medb, each of whom was called "Manè." And each Manè had a nickname, to wit, Manè Fatherlike and Manè Motherlike, and Manè otherlike, and Manè Gentle-pious, Manè Very-pious, Manè Unslow, and Manè Honeyworded, Manè Grasp-them-all, and Manè the Loquacious. Rapine was wrought by them. As to Manè Motherlike and Manè Unslow there were fourteen score in the body of their marauders. Manè Fatherlike had three hundred and fifty. Manè Honeyworded had five hundred. Manè Grasp-them-all had seven hundred. Manè the Loquacious had seven hundred. Each of the others had five hundred in the body of his marauders.

There was a valiant trio of the men of Cúalu of Leinster, namely, the three Red Hounds of Cualu, called Cethach and Clothach and Conall. Now rapine was wrought by them, and twelve score were in the body of their marauders, and they had a troop of madmen. In Conaire's reign a third of the men of Ireland were reavers. He was of sufficient strength and power to drive them out of the land of Erin so as to transfer their marauding to the other side (Great Britain), but after this transfer they returned to their country.

When they had reached the shoulder of the sea, they meet Ingcél the One-eyed and Eiccel and Tulchinne, three great-grandsons of Conmac of Britain, on the raging of the sea. A man ungentle, huge, fearful, uncouth was Ingcél. A single eye in his head, as broad as an oxhide, as black as a chafer, with three pupils therein. Thirteen hundred were in the body of his marauders. The marauders of the men of Erin were more numerous then they.

They go for a sea-encounter on the main. "Ye should not do this," says Ingcél: "do not break the truth of men (fair play) upon us, for ye are more in number than I."

"Nought but a combat on equal terms shall befall thee," say the reavers of Erin.

"There is somewhat better for you," quoth Ingcél. "Let us make peace since ye have been cast out of the land of Erin, and we have been cast out of the land of Alba and Britain. Let us make an agreement between us. Come ye and wreak your rapine in my country, and I will go with you and wreak my rapine in your country.

They follow this counsel, and they gave pledges therefor from this side and from that. There are the sureties that were given to Ingcél by the men of Erin, namely, Fer gair and Gabur (or Fer lee) and Fer rogain, for the destruction that Ingcél should choose to cause in Ireland and for the destruction that the sons of Donn Désa should choose in Alba and Britain.

A lot was cast upon them to see with which of them they should go first. It fell that they should go with Ingcél to his country. So they made for Britain, and there his father and mother and his seven brothers were slain, as we have said before. Thereafter they made for Alba, and there they wrought the destruction, and then they returned to Erin.

'Tis then, now, that Conaire son of Eterscél went towards the Hostel along the Road of Cualu.

'Tis then that the reavers came till they were in the sea off the coast of Bregia overagainst Howth.

Then said the reavers: "Strike the sails, and make one band of you on the sea that ye may not be sighted from land; and let some lightfoot be found from among you to go on shore to see if we could save our honors with

Ingcél. A destruction for the destruction he has given us."

"Who will go on shore to listen? Let some one go," says Ingcél, "who should have there the three gifts, namely, gift of hearing, gift of far sight, and gift of judgment."

"I," says Manè Honeyworded, "have the gift of hearing."

"And I," says Manè Unslow, "have the gift of far sight and of judgment."

"'Tis well for you to go thus," say the reavers: "good is that wise."

Then nine men go on till they were on the Hill of Howth, to know what they might hear and see.

"Be still a while!" says Manè Honeyworded.

"What is that?" asks Manè Unslow.

"The sound of a good king's cavalcade I hear."

"By the gift of far sight, I see," quoth his comrade.

"What seest thou here?"

"I see there," quoth he, "cavalcades splendid, lofty, beautiful, warlike, foreign, somewhat slender, weary, active, keen, whetted, vehement, a good course that shakes a great covering of land. They fare to many heights, with wondrous waters and invers."[5]

"What are the waters and heights and invers that they traverse?"

"Easy to say: Indéoin, Cult, Cuiltén, Máfat, Ammat, Iarmáfat, Finne, Goiste, Guistíne. Gray spears over chariots: ivory-hilted swords on thighs: silvery shields above their elbows. Half red and half white. Garments of every color about them.

"Thereafter I see before them special cattle specially keen, to wit, thrice fifty dark-gray steeds. Small-headed are they, red-nosed, pointed, broad-hoofed, big-nosed, red-chested, fat, easily-stopt, easily-yoked, foray-nimble, keen, whetted, vehement, with their thrice fifty bridles of red enamel upon them."

"I swear by what my tribe swears," says the man of the long sight, "these are the cattle of some good lord. This is my judgment thereof: it is Conaire, son of Eterscél, with multitudes of the men of Erin around him, who has travelled the road."

[5] Mouths of rivers.

Back then they go that they may tell it to the reavers. "This," they say, "is what we have heard and seen."

Of this host, then, there was a multitude, both on this side and on that, namely, thrice fifty boats, with five thousand in them, and ten hundred in every thousand. Then they hoisted the sails on the boats, and steer them thence to shore, till they landed on the Strand of Fuirbthe.

When the boats reached land, then was Mac cecht a-striking fire in Dá Derga's Hostel. At the sound of the spark the thrice fifty boats were hurled out, so that they were on the shoulders of the sea.

"Be silent a while!" said Ingcél. "Liken thou that, O Fer rogain."

"I know not," answers Fer rogain, "unless it is Luchdonn the satirist in Emain Macha, who makes this handsmiting when his food is taken from him perforce: or the scream of Luchdonn in Temair Luachra: or Mac cecht's striking a spark, when he kindles a fire before a king of Erin where he sleeps. Every spark and every shower which his fire would let fall on the floor would broil a hundred calves and two half-pigs."

"May God not bring that man (even Conaire) there tonight!" say Donn Désa's sons. "Sad that he is under the hurt of foes!"

"Meseems," says Ingcél, "it should be no sadder for me than the destruction I gave you. This were my feast that Conaire should chance to come there."

Their fleet is steered to land. The noise that the thrice fifty vessels made in running ashore shook Dá Derga's Hostel so that no spear nor shield remained on rack therein, but the weapons uttered a cry and fell all on the floor of the house.

"Liken thou that, O Conaire," says every one: "what is this noise?"

"I know nothing like it unless it be the earth that has broken, or the Leviathan that surrounds the globe and strikes with its tail to overturn the world, or the barque of the sons of Donn Désa that has reached the shore. Alas that it should not be they who are there! Beloved fosterbrothers of our own were they! Dear were the champions. We should not have feared them tonight."

Then came Conaire, so that he was on the green of the Hostel.

When Mac cecht heard the tumultuous noise, it seemed to him that warriors had attacked his people. Thereat he leapt on to his armour to help them. Vast as the thunder-feat of three hundred did they deem his game in leaping to his weapons. Thereof there was no profit.

Now in the bow of the ship wherein were Donn Désa's sons was the champion, greatly-accoutred, wrathful, the lion hard and awful, Ingcél the One-eyed, great-grandson of Conmac. Wide as an oxhide was the single eye protruding from his forehead, with seven pupils therein, which were black as a chafer. Each of his knees as big as a stripper's caldron; each of his two fists was the size of a reaping-basket: his buttocks as big as a cheese on a withe: each of his shins as long as an outer yoke.

So after that, the thrice fifty boats, and those five thousands—with ten hundred in every thousand,—landed on the Strand of Fuirbthe.

Then Conaire with his people entered the Hostel, and each took his seat within, both tabu and non-tabu. And the three Reds took their seats, and Fer caille with his swine took his seat.

Thereafter Dá Derga came to them, with thrice fifty warriors, each of them having a long head of hair to the hollow of his polls, and a short cloak to their buttocks. Speckled-green drawers they wore, and in their hands were thrice fifty great clubs of thorn with bands of iron.

"Welcome, O master Conaire!" quoth he. "Though the bulk of the men of Erin were to come with thee, they themselves would have a welcome."

When they were there they saw a lone woman coming to the door of the Hostel, after sunset, and seeking to be let in. As long as a weaver's beam was each of her two shins, and they were as dark as the back of a stag-beetle. A greyish, wooly mantle she wore. Her lower hair used to reach as far as her knee. Her lips were on one side of her head.

She came and put one of her shoulders against the door-post of the house, casting the evil eye on the king and the youths who surrounded him in the Hostel. He himself addressed her from within.

"Well, O woman," says Conaire, "if thou art a wizard, what seest thou for us?"

"Truly I see for thee," she answers, "that neither fell nor flesh of thine shall escape from the place into which thou hast come, save what birds will bear away in their claws."

"It was not an evil omen we foreboded, O woman," saith he: "it is not thou that always augurs for us. What is thy name, O woman?"

"Cailb," she answers.

"That is not much of a name," says Conaire.

"Lo, many are my names besides."

"Which be they?" asks Conaire.

"Easy to say," quoth she. "Samon, Sinand, Seisclend, Sodb, Caill, Coll, Díchóem, Dichiúil, Díthim, Díchuimne, Dichruidne, Dairne, Dárine, Déruaine, Egem, Agam, Ethamne, Gním, Cluiche, Cethardam, Níth, Némain, Nóennen, Badb, Blosc, B[l]oár, Huae, óe Aife la Sruth, Mache, Médé, Mod."

On one foot, and holding up one hand, and breathing one breath she sang all that to them from the door of the house.

"I swear by the gods whom I adore," says Conaire, "that I will call thee by none of these names whether I shall be here a long or a short time."

"What dost thou desire?" says Conaire.

"That which thou, too, desirest," she answered.

"'Tis a tabu of mine," says Conaire, "to receive the company of one woman after sunset."

"Though it be a tabu," she replied, "I will not go until my guesting come at once this very night."

"Tell her," says Conaire, "that an ox and a bacon-pig shall be taken out to her, and my leavings: provided that she stays tonight in some other place."

"If in sooth," she says, "it has befallen the king not to have room in his house for the meal and bed of a solitary woman, they will be gotten apart from him from some one possessing generosity—if the hospitality of the Prince in the Hostel has departed."

"Savage is the answer!" says Conaire. "Let her in, though it is a tabu of mine."

Great loathing they felt after that from the woman's converse, and ill-foreboding; but they knew not the cause thereof.

The reavers afterwards landed, and fared forth till they were at Lecca cinn slébe. Ever open was the Hostel. Why it was called a *Bruden* was because it resembles the lips of a man blowing a fire.

Great was the fire which was kindled by Conaire every night, to wit, a "Boar of the Wood." Seven outlets it had. When a log was cut out of its side every flame that used to come forth at each outlet was as big as the blaze of a burning oratory. There were seventeen of Conaire's chariots at every door of the house, and by those that were looking from the vessels that great light was clearly seen through the wheels of the chariots.

"Canst thou say, O Fer rogain, what that great light yonder resembles?"

"I cannot liken it to aught," answers Fer rogain, "unless it be the fire of a king. May God not bring that man there tonight! 'Tis a pity to destroy him!"

"What then deemest thou," says Ingcél, "of that man's reign in the land of Erin?"

"Good is his reign," replied Fer rogain. "Since he assumed the kingship, no cloud has veiled the sun for the space of a day from the middle of spring to the middle of autumn. And not a dewdrop fell from grass till midday, and wind would not touch a beast's tail until nones. And in his reign, from year's end to year's end, no wolf has attacked aught save one bullcalf of each byre; and to maintain this rule there are seven wolves in hostageship at the sidewall in his house, and behind this a further security, even Maclocc, and 'tis he that pleads for them in Conaire's house. In Conaire's reign are the three crowns on Erin, namely, crown of corn-ears, and crown of flowers, and crown of oak mast. In his reign, too, each man deems the other's voice as melodious as the strings of lutes, because of the excellence of the law and the peace and the goodwill prevailing throughout Erin. May God not bring that man there to-night! 'Tis sad to destroy him. 'Tis '*a branch through its blossom,*' 'Tis *a swine that falls before mast.* 'Tis *an infant in age.* Sad is the shortness of his life!"

"This was my luck," says Ingcél, "that *he* should be there, and there should be one Destruction for another. It were not more grievous to me than my father and my mother and my seven brothers, and the king of my country, whom I gave up to you before coming on the transfer of the rapine."

"'Tis true, 'tis true!" say the evildoers who were along with the reavers.

The reavers make a start from the Strand of Fuirbthe, and bring a stone for each man to make a cairn; for this was the distinction which at first the Fians made between a "Destruction" and a "Rout." A pillar-stone they used to plant when there would be a Rout. A cairn, however, they used to make when there would be a Destruction. At this time, then, they made a cairn, for it was a Destruction. Far from the house was this, that they might not be heard or seen therefrom.

For two causes they built their cairn, namely, first, since this was a custom in marauding, and, secondly, that they might find out their losses at the Hostel. Every one that would come safe from it would take his stone from the cairn: thus the stones of those that were slain would be left, and thence they would know their losses. And this is what men skilled in story recount, that for every stone in Carn leca there was one of the reavers killed at the Hostel. From that cairn Leca in Húi Cellaig is so called.

A "boar of a fire" is kindled by the sons of Donn Désa to give warning to Conaire. So *that* is the first warning-beacon that has been made in Erin, and from it to this day every warning-beacon is kindled.

This is what others recount: that it was on the eve of *samain* (All-Saints-day) the destruction of the Hostel was wrought, and that from yonder beacon the beacon of *samain* is followed from that to this, and stones (are placed) in the *samain*-fire.

Then the reavers framed a counsel at the place where they had put the cairn.

"Well, then," says Ingcél to the guides, "what is nearest to us here?"

"Easy to say: the Hostel of Hua Derga, chief-hospitaller of Erin."

"Good men indeed," says Ingcél, "were likely to seek their fellows at that Hostel to-night."

This, then, was the counsel of the reavers, to send one of them to see how things were there.

"Who will go there to espy the house?" say everyone.

"Who should go," says Ingcél, "but I, for 'tis I that am entitled to dues."

Ingcél went to reconnoitre the Hostel with one of the seven pupils of the single eye which stood out of his forehead, to fit his eye into the house in order to destroy the king and the youths who were around him therein. And Ingcél saw them through the wheels of the chariots.

Then Ingcél was perceived from the house. He made a start from it after being perceived.

He went till he reached the reavers in the stead wherein they were. Each circle of them was set around another to hear the tidings—the chiefs of the reavers being in the very centre of the circles. There were Fer gér and Fer gel and Fer rogel and Fer rogain and Lomna the Buffoon, and Ingcél the One-eyed—six in the centre of the circles. And Fer rogain went to question Ingcél.

"How is that, O Ingcél?" asks Fer rogain.

"However it be," answers Ingcél, "royal is the custom, hostful is the tumult: kingly is the noise thereof. Whether a king be there or not, I will take the house for what I have a right to. Thence my turn of rapine cometh."

"We have left it in thy hand, O Ingcél!" say Conaire's fosterbrothers. "But we should not wreak the Destruction till we know who may be therein."

"Question, hast thou seen the house well, O Ingcél?" asks Fer rogain.

"Mine eye cast a rapid glance around it, and I will accept it for my dues as it stands."

"Thou mayest well accept it, O Ingcél," saith Fer rogain: "the foster father of us all is there, Erin's overking, Conaire, son of Eterscél."

"Question, what sawest thou in the champion's high seat of the house, facing the King, on the opposite side?"

### THE ROOM OF CORMAC CONDLONGAS

"I saw there," says Ingcél, "a man of noble countenance, large, with a clear and sparkling eye, an even set of teeth, a face narrow below, broad above. Fair, flaxen, golden hair upon him, and a proper fillet around it. A brooch of silver in his mantle, and in his hand a gold-hilted sword. A shield with five golden circles upon it: a five-barbed javelin in his hand. A visage just, fair, ruddy he hath: he is also beardless. Modest-minded is that man!"

"And after that, whom sawest thou there?"

### THE ROOM OF CORMAC'S NINE COMRADES

"There I saw three men to the west of Cormac, and three to the east of him, and three in front of the same man. Thou wouldst deem that the nine of them had one mother and one father. They are of the same age, equally goodly, equally beautiful, all alike. Thin rods of gold in their mantles. Bent shields of bronze they bear. Ribbed javelins above them. An ivory-hilted sword in the hand of each. An unique feat they have, to wit, each of them takes his sword's point between his two fingers, and they twirl the swords round their fingers, and the swords afterwards extend themselves by themselves. Liken thou *that*, O Fer rogain," says Ingcél.

"Easy," says Fer rogain, "for me to liken them. It is Conchobar's son, Cormac Condlongas, the best hero behind a shield in the land of Erin. Of modest mind is that boy! Evil is what he dreads tonight. He is a champion of valour for feats of arms; he is an hospitaller for householding. These are yon nine who surround him, the three Dúngusses, and the three Doelgusses, and the three Dangusses, the nine comrades of Cormac Condlongas, son of Conchobar. They have never slain men on account of their misery, and they never spared them on account of their prosperity. Good is the hero who is among them, even Cormac Condlongas. I swear what my tribe swears, nine times ten will fall by Cormac in his first onset, and nine times ten will fall by his people, besides a man for each of their weapons, and a man for each of themselves. And Cormac will share prowess with any man before the Hostel, and he will boast of victory over a king or crown-prince or noble of the reavers; and he himself will chance to escape, though all his people be wounded."

"Woe to him who shall wreak this Destruction!" says Lomna Drúth, "even because of that one man, Cormac Condlongas, son of Conchobar." "I swear what my tribe swears," says Lomna son of Donn Désa, "if I could fulfil my counsel, the Destruction would not be attempted were it only because of that one man, and because of the hero's beauty and goodness!"

"It is not feasible to prevent it," says Ingcél: "clouds of weakness come to you. A keen ordeal which will endanger two cheeks of a goat will be opposed by the oath of Fer rogain, who will run. Thy voice, O Lomna," says Ingcél, "hath taken breaking upon thee: thou art a worthless warrior, and I know thee. Clouds of weakness come to you. . . .

Neither old men nor historians shall declare that I quitted the Destruction, until I shall wreak it."

"Reproach not our honour, O Ingcél," say Gér and Gabur and Fer rogain. "The Destruction shall be wrought unless the earth break under it, until all of us are slain thereby."

"Truly, then, thou hast reason, O Ingcél," says Lomna Drúth son of Donn Désa. "Not to *thee* is the loss caused by the Destruction. Thou wilt carry off the head of the king of a foreign country, with thy slaughter of another; and thou and thy brothers will escape from the Destruction, even Ingcél and Ecell and the Yearling of the Rapine."

"Harder, however, it is for me," says Lomna Drúth:

" woe is me before every one! woe is me after every one!
'Tis my head that will be first tossed about there to-night
after an hour among the chariot-shafts, where devilish foes
will meet. It will be flung into the Hostel thrice, and thrice
will it be flung forth. Woe to him that comes! woe to
him with whom one goes! woe to him to whom one goes!
Wretches are they that go! wretches are they to whom they
go! "

" There is nothing that will come to me," says Ingcél, " in
place of my mother and my father and my seven brothers,
and the king of my district, whom ye destroyed with me.
There is nothing that I shall not endure henceforward. "

" Though a . . . should go through them," say Gér and
Gabur and Fer rogain, " the Destruction will be wrought by
thee to-night."

" Woe to him who shall put them under the hands of
foes! " says Lomna. " And whom sawest thou afterwards? "

### The Room of the Picts, this

" I saw another room there, with a huge trio in it: three
brown, big men: three round heads of hair on them, even,
equally long at nape and forehead. Three short black cowls
about them reaching to their elbows: long hoods were on the
cowls. Three black, huge swords they had, and three black
shields they bore, with three dark broad-green javelins
above them. Thick as the spit of a caldron was the shaft
of each. Liken thou that, O Fer rogain! "

" Hard it is for me to find their like. I know not in
Erin that trio, unless it be yon trio of Pictland, who went
into exile from their country, and are now in Conaire's
household. These are their names: Dublonges son of Trebúat, and Trebúat son of Húa-Lonsce, and Curnach son of
Húa Fáich. The three who are best in Pictland at taking
arms are that trio. Nine decads will fall at their hands in
their first encounter, and a man will fall for each of their
weapons, besides one for each of themselves. And they will
share prowess with every trio in the Hostel. They will boast
a victory over a king or a chief of the reavers; and they

will afterwards escape though wounded. Woe to him who
shall wreak the Destruction, though it be only on account
of those three!"

Says Lomna Druth: "I swear to God what my tribe
swears, if my counsel were taken, the Destruction would
never be wrought."

"Ye cannot," says Ingcél: "clouds of weakness are coming to you. A keen ordeal which will endanger, etc. And
whom sawest thou there afterwards?"

## The Room of the Pipers

"There I beheld a room with nine men in it. Hair fair
and yellow was on them: they all are equally beautiful.
Mantles speckled with colour they wore, and above them
were nine bagpipes, four-tuned, ornamented. Enough light
in the palace were the ornament on these four-tuned pipes.
Liken thou them, O Fer rogain."

"Easy for me to liken them," says Fer rogain. "Those
are the nine pipers that came to Conaire out of the Elfmound of Bregia, because of the noble tales about him.
These are their names: Bind, Robind, Riarbind, Sibè, Dibè,
Deichrind, Umall, Cumal, Ciallglind. They are the best
pipers in the world. Nine enneads will fall before them,
and a man for each of their weapons, and a man for each
of themselves. And each of them will boast a victory over
a king or a chief of the reavers. And they will escape from
the Destruction; for a conflict with them will be a conflict
with a shadow. They will slay, but they will not be slain,
for they are out of an elfmound. Woe to him who shall
wreak the Destruction, though it be only because of those
nine!"

"Ye cannot," says Ingcél. "Clouds of weakness come
to you," etc. "And after that, whom sawest thou there?"

## The Room of Conaire's Majordomo

"There I saw a room with one man in it. Rough cropt hair upon him. Though a sack of crab-apples should be flung on his head, not one of them would fall on the floor, but every apple would stick on his hair. His fleecy mantle was over him in the house. Every quarrel therein about seat or bed comes to his decision. Should a needle drop in the house, its fall would be heard when he speaks. Above him is a huge black tree, like a millshaft, with its paddles and its cap and its spike. Liken thou him, O Fer rogain!"

"Easy for me is this. Tuidle of Ulaid is he, the steward of Conaire's household. 'Tis needful to hearken to the decision of that man, the man that rules seat and bed and food for each. 'Tis his household staff that is above him. That man will fight with you. I swear what my tribe swears, the dead at the Destruction slain by him will be more numerous than the living. Thrice his number will fall by him, and he himself will fall there. Woe to him who shall wreak the Destruction!" etc.

"Ye cannot," says Ingcél. "Clouds of weakness come upon you. What sawest thou there after that?"

## The Room of Mac cecht, Conaire's battle-soldier

There I beheld another room with a trio in it, three half-furious nobles: the biggest of them in the middle, very noisy . . . rock-bodied, angry, smiting, dealing strong blows, who beats nine hundred in battle-conflict. A wooden shield, dark, covered with iron, he bears, with a hard . . . rim, a shield whereon would fit the proper litter of four troops of ten weaklings on its . . . of . . . leather. A . . . boss thereon, the depth of a caldron, fit to cook four oxen, a hollow maw, a great boiling, with four swine in its mid-maw great . . . At his two smooth sides are two five-thwarted boats fit for three parties of ten in each of his two strong fleets.

A spear he hath, blue-red, hand-fitting, on its puissant

shaft. It stretches along the wall on the roof and rests on the ground. An iron point upon it, dark-red, dripping. Four amply-measured feet between the two points of its edge.

Thirty amply-measured feet in his deadly-striking sword from dark point to iron hilt. It shews forth fiery sparks which illumine the Mid-court House from roof to ground.

'Tis a strong countenance that I see. A swoon from horror almost befell me while staring at those three. There is nothing stranger.

Two bare hills were there by the man with hair. Two loughs by a mountain of the . . . of a blue-fronted wave: two hides by a tree. Two boats near them full of thorns of a white thorn tree on a circular board. And there seems to me somewhat like a slender stream of water on which the sun is shining, and its trickle down from it, and a hide arranged behind it, and a palace house-post shaped like a great lance above it. A good weight of a plough-yoke is the shaft that is therein. Liken thou that, O Fer rogain!

"Easy, meseems, to liken him! That is Mac cecht son of Snaide Teichid; the battle-soldier of Conaire son of Eterscél. Good is the hero Mac cecht! Supine he was in his room, in his sleep, when thou beheldest him. The two bare hills which thou sawest by the man with hair, these are his two knees by his head. The two loughs by the mountain which thou sawest, these are his two eyes by his nose. The two hides by a tree which thou sawest, these are his two ears by his head. The two five-thwarted boats on a circular board, which thou sawest, these are his two sandals on his shield. The slender stream of water which thou sawest, whereon the sun shines, and its trickle down from it, this is the flickering of his sword. The hide which thou sawest arranged behind him, that is his sword's scabbard. The palace-housepost which thou sawest, that is his lance; and he brandishes this spear till its two ends meet, and he hurls a wilful cast of it when he pleases. Good is the hero, Mac cecht!"

"Six hundred will fall by him in his first encounter, and a man for each of his weapons, besides a man for himself.

And he will share prowess with every one in the Hostel, and he will boast of triumph over a king or chief of the reavers in front of the Hostel. He will chance to escape though wounded. And when he shall chance to come upon you out of the house, as numerous as hailstones, and grass on a green, and stars of heaven will be your cloven heads and skulls, and the clots of your brains, your bones and the heaps of your bowels, crushed by him and scattered throughout the ridges."

Then with trembling and terror of Mac cecht they flee over three ridges.

They took the pledges among them again, even Gér and Gabur and Fer rogain.

"Woe to him that shall wreak the Destruction!" says Lomna Drúth; "your heads will depart from you."

"Ye cannot," says Ingcél: "clouds of weakness are coming to you" etc.

"True indeed, O Ingcél," says Lomna Drúth son of Donn Désa. "Not unto thee is the loss caused by the Destruction. Woe is me for the Destruction, for the first head that will reach the Hostel will be mine!"

"'Tis harder for *me*," says Ingcél: "'tis *my* destruction that has been . . . there.

"Truly then," says Ingcél, "maybe I shall be the corpse that is frailest there," etc.

"And afterwards whom sawest thou there?"


### THE ROOM OF CONAIRE'S THREE SONS, OBALL AND OBLIN AND CORPRE

"There I beheld a room with a trio in it, to wit, three tender striplings, wearing three silken mantles. In their mantles were three golden brooches. Three golden-yellow manes were on them. When they undergo head-cleansing their golden-yellow mane reaches the edge of their haunches. When they raise their eye it raises the hair so that it is not lower than the tips of their ears, and it is as curly as a ram's head. A . . . of gold and a palace-flambeau above each of them. Every one who is in the house spares them, voice and deed and word. Liken thou that, O Fer rogain," says Ingcél.

Fer rogain wept, so that his mantle in front of him became moist. And no voice was gotten out of his head till a third of the night had passed.

"O little ones," says Fer rogain, "I have good reason for what I do! Those are three sons of the king of Erin: Oball and Oblíne and Corpre Findmor."

"It grieves us if the tale be true," say the sons of Donn Désa. "Good is the trio in that room. Manners of ripe maidens have they, and hearts of brothers, and valours of bears, and furies of lions. Whosoever is in their company and in their couch, and parts from them, he sleeps not and eats not at ease till the end of nine days, from lack of their companionship. Good are the youths for their age! Thrice ten will fall by each of them in their first encounter, and a man for each weapon, and three men for themselves. And one of the three will fall there. Because of that trio, woe to him that shall wreak the Destruction!"

'Ye cannot," says Ingcél: "clouds of weakness are coming to you, etc. And whom sawest thou afterwards?"


### THE ROOM OF THE FOMORIANS

I beheld there a room with a trio in it, to wit, a trio horrible, unheard-of, a triad of champions, etc.

.   .   .   .   .   .   .   .   .   .

Liken thou that, O Fer rogain?

"'Tis hard for me to liken that trio. Neither of the men of Erin nor of the men of the world do I know it, unless it be the trio that Mac cecht brought out of the land of the Fomorians by dint of duels. Not one of the Fomorians was found to fight him, so he brought away those three, and they are in Conaire's house as sureties that, while Conaire is reigning, the Fomorians destroy neither corn nor milk in Erin beyond their fair tribute. Well may their aspect be loathy! Three rows of teeth in their heads from one ear to another. An ox with a bacon-pig, this is the ration of each of them, and that ration which they put into their mouths is visible till it comes down past their navels. Bodies of bone (i. e. without a joint in them) all those three have. I swear what my tribe swears, more will be killed by them at the Destruction than those they leave alive. Six hundred warriors will fall by them in their first conflict, and a man for each of their weapons, and one for each of the three themselves. And they will boast a triumph over a king or chief of the reavers. It will not be more than with a bite or a blow or a kick that each of those men will kill, for no arms are allowed them in the house, since they are in 'hostageship at the wall' lest they do a misdeed therein. I swear what my tribe swears, if they had armour on them, they would slay us all but a third. Woe to him that shall wreak the Destruction, because it is not a combat against sluggards."

"Ye cannot," says Ingcél, etc. "And whom sawest thou there after that?"

### The Room of Munremar son of Gerrchenn and Birderg son of Ruan and Mál son of Telband

"I beheld a room there, with a trio in it. Three brown, big men, with three brown heads of short hair. Thick calf-bottoms (ankles?) they had. As thick as a man's waist was each of their limbs. Three brown and curled masses of hair upon them, with a thick head: three cloaks, red and speckled, they wore: three black shields with clasps of gold, and three five-barbed javelins; and each had in hand an ivory-hilted sword. This is the feat they perform with their swords: they throw them high up, and they throw the scabbards after them, and the swords, before reaching the ground, place themselves in the scabbards. Then they throw the scabbards first, and the swords after them, and the scabbards meet the swords and place themselves round them before they reach the ground. Liken thou that, O Fer rogain!"

"Easy for me to liken them! Mál son of Telband, and Munremar son of Gerrchenn, and Birderg son of Rúan. Three crown-princes, three champions of valour, three heroes the best behind weapons in Erin! A hundred heroes will fall by them in their first conflict, and they will share prowess with every man in the Hostel, and they will boast of the victory over a king or chief of the reavers, and afterwards they will chance to escape. The Destruction should not be wrought even because of those three."

"Woe to him that shall wreak the Destruction!" says Lomna. "Better were the victory of saving them than the victory of slaying them! Happy he who should save them! Woe to him that shall slay them!"

"It is not feasible," says Ingcél, etc. "And afterwards whom sawest thou?"

## The Room of Conall Cernach

"There I beheld in a decorated room the fairest man of Erin's heroes. He wore a tufted purple cloak. White as snow was one of his cheeks, the other was red and speckled like foxglove. Blue as hyacinth was one of his eyes, dark as a stag-beetle's back was the other. The bushy head of fair golden hair upon him was as large as a reaping-basket, and it touches the edge of his haunches. It is as curly as a ram's head. If a sackful of red-shelled nuts were spilt on the crown of his head, not one of them would fall on the floor, but remain on the hooks and plaits and swordlets of their hair. A gold hilted sword in his hand; a blood-red shield which has been speckled with rivets of white bronze between plates of gold. A long, heavy, three-ridged spear: as thick as an outer yoke is the shaft that is in it. Liken thou that, O Fer rogain!"

"Easy for me to liken him, for the men of Erin know that scion. That is Conall Cernach, son of Amorgen. He has chanced to be along with Conaire at this time. 'Tis he whom Conaire loves beyond every one, because of his resemblance to him in goodness of form and shape. Goodly is the hero that is there, Conall Cernach! To that blood-red shield on his fist, which has been speckled with rivets of white bronze, the Ulaid have given a famous name, to wit, the *Bricriu* of Conall Cernach.

"I swear what my tribe swears, plenteous will be the rain of red blood over it to-night before the Hostel! That ridged spear above him, many will there be unto whom to-night, before the Hostel, it will deal drinks of death. Seven doorways there are out of the house, and Conall Cernach will contrive to be at each of them, and from no doorway will he be absent. Three hundred will fall by Conall in his first conflict, besides a man for each (of his) weapons and one for himself. He will share prowess with every one in the Hostel, and when he shall happen to sally upon you from the house, as numerous as hailstones and grass on green and stars of heaven will be your half-heads and cloven skulls, and your bones under the point of his sword. He will succeed in escaping though wounded. Woe to him that shall wreak the Destruction, were it but for this man only!"

"Ye cannot," says Ingcél. "Clouds," etc.

"And after that whom sawest thou?"

## The Room of Conaire Himself

"There I beheld a room, more beautifully decorated than the other rooms of the house. A silvery curtain around it, and there were ornaments in the room. I beheld a trio in it. The outer two of them were, both of them, fair, with their hair and eyelashes; and they are as bright as snow. A very lovely blush on the cheek of each of the twain. A tender lad in the midst between them. The ardour and energy of a king has he, and the counsel of a sage. The mantle I saw around him is even as the mist of Mayday. Diverse are the hue and semblance each moment shewn upon it. Lovelier is each hue than the other. In front of him in the mantle I beheld a wheel of gold which reached from his chin to his navel. The colour of his hair was like the sheen of smelted gold. Of all the world's forms that I beheld, this is the most beautiful. I saw his golden-hilted glaive down beside him. A forearm's length of the sword was outside the scabbard. That forearm, a man down in the front of the house could see a fleshworm by the shadow of the sword!

Sweeter is the melodious sounding of the sword than the melodious sound of the golden pipes that accompany music in the palace."

" Then," quoth Ingcél, " I said, gazing at him:

I see a high, stately prince, etc.

I see a famous king, etc.

I see his white prince's diadem, etc.

I see his two blue-bright cheeks, etc.

I see his high wheel . . . round his head . . . which is over his yellow-curly hair.

I see his mantle red, many-coloured, etc.

I see therein a huge brooch of gold, etc.

I see his beautiful linen frock . . . from ankle to knee-caps.

I see his sword golden-hilted, inlaid, its in scabbard of white silver, etc.

I see his shield bright, chalky, etc.

A tower of inlaid gold," etc.

Now the tender warrior was asleep, with his feet in the lap of one of the two men and his head in the lap of the other. Then he awoke out of his sleep, and arose, and chanted this lay:

" The howl of Ossar (Conaire's dog) . . . cry of warriors on the summit of Tol Géisse; a cold wind over edges peri-lous: a night to destroy a king is this night."

He slept again, and awoke thereout, and sang this rhetoric:

" The howl of Ossar . . . a battle he announced: enslave-ment of a people: sack of the Hostel: mournful are the champions: men wounded: wind of terror: hurling of javel-ins: trouble of unfair fight: wreck of houses: Tara waste: a foreign heritage: like is lamenting Conaire: destruction of corn: feast of arms: cry of screams: destruction of Erin's king: chariots a-tottering: oppression of the king of Tara: lamentations will overcome laughter: Ossar's howl."

He said the third time:

" Trouble hath been shewn to me: a multitude of elves: a host supine; foes' prostration: a conflict of men on the Dodder [6]: oppression of Tara's king: in youth he was de-

---

[6] A small river near Dublin, which is said to have passed through the Bruden.—W. S.

stroyed: lamentations will overcome laughter: Ossar's howl."

"Liken thou, O Fer rogain, him who has sung that lay."

"Easy for me to liken him," says Fer rogain. No "conflict without a king" this. He is the most splendid and noble and beautiful and mighty king that has come into the whole world. He is the mildest and gentlest and most perfect king that has come to it, even Conaire son of Eterscél. 'Tis he that is overking of all Erin. There is no defect in that man, whether in form or shape or vesture: whether in size or fitness or proportion, whether in eye or hair or brightness, whether in wisdom or skill or eloquence, whether in weapon or dress or appearance, whether in splendour or abundance or dignity, whether in knowledge or valour or kindred.

"Great is the tenderness of the sleepy simple man till he has chanced on a deed of valour. But if his fury and his courage be awakened when the champions of Erin and Alba are at him in the house, the Destruction will not be wrought so long as he is therein. Six hundred will fall by Conaire before he shall attain his arms, and seven hundred will fall by him in his first conflict after attaining his arms. I swear to God what my tribe swears, unless drink be taken from him, though there be no one else in the house, but he alone, he would hold the Hostel until help would reach it which the man would prepare for him from the Wave of Clidna [7] and the Wave of Assaroe [8] while ye are at the Hostel.

"Nine doors there are to the house, and at each door a hundred warriors will fall by his hand. And when every one in the house has ceased to ply his weapon, 'tis then he will resort to a deed of arms. And if he chance to come upon you out of the house, as numerous as hailstones and grass on a green will be your halves of heads and your cloven skulls and your bones under the the edge of his sword.

"'Tis my opinion that he will not chance to get out of the house. Dear to him are the two that are with him in the room, his two fosterers, Dris and Snithe. Thrice fifty war-

---

[7] In the bay of Glandore, co. Cork.—W. S.
[8] At Ballyshannon, co. Donegal.—W. S.

riors will fall before each of them in front of the Hostel, and not farther than a foot from him, on this side and that, will they too fall."

"Woe to him who shall wreak the Destruction, were it only because of that pair and the prince that is between them, the over-king of Erin, Conaire son of Eterscél! Sad were the quenching of that reign!" says Lomna Drúth, son of Donn Désa.

"Ye cannot," says Ingcél. "Clouds of weakness are coming to you," etc.

"Good cause hast thou, O Ingcél," says Lomna son of Donn Désa. "Not unto *thee* is the loss caused by the Destruction: for thou wilt carry off the head of the king of another country, and thyself will escape. Howbeit 'tis hard for me, for I shall be the first to be slain at the Hostel."

"Alas for me!" says Ingcél, "peradventure I shall be the frailest corpse," etc.

"And whom sawest thou afterwards?"

## The Room of the Rearguards

"There I saw twelve men on silvery hurdles all around that room of the king. Light yellow hair was on them. Blue kilts they wore. Equally beautiful were they, equally hardy, equally shapely. An ivory-hilted sword in each man's hand, and they cast them not down; but it is the horse-rods in their hands that are all round the room. Liken thou that, O Fer rogain."

"Easy for me to say. The king of Tara's guardsmen are there. These are their names: three Londs of Liffey-plain: three Arts of Ath cliath (*Dublin*): three Buders of Buagnech: and three Trénfers of Cuilne. I swear what my tribe swears, that many will be the dead by them around the Hostel.

And they will escape from it although they are wounded. Woe to him who shall wreak the Destruction were it only because of that band! And afterwards whom sawest thou there?"

### Le fri flaith son of Conaire, whose likeness this is

"There I beheld a red-freckled boy in a purple cloak. He is always a-wailing in the house. A stead wherein is the king of a cantred, whom each man takes from bosom to bosom.

"So he is with a blue silvery chair under his seat in the midst of the house, and he always a-wailing. Truly then, sad are his household listening to him! Three heads of hair on that boy, and these are the three: green hair and purple hair and all-golden hair. I know not whether they are many appearances which the hair receives, or whether they are three kinds of hair which are naturally upon him. But I know that evil is the thing he dreads to-night. I beheld thrice fifty boys on silvern chairs around him, and there were fifteen bulrushes in the hand of that red-freckled boy, with a thorn at the end of each of the rushes. And we were fifteen men, and our fifteen right eyes were blinded by him, and he blinded one of the seven pupils which was in my head" saith Ingcél. "Hast thou his like, O Fer rogain?"

"Easy for me to liken him!" Fer rogain wept till he shed his tears of blood over his cheeks. "Alas for him!" quoth he. This child is a ' scion of contention ' for the men of Erin with the men of Alba for hospitality, and shape, and form and horsemanship. Sad is his slaughter! 'Tis a ' swine that goes before mast,' 'tis a babe in age! the best crown-prince that has ever come into Erin! The child of Conaire son of Eterscél, Lé fri flaith is his name. Seven years there are in his age. It seems to me very likely that he is miserable because of the many appearances on his hair and the various hues that the hair assumes upon him. This is his special household, the thrice fifty lads that are around him."

"Woe," says Lomna, "to him that shall wreak the Destruction, were it only because of that boy!"

"Ye cannot," says Ingcél. "Clouds of weakness are coming on you, etc." "And after that whom sawest thou there?"

## The Room of the Cupbearers

"There I saw six men in front of the same room. Fair yellow manes upon them: green mantles about them: tin brooches at the opening of their mantles. Half-horses (centaurs) are they, like Conall Cernach. Each of them throws his mantle round another and is as swift as a mill-wheel. Thine eye can hardly follow them. Liken thou those, O Fer rogain!"

"This is easy for me. Those are the King of Tara's six cupbearers, namely Uan and Broen and Banna, Delt and Drucht and Dathen. That feat does not hinder them from their skinking, and it blunts not their intelligence thereat. Good are the warriors that are there! Thrice their number will fall by them. They will share prowess with any six in the Hostel, and they will escape from their foes, for they are out of the elfmounds. They are the best cupbearers in Erin. Woe to him that shall wreak the Destruction were it nly because of them!"

'Ye cannot," says Ingcél. "Clouds, etc." "And after that, whom sawest thou there?"

## Th· Room of Tulchinne the Juggler

"There I beheld a great champion, in front of the same room, on the floor of the house. The shame of baldness is on him. White as mountain cotton-grass is each hair that grows through his head. Earrings of gold around his ears. A mantle speckled, coloured, he wore. Nine swords in his hand, and nine silvern shields, and nine apples of gold. He throws each of them upwards, and none of them falls on the ground, and there is only one of them on his palm; each of them rising and falling past another is just like the movement to and fro of bees on a day of beauty. When he was swiftest, I beheld him at the feat, and as I looked, they uttered a cry about him and they were all on the house-floor. Then the Prince who is in the house said to the juggler: 'We have come together since thou wast a little boy, and till to-night thy juggling never failed thee.'

" 'Alas, alas, fair master Conaire, good cause have I. A keen, angry eye looked at me: a man with the third of a pupil which sees the going of the nine bands. Not much to him is that keen, wrathful sight! Battles are fought with it,' saith he. 'It should be known till doomsday that there is evil in front of the Hostel.'

" Then he took the swords in his hand, and the silvern shields and the apples of gold; and again they uttered a cry and were all on the floor of the house. That amazed him, and he gave over his play and said:

' O Fer caille, arise! Do not . . . its slaughter. Sacrifice thy pig! Find out who is in front of the house to injure the men of the Hostel.'

' There,' said he, ' are Fer Cualngi, Fer lé, Fer gar, Fer rogel, Fer rogain. They have announced a deed which is not feeble, the annihilation of Conaire by Donn Désa's five sons, by Conaire's five loving foster-brothers.'

" Liken thou that, O Fer rogain! Who has chanted that lay?"

" Easy for me to liken him," says Fer rogain. " Taul-chinne the chief juggler of the King of Tara; he is Conaire's conjurer. A man of great might is that man. Thrice nine will fall by him in his first encounter, and he will share prowess with every one in the Hostel, and he will chance to escape therefrom though wounded. What then? Even on account of this man only the Destruction should not be wrought."

" Long live he who should spare him! " says Lomna Drúth.

" Ye cannot," says Ingcél, etc.

## THE ROOM OF THE SWINEHERDS

" I beheld a trio in the front of the house: three dark crowntufts on them: three green frocks around them: three dark mantles over them: three forked . . . (?) above them on the side of the wall. Six black greaves they had on the mast. Who are yon, O Fer rogain?"

" Easy to say," answers Fer rogain: " the three swine-herds of the king, Dub and Donn and Dorcha: three brothers are they, three sons of Mapher of Tara. Long live he who should protect them! woe to him who shall slay them! for greater would be the triumph of protecting them than the triumph of slaying them!"

"Ye cannot," says Ingcél, etc.

## THE ROOM OF THE PRINCIPAL CHARIOTEERS

"I beheld another trio in front of them: three plates of gold on their foreheads: three short aprons they wore, of grey linen embroidered with gold: three crimson capes about them: three goads of bronze in their hands. Liken thou that, O Fer rogain!"

"I know them," he answered. "Cul and Frecul and Forcul, the three charioteers of the King: three of the same age: three sons of Pole and Yoke. A man will perish by each of their weapons, and they will share the triumph of slaughter."

## THE ROOM OF CUSCRAD SON OF CONCHOBAR

"I beheld another room. Therein were eight swordsmen, and among them a stripling. Black hair is on him, and very stammering speech has he. All the folk of the Hostel listen to his counsel. Handsomest of men he is: he wears a shirt and a bright-red mantle, with a brooch of silver therein."

"I know him," says Fer rogain: "'tis Cuscraid Menn of Armagh, Conchobar's son, who is in hostageship with the king. And his guards are those eight swordsmen around him, namely, two Flanns, two Cummains, two Aeds, two Crimthans. They will share prowess with every one in the Hostel, and they will chance to escape from it with their fosterling."

## THE ROOM OF THE UNDER-CHARIOTEERS

"I beheld nine men: on the mast were they. Nine capes they wore, with a purple loop. A plate of gold on the head of each of them. Nine goads in their hands. Liken thou."

" I know those," quoth Fer rogain: " Riado, Riamcobur, Ríade, Buadon, Búadchar, Buadgnad, Eirr, Ineirr, Argatlam —nine charioteers in apprenticeship with the three chief charioteers of the king. A man will perish at the hands of each of them," etc.

### The Room of the Englishmen

" On the northern side of the house I beheld nine men. Nine very yellow manes were on them. Nine linen frocks somewhat short were round them: nine purple plaids over them without brooches therein. Nine broad spears, nine red curved shields above them."

" We know them," quoth he. " Oswald and his two foster-brothers, Osbrit Longhand and his two foster-brothers, Lindas and his two foster-brothers. Three crown-princes of England who are with the king. That set will share victorious prowess," etc.

### The Room of the Equerries

" I beheld another trio. Three cropt heads of hair on them, three frocks they wore, and three mantles wrapt around them. A whip in the hand of each."

" I know those," quoth Fer rogain. " Echdruim, Echriud, Echrúathar, the three horsemen of the king, that is, his three equerries. Three brothers are they, three sons of Argatron. Woe to him who shall wreak the Destruction, were it only because of that trio."

### The Room of the Judges

" I beheld another trio in the room by them. A handsome man who had got his baldness newly. By him were two young men with manes upon them. Three mixed plaids they wore. A pin of silver in the mantle of each of them. Three suits of armour above them on the wall. Liken thou that, O Fer rogain ! "

"I know those," quoth he. "Fergus Ferde, Fergus Fordae and Domáine Mossud, those are the king's three judges. Woe to him who shall wreak the Destruction were it only because of that trio! A man will perish by each of them."

### The Room of the Harpers

"To the east of them I beheld another ennead. Nine branchy, curly manes upon them. Nine grey, floating mantles about them: nine pins of gold in their mantles. Nine rings of crystal round their arms. A thumb-ring of gold round each man's thumb: an ear-tie of gold round each man's ear: a torque of silver round each man's throat. Nine bags with golden faces above them on the wall. Nine rods of white silver in their hands. Liken thou them."

"I know those," quoth Fer rogain. "They are the king's nine harpers, with their nine harps above them: Side and Dide, Dulothe and Deichrinne, Caumul and Cellgen, Ol and Olene and Olchói. A man will perish by each of them."

### The Room of the Conjurers

"I saw another trio on the dais. Three bedgowns girt about them. Four-cornered shields in their hands, with bosses of gold upon them. Apples of silver they had, and small inlaid spears."

"I know them," says Fer rogain. "Cless and Clissíne and Clessamun, the king's three conjurers. Three of the same age are they: three brothers, three sons of Naffer Rochless. A man will perish by each of them."

### The Room of the Three Lampooneers

"I beheld another trio hard by the room of the King himself. Three blue mantles around them, and three bedgowns with red insertion over them. Their arms had been hung above them on the wall."

"I know those," quoth he. "Dris and Draigen and Aittít ('Thorn and Bramble and Furze'), the king's three lampooners, three sons of Sciath foilt. A man will perish by each of their weapons."

### THE ROOM OF THE BADBS

"I beheld a trio, naked, on the roof-tree of the house: their jets of blood coming through them, and the ropes of their slaughter on their necks."

"Those I know," saith he, "three . . . of awful boding. Those are the three that are slaughtered at every time."

### THE ROOM OF THE KITCHENERS

"I beheld a trio cooking, in short inlaid aprons: a fair grey man, and two youths in his company."

"I know those," quoth Fer rogain: "they are the King's three chief kitcheners, namely, the Dagdae and his two fosterlings, Séig and Segdae, the two sons of Rofer Singlespit. A man will perish by each of them," etc.

"I beheld another trio there. Three plates of gold over their heads. Three speckled mantles about them: three linen shirts with red insertion: three golden brooches in their mantles: three wooden darts above them on the wall."

"Those I know," says Fer rogain: "the three poets of that king: Sui and Rodui and Fordui: three of the same age, three brothers: three sons of Maphar of the Mighty Song. A man will perish for each of them, and every pair will keep between them one man's victory. Woe to him who shall wreak the Destruction!" etc.

### THE ROOM OF THE SERVANT-GUARDS

"There I beheld two warriors standing over the king. Two curved shields they had, and two great pointed swords. Red kilts they wore, and in the mantles pins of white silver."

"Bole and Root are those," quoth he, "the king's two guards, two sons of Maffer Toll."

## The Room of the King's Guardsmen

"I beheld nine men in a room there in front of the same room. Fair yellow manes upon them: short aprons they wore and spotted capes: they carried smiting shields. An ivory-hilted sword in the hand of each of them, and whoever enters the house they essay to smite him with the swords. No one dares to go to the room of the King without their consent. Liken thou that, O Fer rogain!"

"Easy for me is that. Three Mochmatnechs of Meath, three Buageltachs of Bregia, three Sostachs of Sliab Fuait, the nine guardsmen of that King. Nine decads will fall by them in their first conflict, etc. Woe to him that shall wreak the Destruction because of them only!"

"Ye cannot," says Ingcél. "Clouds of weakness," etc. "And whom sawest thou then?"

## The Room of Nia and Bruthne, Conaire's Two Waiters

"There I beheld another room, and a pair was in it, and they are 'oxtubs,' stout and thick. Aprons they wore, and the men were dark and brown. They had short backhair on them, but high upon their foreheads. They are as swift as a waterwheel, each of them past another, one of them to the King's room, the other to the fire. Liken thou those, O Fer rogain!"

"Easy to me. They are Nia and Bruthne, Conaire's two table-servants. They are the pair that is best in Erin for their lord's advantage. What causes brownness to them and height to their hair is their frequent haunting of the fire. In the world is no pair better in their art than they. Thrice nine men will fall by them in their first encounter, and they will share prowess with every one, and they will chance to escape. And after that whom sawest thou?"

### The Room of Sencha and Dubthach and Gobniu Son of Lurgnech

" I beheld the room that is next to Conaire. Three chief champions, in their first greyness, are therein. As thick as a man's waist is each of their limbs. They have three black swords, each as long as a weaver's beam. These swords would split a hair on water. A great lance in the hand of the midmost man, with fifty rivets through it. The shaft therein is a good load for the yoke of a plough-team. The midmost man brandishes that lance so that its edge-studs hardly stay therein, and he strikes the haft thrice against his palm. There is a great boiler in front of them, as big as a calf's caldron, wherein is a black and horrible liquid. Moreover he plunges the lance into that black fluid. If its quenching be delayed it flames on its shaft and then thou wouldst suppose that there is a fiery dragon in the top of the house. Liken thou that, O Fer rogain!"

" Easy to say. Three heroes who are best at grasping weapons in Erin, namely, Sencha the beautiful son of Ailill, and Dubthach Chafer of Ulaid, and Goibnenn son of Lurgnech. And the *Luin* of Celtchar son of Uthider which was found in the battle of Mag Tured, this is in the hand of Dubthach Chafer of Ulaid. That feat is usual for it when it is ripe to pour forth a foeman's blood. A caldron full of poison is needed to quench it when a deed of man-slaying is expected. Unless this come to the lance, it flames on its haft and will go through its bearer or the master of the palace wherein it is. If it be a blow that is to be given thereby it will kill a man at every blow, when it is at that feat, from one hour to another, though it may not reach him. And if it be a cast, it will kill nine men at every cast, and one of the nine will be a king or crown-prince or chieftain of the reavers.

" I swear what my tribe swears, there will be a multitude unto whom tonight the *Luin* of Celtchar will deal drinks of death in front of the Hostel. I swear to God what my tribe swears that, in their first encounter, three hundred will fall by that trio, and they will share prowess with every three in the Hostel tonight. And they will boast of victory over a king or chief of the reavers, and the three will chance to escape."

"Woe," says Lomna Drúth, "to him who shall wreak the Destruction, were it only because of that trio!"

"Ye cannot," says Ingcél, etc. "And after that, whom sawest thou there?"

## THE ROOM OF THE THREE MANX GIANTS

"There I beheld a room with a trio in it. Three men mighty, manly, overbearing, which see no one abiding at their three hideous crooked aspects. A fearful view because of the terror of them. A . . . dress of rough hair covers them . . . of cow's hair, without garments enwrapping down to the right heels. With three manes, equine, awful, majestic, down to their sides. Fierce heroes who wield against foeman hard-smiting swords. A blow, they give with three iron flails having seven chains triple-twisted, three-edged, with seven iron knobs at the end of every chain : each of them as heavy as an ingot of ten smeltings. Three big brown men. Dark equine back-manes on them, which reach their two heels. Two good thirds of an oxhide in the girdle round each one's waist, and each quadrangular clasp that closes it as thick as a man's thigh. The raiment that is round them is the dress that grows through them. Tresses of their back-manes were spread, and a long staff of iron, as long and thick as an outer yoke was in each man's hand, and an iron chain out of the end of every club, and at the end of every chain an iron pestle as long and thick as a middle yoke. They stand in their sadness in the house, and enough is the horror of their aspect. There is no one in the house that would not be avoiding them. Liken thou that, O Fer rogain!"

Fer rogain was silent. "Hard for me to liken them. I know none such of the world's men unless they be yon trio of giants to whom Cúchulainn gave quarter at the beleaguerment of the Men of Falga, and when they were getting quarter they killed fifty warriors. But Cúchulainn would not let them be slain, because of their wondrousness. These are the names of the three: Srubdaire son of Dordbruige, and Conchenn of Cenn maige, and Fiad sceme son of Scípe. Conaire bought them from Cúchulainn for . . . so they are along with him. Three hundred will fall by them in their first encounter, and they will surpass in prowess every three in the Hostel; and if they come forth upon you, the fragments of you will be fit to go through the sieve of a cornkiln, from the way in which they will destroy you with the flails of iron. Woe to him that shall wreak the Destruction, though it were only on account of those three! For to combat against them is not a ' paean round a sluggard.' "

" Ye cannot," says Ingcél. " Clouds of weakness are coming to you," etc. "And after that, whom sawest thou there ? "

### THE ROOM OF DÁ DERGA

" There I beheld another room, with one man therein and in front of him two servants with two manes upon them, one of the two dark, the other fair. Red hair on the warrior, and red eyebrows. Two ruddy cheeks he had, and an eye very blue and beautiful. He wore a green cloak and a shirt with a white hood and a red insertion. In his hand was a sword with a hilt of ivory, and he supplies attendance of every room in the house with ale and food, and he is quick-footed in serving the whole host. Liken thou that, O Fer rogain ! "

" I know those men. That one is Dá Derga. 'Tis by him that the Hostel was built, and since it was built its doors have never been shut save on the side to which the wind comes—the valve is closed against it—and since he began housekeeping his caldron was never taken from the fire, but it has been boiling food for the men of Erin. The pair before him, those two youths, are his fosterlings, two sons of the king of Leinster, namely Muredach and Corpre. Three decads will fall by that trio in front of their house and they will boast of victory over a king or a chief of the reavers. After this they will chance to escape from it."

" Long live he who should protect them ! " says Lomna.

" Better were triumph of saving them than triumph of slaying them! They should be spared were it only on account of that man. 'Twere meet to give that man quarter," says Lomna Drúth.

" Ye cannot," says Ingcél. " Clouds," etc. "And after that whom sawest thou there?"

## The Room of the Three Champions from the Elfmounds

" There I beheld a room with a trio in it. Three red mantles they wore, and three red shirts, and three red heads of hair were on them. Red were they all together with their teeth. Three red shields above them. Three red spears in their hands. Three red horses in their bridles in front of the Hostel. Liken thou that, O Fer rogain!"

" Easily done. Three champions who wrought falsehood in the elfmounds. This is the punishment inflicted upon them by the king of the elfmounds, to be destroyed thrice by the King of Tara. Conaire son of Eterscél is the last king by whom they are destroyed. Those men will escape from you. To fulfil their own destruction, they have come. But they will not be slain, nor will they slay anyone. And after that whom sawest thou?"

## The Room of the Doorwards

" There I beheld a trio in the midst of the house at the door. Three holed maces in their hands. Swift as a hare was each of them round the other towards the door. Aprons were on them, and they had gray and speckled mantles. Liken thou that, O Fer rogain!"

" Easily done: Three doorwardens of Tara's King are those, namely Echur ('Key') and Tochur and Tecmang, three sons of Ersa ('Doorpost') and Comla ('Valve'). Thrice their number will fall by them, and they will share a man's triumph among them. They will chance to escape though wounded."

" Woe to him that shall wreak!" etc., says Lomna Drúth.

" Ye cannot," says Ingcél, etc.   " And after that whom sawest thou? "

### THE ROOM OF FER CAILLE

" There I beheld at the fire in front a man with black cropt hair, having only one eye and one foot and one hand, having on the fire a pig bald, black, singed, squealing continually, and in his company a great big-mouthed woman. Liken thou that, O Fer rogain! "

" Easily done:   Fer caille with his pig and his wife Cichuil.   They (the wife and the pig) are his proper instruments on the night that ye destroy Conaire King of Erin.   Alas for the guest who will run between them!   Fer caille with his pig is one of Conaire's tabus."

" Woe to him who shall wreak the Destruction! " says Lomna.

" Ye cannot," quoth Ingcél.   " And after that, whom sawest thou there? "

### THE ROOM OF THE THREE SONS OF BÁITHIS OF BRITAIN

" There I beheld a room with three enneads in it.   Fair yellow manes upon them, and they are equally beautiful. Each of them wore a black cape, and there was a white hood on each mantle, a red tuft on each hood, and an iron brooch at the opening of every mantle, and under each man's cloak a huge black sword, and the swords would split a hair on water.   They bore shields with scalloped edges.   Liken thou them, O Fer rogain! "

" Easily done.   That is the robber-band of the three sons of Báithis of Britain.   Three enneads will fall by them in their first conflict, and among them they will share a man's triumph.   And after that whom sawest thou? "

### THE ROOM OF THE MIMES

" There I beheld a trio of jesters hard by the fire.   Three dun mantles they wore.   If the men of Erin were in one place, even though the corpse of his mother or his father were in front of each, not one could refrain from laughing at them. Wheresoever the king of a cantred is in the house, not one of them attains his seat on his bed because of that trio of jesters. Whenever the king's eye visits them it smiles at every glance. Liken thou that, O Fer rogain!"

"Easily done. Mael and Mlithe and Admlithe—those are the king of Erin's three jesters. By each of them a man will perish, and among them they will share a man's triumph."

"Woe to him that will wreak the Destruction!" says Lomna, etc. "And after that whom sawest thou there?"

## The Room of the Cupbearers

"There I beheld a room with a trio in it. Three grey-floating mantles they wore. There was a cup of water in front of each man, and on each cup a bunch of watercress. Liken thou that, O Fer rogain!"

"Easily done. Black and Dun and Dark: they are the King of Tara's three cupbearers, to wit, the sons of Day and Night. And after that, whom sawest thou there?"

## The Room of Nár the Squinter-with-the-left-eye

"There I beheld a one-eyed man asquint with a ruinous eye. A swine's head he had on the fire, continually squealing. Liken thou that, O Fer rogain!"

"Easy for me to name the like. He is Nár the Squinter with the left eye, the swineherd of Bodb of the Elfmound on Femen, 'tis he that is over the cooking. Blood hath been spilt at every feast at which he has ever been present."

"Rise up, then, ye champions!" says Ingcél, "and get you on to the house!"

With that the reavers march to the Hostel, and made a murmur about it.

"Silence a while!" says Conaire, "what is this?"

"Champions at the house," says Conall Cernach.

"There are warriors for them here," answers Conaire.

"They will be needed tonight," Conall Cernach rejoins.

Then went Lomna Drúth before the host of reavers into the Hostel. The doorkeepers struck off his head. Then the head was thrice flung into the Hostel, and thrice cast out of it, as he himself had foretold.

Then Conaire himself sallies out of the Hostel together with some of his people, and they fight a combat with the host of reavers, and six hundred fell by Conaire before he could get to his arms. Then the Hostel is thrice set on fire, and thrice put out from thence: and it was granted that the Destruction would never have been wrought had not work of weapons been taken from Conaire.

Thereafter Conaire went to seek his arms, and he dons his battle-dress, and falls to plying his weapons on the reavers, together with the band that he had. Then, after getting his arms, six hundred fell by him in his first encounter.

After this the reavers were routed. "I have told you," says Fer rogain son of Donn Désa, "that if the champions of the men of Erin and Alba attack Conaire at the house, the Destruction will not be wrought unless Conaire's fury and valour be quelled."

"Short will his time be," say the wizards along with the reavers. This was the quelling they brought, a scantness of drink that seized him.

Thereafter Conaire entered the house, and asked for a drink.

"A drink to me, O master Mac cecht!" says Conaire.

Says Mac cecht: "This is not the order that I have hitherto had from thee, to give thee a drink. There are spencers and cupbearers who bring drink to thee. The order I have hitherto had from thee is to protect thee when the champions of the men of Erin and Alba may be attacking thee around the Hostel. Thou wilt go safe from them, and no spear shall enter thy body. Ask a drink of thy spencers and thy cupbearers."

Then Conaire asked a drink of his spencers and his cupbearers who were in the house.

" In the first place there is none," they say; " all the liquids that had been in the house have been spilt on the fires."

The cupbears found no drink for him in the Dodder (a river), and the Dodder had flowed through the house.

Then Conaire again asked for a drink. " A drink to me, O fosterer, O Mac cecht! 'Tis equal to me what death I shall go to, for anyhow I shall perish."

Then Mac cecht gave a choice to the champions of valour of the men of Erin who were in the house, whether they cared to protect the King or to seek a drink for him.

Conall Cernach answered this in the house—and cruel he deemed the contention, and afterwards he had always a feud with Mac cecht. — " Leave the defence of the King to *us*," says Conall, "and go thou to seek the drink, for of thee it is demanded."

So then Mac cecht fared forth to seek the drink, and he took Conaire's son, Lé fri flaith, under his armpit, and Conaire's golden cup, in which an ox with a bacon-pig would be boiled; and he bore his shield and his two spears and his sword, and he carried the caldron-spit, a spit of iron.

He burst forth upon them, and in front of the Hostel he dealt nine blows of the iron spit, and at every blow nine reavers fell. Then he makes a sloping feat of the shield and an edge-feat of the sword about his head, and he delivered a hostile attack upon them. Six hundred fell in his first encounter, and after cutting down hundreds he goes through the band outside.

The doings of the folk of the Hostel, this is what is here examined, presently.

Conall Cernach arises, and takes his weapons, and wends over the door of the Hostel, and goes round the house. Three hundred fell by him, and he hurls back the reavers over three ridges out from the Hostel, and boasts of triumph over a king, and returns, wounded, into the Hostel.

Cormac Condlongas sallies out, and his nine comrades with him, and they deliver their onsets on the reavers. Nine enneads fall by Cormac and nine enneads by his people, and a man for each weapon and a man for each man. And Cormac boasts of the death of a chief of the reavers. They succeed in escaping though they be wounded.

The trio of Picts sally forth from the Hostel, and take to plying their weapons on the reavers. And nine enneads fall by them, and they chance to escape though they be wounded.

The nine pipers sally forth and dash their warlike work on the reavers; and then they succeed in escaping.

Howbeit then, but it is long to relate, 'tis weariness of mind, 'tis confusion of the senses, 'tis tediousness to hearers, 'tis superfluity of narration to go over the same things twice. But the folk of the Hostel came forth in order, and fought their combats with the reavers, and fell by them, as Fer rogain and Lomna Drúth had said to Ingcél, to wit, that the folk of every room would sally forth still and deliver their combat, and after that escape. So that none were left in the Hostel in Conaire's company save Conall and Sencha and Dubthach.

Now from the vehement ardour and the greatness of the contest which Conaire had fought, his great drouth of thirst attacked him, and he perished of a consuming fever, for he got not his drink. So when the king died those three sally out of the Hostel, and deliver a wily stroke of reaving on the reavers, and fare forth from the Hostel, wounded, to-broken and maimed.

Touching Mac cecht, however, he went his way till he reached the Well of Casair, which was near him in Crích Cualann; but of water he found not therein the full of his cup, that is, Conaire's golden cup which he had brought in his hand. Before morning he had gone round the chief rivers of Erin, to wit, Bush, Boyne, Bann, Barrow, Neim, Luae, Láigdae, Shannon, Suir, Sligo, Sámair, Find, Ruirthech, Slaney, and in them he found not the full of his cup of water.

Then before morning he had travelled to the chief lakes of Erin, to wit, Lough Derg, Loch Luimnig, Lough Foyle, Lough Mask, Loug Corrib, Loch Láig, Loch Cúan, Lough Neagh, Mórloch, and of water he found not therein the full of his cup.

He went his way till he reached Uaran Garad on Magh Ai. It could not hide itself from him: so he brought thereout the full of his cup, and the boy fell under his covering.

After this he went on and reached Dá Derga's Hostel before morning.

When Mac cecht went across the third ridge towards the house, 'tis there were twain striking off Conaire's head. Then Mac cecht strikes off the head of one of the two men who were beheading Conaire. The other man then was fleeing forth with the king's head. A pillar-stone chanced to be under Mac cecht's feet on the floor of the Hostel. He hurls it at the man who had Conaire's head and drove it through his spine, so that his back broke. After this Mac cecht beheads him. Mac cecht then spilt the cup of water into Conaire's gullet and neck. Then said Conaire's head, after the water had been put into its neck and gullet:

"A good man Mac cecht! an excellent man Mac cecht!
A good warrior without, good within,
He gives a drink, he saves a king, he doth a deed.
Well he ended the champions I found.
He sent a flagstone on the warriors.
Well he hewed by the door of the Hostel ... Fer lé,
So that a spear is against one hip.
Good should I be to far-renowned Mac cecht
If I were alive. A good man!"

After this Mac cecht followed the routed foe.

'Tis this that some books relate, that but a very few fell around Conaire, namely, nine only. And hardly a fugitive escaped to tell the tidings to the champions who had been at the house.

Where there had been five thousand—and in every thousand ten hundred—only one set of five escaped, namely Ingcél, and his two brothers Echell and Tulchinne, the "Yearling of the Reavers"—three great-grandsons of Conmac, and the two Reds of Róiriu who had been the first to wound Conaire.

Thereafter Ingcél went into Alba, and received the kingship after his father, since he had taken home triumph over a king of another country.

This, however, is the recension in other books, and it is more probably truer. Of the folk of the Hostel forty or fifty fell, and of the reavers three fourths and one fourth of them only escaped from the Destruction.

Now when Mac cecht was lying wounded on the battle-field, at the end of the third day, he saw a woman passing by.

"Come hither, O woman!" says Mac cecht.

"I dare not go thus," says the woman, "for horror and fear of thee."

"There *was* a time when I had this, O woman, even horror and fear of me on some one. But now thou shouldst fear nothing. I accept thee on the truth of my honour and my safeguard."

Then the woman goes to him.

"I know not," says he, "whether it is a fly or a gnat, or an ant that nips me in the wound."

It happened that it was a hairy wolf that was there, as far as its two shoulders in the wound!

The woman seized it by the tail, and dragged it out of the wound, and it takes the full of its jaws out of him.

"Truly," says the woman, "this is 'an ant of ancient land.'"

Says Mac cecht "I swear to God what my people swears, I deemed it no bigger than a fly, or a gnat, or an ant."

And Mac cecht took the wolf by the throat, and struck it a blow on the forehead, and killed it with a single blow.

Then Lé fri flaith, son of Conaire, died under Mac cecht's armpit, for the warrior's heat and sweat had dissolved him.

Thereafter Mac cecht, having cleansed the slaughter, at the end of the third day, set forth, and he dragged Conaire with him on his back, and buried him at Tara, as some say. Then Mac cecht departed into Connaught, to his own country, that he might work his cure in Mag Bréngair. Wherefore the name clave to the plain from Mac cecht's misery, that is, Mag Brén-guir.

Now Conall Cernach escaped from the Hostel, and thrice fifty spears had gone through the arm which upheld his shield. He fared forth till he reached his father's house, with half his shield in his hand, and his sword, and the fragments of his two spears. Then he found his father before his garth in Taltiu.

"Swift are the wolves that have hunted thee, my son," saith his father.

" 'Tis this that has wounded us, thou old hero, an evil conflict with warriors," Conall Cernach replied.

" Hast thou then news of Dá Derga's Hostel?" asked Amorgin. " Is thy lord alive?"

" He is *not* alive," says Conall.

" I swear to God what the great tribes of Ulaid swear, it is cowardly for the man who went thereout alive, having left his lord with his foes in death."

" My wounds are not white, thou old hero," says Conall.

He shews him his shield-arm, whereon were thrice fifty wounds: this is what was inflicted upon it. The shield that guarded it is what saved it. But the right arm had been played upon, as far as two thirds thereof, since the shield had not been guarding it. That arm was mangled and maimed and wounded and pierced, save that the sinews kept it to the body without separation.

" That arm fought tonight, my son," says Amorgein.

" True is that, thou old hero," says Conall Cernach. " Many there are unto whom it gave drinks of death tonight in front of the Hostel."

Now as to the reavers, every one of them that escaped from the Hostel went to the cairn which they had built on the night before last, and they brought thereout a stone for each man not mortally wounded. So this is what they lost by death at the Hostel, a man for every stone that is (now) in Carn Lecca.

It endeth: Amen: it endeth.

# THE STORY OF THE VOLSUNGS AND NIBLUNGS

TRANSLATED BY
EIRÍKR MAGNÚSSON AND WILLIAM MORRIS

## TRANSLATOR'S PREFACE

IN *offering to the reader this translation of the most complete and dramatic form of the great Epic of the North, we lay no claim to special critical insight, nor do we care to deal at all with vexed questions, but are content to abide by existing authorities, doing our utmost to make our rendering close and accurate, and, if it might be so, at the same time, not over prosaic: it is to the lover of poetry and nature, rather than to the student, that we appeal to enjoy and wonder at this great work, now for the first time, strange to say, translated into English: this must be our excuse for speaking here, as briefly as may be, of things that will seem to the student over well known to be worth mentioning, but which may give some ease to the general reader who comes across our book.*

*The prose of the Völsunga Saga was composed probably some time in the twelfth century, from floating traditions no doubt; from songs which, now lost, were then known, at least in fragments, to the Sagaman; and finally from songs, which, written down about his time, are still existing: the greater part of these last the reader will find in this book; some inserted amongst the prose text by the original story-teller, and some by the present translators, and the remainder in the latter part of the book, put together as nearly as may be in the order of the story, and forming a metrical version of the greater portion of it.*

*These Songs from the Elder Edda we will now briefly compare with the prose of the Volsung Story, premising that these are the only metrical sources existing of those from which the Sagaman told his tale.*

*Except for the short snatch on p. 290 of our translation, nothing is now left of these till we come to the episode of Helgi Hundings-bane, Sigurd's half-brother; there are two songs left relating to this, from which the prose is put together; to a certain extent they cover the same ground; but the latter half of the second is, wisely as we think, left untouched by the Sagaman, as its interest is of itself too great not to encumber the progress of the main story; for the sake of its wonderful beauty, however, we could not refrain from rendering it, and it will be found first among the metrical translations that form the second part of this book.*

*Of the next part of the Saga, the deaths of Sinfjotli and Sigmund, and the journey of Queen Hjordis to the court of King Alf, there is no trace left of any metrical origin; but we meet the Edda once more where Regin tells the tale of his kin to Sigurd, and where Sigurd defeats and slays the sons of Hunding: this lay is known as the Lay of Regin.*

*The short chap. xvi. is abbreviated from a long poem called the Prophecy of Gripir (the Grifir of the Saga), where the whole story to come is told with some detail, and which certainly, if drawn out at length into the prose, would have forestalled the interest of the tale.*

*In the slaying of the Dragon the Saga adheres very closely to the Lay of Fafnir; for the insertion of the song of the birds to Sigurd the present translators are responsible.*

*Then comes the waking of Brynhild, and her wise redes to Sigurd, taken from the Lay of Sigrdrifa, the greater part of which, in its metrical form, is inserted by the Sagaman into his prose; but the stanzas relating Brynhild's awaking we have inserted into the text; the latter part, omitted in the prose, we have translated for the second part of our book.*

*Of Sigurd at Hlymdale, of Gudrun's dream, the magic potion of Grimhild, the wedding of Sigurd consequent on that potion; of the wooing of Brynhild for Gunnar, her marriage to him, of the quarrel of the Queens, the brooding grief and wrath of Brynhild, and the interview of Sigurd with her—of all this, the most dramatic and best-considered part of the tale, there is now no more left that retains its metrical form than the few snatches preserved by the Sagaman, though many of the incidents are alluded to in other poems.*

*Chap. xxx. is met by the poem called the Short Lay of Sigurd, which, fragmentary apparently at the beginning, gives us something of Brynhild's awakening wrath and jealousy, the slaying of Sigurd, and the death of Brynhild herself; this poem we have translated entire.*

*The Fragments of the Lay of Brynhild are what is left of a poem partly covering the same ground as this last, but giving a different account of Sigurd's slaying; it is very incomplete, though the Sagaman has drawn some incidents from it; the reader will find it translated in our second part.*

*But before the death of the heroine we have inserted entire into the text as chap. xxxi. the First Lay of Gudrun, the most lyrical, the most complete, and the most beautiful of all the Eddaic poems; a poem that any age or language might count among its most precious possessions.*

*From this point to the end of the Saga it keeps closely to the Songs of Edda; in chap. xxxii. the Sagaman has rendered into prose the Ancient Lay of Gudrun, except for the beginning, which gives again another account of the death of Sigurd: this lay also we have translated.*

*The grand poem, called the Hell-ride of Brynhild, is not represented directly by anything in the prose except that the Sagaman has supplied from it a link or two wanting in the Lay of Sigrdrifa; it will be found translated in our second part.*

*The betrayal and slaughter of the Giukings or Niblungs, and the fearful end of Atli and his sons, and court, are recounted in two lays, called the Lays of Atli; the longest of these, the Greenland Lay of Atli, is followed closely by the Sagaman; the shorter one we have translated.*

*The end of Gudrun, of her daughter by Sigurd, and of her sons by her last husband Jonakr, treated of in the last four chapters of the Saga, are very grandly and poetically given in the songs called the Whetting of Gudrun, and the Lay of Hamdir, which are also among our translations.*

*These are all the songs of the Edda which the Sagaman has dealt with; but one other, the Lament of Oddrun, we have translated on account of its intrinsic merit.*

*As to the literary quality of this work we might say much, but we think we may well trust the reader of poetic insight to break through whatever entanglement of strange manners or unused element may at first trouble him, and to meet the nature and beauty with which it is filled: we cannot doubt that such a reader will be intensely touched by finding, amidst all its wildness and remoteness, such a startling realism, such subtilty, such close sympathy with all the passions that may move himself to-day.*

*In conclusion, we must again say how strange it seems to us, that this Volsung Tale, which is in fact an unversified poem, should never before have been translated into English. For this is the Great Story of the North, which should be to all our race what the Tale of Troy was to the Greeks—to all our race first, and afterwards, when the change of the world has made our race nothing more than a name of what has been—a story too—then should it be to those that come after us no less than the Tale of Troy has been to us.*

[The following text and notes are from the edition by H. H. Sparling.]

# THE NAMES OF THOSE WHO ARE MOST NOTEWORTHY IN THIS STORY

## VOLSUNGS

SIGI, son of Odin.

RERIR, son of Sigi, king of Hunland.

VOLSUNG, son of Rerir.

SIGMUND, son  }
SIGNY, daughter } of Volsung.

SINFJOTLI, son of Sigmund and Signy.

HELGI, son of Sigmund by Borgny.

SIGURD FAFNIR'S-BANE, posthumous son of Sigmund by Hjordis.

SWANHILD, his daughter, by GUDRUN, Giuki's daughter.

## PEOPLE WHO DEAL WITH THE VOLSUNGS BEFORE SIGURD MEETS BRYNHILD

SIGGEIR, king of Gothland, husband of Signy.

BORGNY, first wife of Sigmund.

HJORDIS, his second wife.

KING EYLIMI, her father.

HJALPREK, king of Denmark.

ALF, his son, second husband of Hjordis.

REGIN, the king's smith.

FAFNIR, his brother, turned into a dragon.

OTTER, his brother, slain by Loki.

HREIDMAR, the father of these brothers.

ANDVARI, a dwarf, first owner of the hoard of the Niblungs, on which he laid a curse when it was taken from him by Loki.

## GIUKINGS OR NIBLUNGS

KING GIUKI.

GRIMHILD, his wife.

GUNNAR, )
HOGNI,  } sons of Giuki.
GUTTORM, )

GUDRUN, daughter of Giuki, wife of SIGURD FAFNIR'S-BANE.

## BUDLUNGS

KING BUDLI.

ATLI, his son, second husband of GUDRUN,

BRYNHILD, daughter of Budli, first betrothed and love of SIGURD
 FAFNIR'S-BANE, wife of Gunnar, son of Giuki.
BEKKHILD, daughter of Budli, wife of Heimir of Hlymdale.

## OTHERS WHO DEAL WITH SIGURD AND THE GIUKINGS

HEIMER OF HLYMDALE, foster-father of BRYNHILD.
GLAUMVOR, second wife of Gunnar.
KOSTBERA, wife of Hogni.
VINGI, an evil counsellor of King Atli.
NIBLUNG, the son of Hogni, who helps GUDRUN in the slaying of Atli.
JORMUNREK, king of the Goths, husband of Swanhild.
RANDVER, his son.
BIKKI, his evil counsellor.
JONAKR, GUDRUN's third husband.
SORLI, HAMDIR, AND ERP, the sons of Jonakr and GUDRUN.

# A PROLOGUE IN VERSE

O HEARKEN, ye who speak the English Tongue,
  How in a waste land ages long ago,
The very heart of the North bloomed into song
  After long brooding o'er this tale of woe!
  Hearken, and marvel how it might be so,
That such a sweetness so well crowned could be
Betwixt the ice-hills and the cold grey sea.

Or rather marvel not, that those should cling
  Unto the thoughts of great lives passed away,
Whom God has stripped so bare of everything,
  Save the one longing to wear through their day,
  In fearless wise; the hope the Gods to stay,
When at that last tide gathered wrong and hate
Shall meet blind yearning on the Fields of Fate.

Yea, in the first grey dawning of our race,
  This ruth-crowned tangle to sad hearts was dear.
Then rose a seeming sun, the lift gave place
  Unto a seeming heaven, far off, but clear;
  But that passed too, and afternoon is here;
Nor was the morn so fruitful or so long
But we may hearken when ghosts moan of wrong.

For as amid the clatter of the town
  When eve comes on with unabated noise,
The soaring wind will sometimes drop adown
  And bear unto our chamber the sweet voice
  Of bells that 'mid the swallows do rejoice,
Half-heard, to make us sad, so we awhile
With echoed grief life's dull pain may beguile.

Naught vague, naught base our tale, that seems to say,—
　'Be wide-eyed, kind; curse not the hand that smites;
Curse not the kindness of a past good day,
　Or hope of love; cast by all earth's delights,
　For very love: through weary days and nights,
Abide thou, striving howsoe'er in vain,
The inmost love of one more heart to gain!'

So draw ye round and hearken, English Folk,
　Unto the best tale pity ever wrought!
Of how from dark to dark bright Sigurd broke,
　Of Brynhild's glorious soul with love distraught,
　Of Gudrun's weary wandering unto naught,
Of utter love defeated utterly,
Of grief too strong to give Love time to die!

                                    WILLIAM MORRIS.

# THE STORY OF THE
# VOLSUNGS AND NIBLUNGS

## CHAPTER I

### OF SIGI, THE SON OF ODIN

HERE begins the tale, and tells of a man who was named Sigi, and called of men the son of Odin; another man withal is told of in the tale, hight Skadi, a great man and mighty of his hands; yet was Sigi the mightier and the higher of kin, according to the speech of men of that time. Now Skadi had a thrall with whom the story must deal somewhat, Bredi by name, who was called after that work which he had to do; in prowess and might of hand he was equal to men who were held more worthy, yea, and better than some thereof.

Now it is to be told that, on a time, Sigi fared to the hunting of the deer, and the thrall with him; and they hunted deer day-long till the evening; and when they gathered together their prey in the evening, lo, greater and more by far was that which Bredi had slain than Sigi's prey; and this thing he much misliked, and he said that great wonder it was that a very thrall should out-do him in the hunting of deer: so he fell on him and slew him, and buried the body of him thereafter in a snow-drift.

Then he went home at evening tide and says that Bredi had ridden away from him into the wild-wood. "Soon was he out of my sight," he says, "and naught more I wot of him."

Skadi misdoubted the tale of Sigi, and deemed that this was a guile of his, and that he would have slain Bredi. So he sent men to seek for him, and to such an end came their seeking, that they found him in a certain snow-drift; then said Skadi, that men should call that snow-drift Bredi's Drift from henceforth; and thereafter have folk followed, so that in such wise they call every drift that is right great.

Thus it is well seen that Sigi has slain the thrall and murdered him; so he is given forth to be a wolf in holy places,[1] and may no more abide in the land with his father; therewith Odin bare him fellowship from the land, so long a way, that right long it was, and made no stay till he brought him to certain war-ships. So Sigi falls to lying out a-warring with the strength that his father gave him or ever they parted; and happy was he in his warring, and ever prevailed, till he brought it about that he won by his wars land and lordship at the last; and thereupon he took to him a noble wife, and became a great and mighty king, and ruled over the land of the Huns, and was the greatest of warriors. He had a son by his wife, who was called Rerir, who grew up in his father's house, and soon became great of growth, and shapely.

## CHAPTER II

### Of the Birth of Volsung, the Son of Rerir, Who was the Son of Sigi

Now Sigi grew old, and had many to envy him, so that at last those turned against him whom he trusted most; yea, even the brothers of his wife; for these fell on him at his unwariest, when there were few with him to withstand them, and brought so many against him, that they prevailed against him, and there fell Sigi and all his folk with him. But Rerir, his son, was not in this trouble, and he brought together so mighty a strength of his friends and the great men of the land, that he got to himself both the lands and kingdom of Sigi his father; and so now, when he deems that the feet under him stand firm in his rule, then he calls to mind that which he had against his mother's

---

[1] "Wolf in holy places," a man put out of the pale of society for his crimes, an outlaw.

brothers, who had slain his father. So the king gathers
together a mighty army, and therewith falls on his kinsmen,
deeming that if he made their kinship of small account,
yet none the less they had first wrought evil against him.
So he wrought his will herein, in that he departed not
from strife before he had slain all his father's banesmen,
though dreadful the deed seemed in every wise. So now he
gets land, lordship, and fee, and is become a mightier man
than his father before him.

Much wealth won in war gat Rerir to himself, and wedded
a wife withal, such as he deemed meet for him, and long
they lived together, but had no child to take the heritage
after them; and ill-content they both were with that, and
prayed the Gods with heart and soul that they might get
them a child. And so it is said that Odin hears their prayer,
and Freyia no less hearkens wherewith they prayed unto
her : so she, never lacking for all good counsel, calls to her her
casket-bearing may,[1] the daughter of Hrimnir the giant, and
sets an apple in her hand, and bids her bring it to the king.
She took the apple, and did on her the gear of a crow, and
went flying till she came whereas the king sat on a mound,
and there she let the apple fall into the lap of the king;
but he took the apple, and deemed he knew whereto it would
avail; so he goes home from the mound to his own folk,
and came to the queen, and some deal of that apple she ate.

So, as the tale tells, the queen soon knew that she was
big with child, but a long time wore or ever she might give
birth to the child: so it befell that the king must needs go
to the wars, after the custom of kings, that he may keep his
own land in peace: and in this journey it came to pass
that Rerir fell sick and got his death, being minded to go
home to Odin, a thing much desired of many folk in those
days.

Now no otherwise it goes with the queen's sickness than
heretofore, nor may she be the lighter of her child, and
six winters wore away with the sickness still heavy on her;
so that at the last she feels that she may not live long;
wherefore now she bade cut the child from out of her; and
it was done even as she bade; a man-child was it, and great

[1] A maid.

of growth from his birth, as might well be; and they say that the youngling kissed his mother or ever she died; but to him is a name given, and he is called Volsung; and he was king over Hunland in the room of his father. From his early years he was big and strong, and full of daring in all manly deeds and trials, and he became the greatest of warriors, and of good hap in all the battles of his warfaring.

Now when he was fully come to man's estate, Hrimnir the giant sends to him Ljod his daughter; she of whom the tale told, that she brought the apple to Rerir, Volsung's father. So Volsung weds her withal; and long they abode together with good hap and great love. They had ten sons and one daughter, and their eldest son was hight Sigmund, and their daughter Signy; and these two were twins, and in all wise the foremost and the fairest of the children of Volsung the king, and mighty, as all his seed was; even as has been long told from ancient days, and in tales of long ago, with the greatest fame of all men, how that the Volsungs have been great men and high-minded and far above the most of men both in cunning and in prowess and all things high and mighty.

So says the story that king Volsung let build a noble hall in such a wise, that a big oak-tree stood therein, and that the limbs of the tree blossomed fair out over the roof of the hall, while below stood the trunk within it, and the said trunk did men call Branstock.

## CHAPTER III

### Of the Sword that Sigmund, Volsung's son, drew from the Branstock

There was a king called Siggeir, who ruled over Gothland, a mighty king and of many folk; he went to meet Volsung, the king, and prayed him for Signy his daughter to wife; and the king took his talk well, and his sons withal, but she was loth thereto, yet she bade her father rule in this as in all other things that concerned her; so the king took such rede[1]

[1] Rede (A.S. *ræd*), counsel, advice, a tale or prophecy.

that he gave her to him, and she was betrothed to King Siggeir; and for the fulfilling of the feast and the wedding, was King Siggeir to come to the house of King Volsung. The king got ready the feast according to his best might, and when all things were ready, came the king's guests and King Siggeir withal at the day appointed, and many a man of great account had Siggeir with him.

The tale tells that great fires were made endlong the hall, and the great tree aforesaid stood midmost thereof; withal folk say that, whenas men sat by the fires in the evening, a certain man came into the hall unknown of aspect to all men; and suchlike array he had, that over him was a spotted cloak, and he was bare-foot, and had linen-breeches knit tight even unto the bone, and he had a sword in his hand as he went up to the Branstock, and a slouched hat upon his head: huge he was, and seeming-ancient, and one-eyed.[2] So he drew his sword and smote it into the tree-trunk so that it sank in up to the hilts; and all held back from greeting the man. Then he took up the word, and said—

"Whoso draweth this sword from this stock, shall have the same as a gift from me; and shall find in good sooth that never bare he better sword in hand than is this."

Therewith out went the old man from the hall, and none knew who he was or whither he went.

Now men stand up, and none would fain be the last to lay hand to the sword, for they deemed that he would have the best of it who might first touch it; so all the noblest went thereto first, and then the others, one after other; but none who came thereto might avail to pull it out, for in nowise would it come away howsoever they tugged at it; but now up comes Sigmund, King Volsung's son, and sets hand to the sword, and pulls it from the stock, even as if it lay loose before him; so good that weapon seemed to all, that none thought he had seen such a sword before, and Siggeir would fain buy it of him at thrice its weight of gold, but Sigmund said—

"Thou mightest have taken the sword no less than I

[2] The man is Odin, who is always so represented, because he gave his eye as a pledge for a draught from the fountain of Mimir, the source of all wisdom.

from there whereas it stood, if it had been thy lot to bear it; but now, since it has first of all fallen into my hand, never shalt thou have it, though thou biddest therefor all the gold thou hast."

King Siggeir grew wroth at these words,· and deemed Sigmund had answered him scornfully, but whereas he was a wary man and a double-dealing, he made as if he heeded this matter in nowise, yet that same evening he thought how he might reward it, as was well seen afterwards.

## CHAPTER IV

### How King Siggier wedded Signy, and bade King Volsung and his son to Gothland

Now it is to be told that Siggeir goes to bed by Signy that night, and the next morning the weather was fair; then says King Siggeir that he will not bide, lest the wind should wax, or the sea grow impassable; nor is it said that Volsung or his sons letted him herein, and that the less, because they saw that he was fain to get him gone from the feast. But now says Signy to her father—

"I have no will to go away with Siggeir, neither does my heart smile upon him; and I wot, by my fore-knowledge, and from the fetch[1] of our kin, that from this counsel will great evil fall on us if this wedding be not speedily undone."

"Speak in no such wise, daughter!" said he; "for great shame will it be to him, yea, and to us also, to break troth with him, he being sackless;[2] and in naught may we trust him, and no friendship shall we have of him, if these matters are broken off; but he will pay us back in as evil wise as he may; for that alone is seemly, to hold truly to troth given."

So King Siggeir got ready for home, and before he went from the feast he bade King Volsung, his father-in-law, come see him in Gothland, and all his sons with him, whenas three months should be overpast, and to bring such following with him, as he would have, and as he deemed meet

---

[1] Wraith, or familiar spirit.　　[2] Blameless.

for his honour; and thereby will Siggeir the king pay back for the shortcomings of the wedding-feast, in that he would abide thereat but one night only, a thing not according to the wont of men. So King Volsung gave his word to come on the day named, and the kinsmen-in-law parted, and Siggeir went home with his wife.

## CHAPTER V

### OF THE SLAYING OF KING VOLSUNG

Now tells the tale of King Volsung and his sons that they go at the time appointed to Gothland at the bidding of King Siggeir, and put off from the land in three ships, all well manned, and have a fair voyage, and made Gothland late of an evening tide.

But that same night came Signy and called her father and brothers to a privy talk, and told them what she deemed King Siggier was minded to do, and how that he had drawn together an army no man may meet. "And," says she, "he is minded to do guilefully by you; wherefore I bid you get ye gone back again to your own land, and gather together the mightiest power ye may, and then come back hither and avenge you; neither go ye now to your undoing, for ye shall surely fail not to fall by his wiles if ye turn not on him even as I bid you."

Then spake Volsung the king, "All people and nations shall tell of the word I spake, yet being unborn, wherein I vowed a vow that I would flee in fear from neither fire nor the sword; even so have I done hitherto, and shall I depart therefrom now I am old? Yea withal never shall the maidens mock these my sons at the games, and cry out at them that they fear death; once alone must all men need die, and from that season shall none escape; so my rede it is that we flee nowhither, but do the work of our hands in as manly wise as we may; a hundred fights have I fought, and whiles I had more, and whiles I had less, and yet ever had I the victory, nor shall it ever be heard tell of me that I fled away or prayed for peace."

Then Signy wept right sore, and prayed that she might not go back to King Siggeir, but King Volsung answered—

"Thou shalt surely go back to thine husband, and abide with him, howsoever it fares with us."

So Signy went home, and they abode there that night; but in the morning, as soon as it was day, Volsung bade his men arise and go aland and make them ready for battle; so they went aland, all of them all-armed, and had not long to wait before Siggeir fell on them with all his army, and the fiercest fight there was betwixt them; and Siggeir cried on his men to the onset all he might; and so the tale tells that King Volsung and his sons went eight times right through Siggeir's folk that day, smiting and hewing on either hand, but when they would do so even once again, King Volsung fell amidst his folk and all his men withal, saving his ten sons, for mightier was the power against them than they might withstand.

But now are all his sons taken, and laid in bonds and led away; and Signy was ware withal that her father was slain, and her brothers taken and doomed to death; that she called King Siggeir apart to talk with her, and said—

"This will I pray of thee, that thou let not slay my brothers hastily, but let them be set awhile in the stocks, for home to me comes the saw that says, *Sweet to eye while seen:* but longer life I pray not for them, because I wot well that my prayer will not avail me."

Then answered Siggeir—

"Surely thou art mad and witless, praying thus for more bale for thy brothers than their present slaying; yet this will I grant thee, for the better it likes me the more they must bear, and the longer their pain is or ever death come to them."

Now he let it be done even as she prayed, and a mighty beam was brought and set on the feet of those ten brethren in a certain place of the wild-wood, and there they sit day-long until night; but at midnight, as they sat in the stocks, there came on them a she-wolf from out the wood; old she was, and both great and evil of aspect; and the first thing she did was to bite one of those brethren till he died, and then she ate him up withal, and went on her way.

But the next morning Signy sent a man to the brethren, even one whom she most trusted, to wot of the tidings; and when he came back he told her that one of them was dead, and great and grievous she deemed it, if they should all fare in like wise, and yet naught might she avail them.

Soon is the tale told thereof: nine nights together came the she-wolf at midnight, and each night slew and ate up one of the brethren, until all were dead, save Sigmund only; so now, before the tenth night came, Signy sent that trusty man to Sigmund, her brother, and gave honey into his hand, bidding him do it over Sigmund's face, and set a little deal of it in his mouth; so he went to Sigmund and did as he was bidden, and then came home again; and so the next night came the she-wolf according to her wont, and would slay him and eat him even as his brothers; but now she sniffs the breeze from him, whereas he was anointed with the honey, and licks his face all over with her tongue, and then thrusts her tongue into the mouth of him. No fear he had thereof, but caught the she-wolf's tongue betwixt his teeth, and so hard she started back thereat, and pulled herself away so mightily, setting her feet against the stocks, that all was riven asunder; but he ever held so fast that the tongue came away by the roots, and thereof she had her bane.

But some men say that this same she-wolf was the mother of King Siggeir, who had turned herself into this likeness by troll's lore and witchcraft.[1]

## CHAPTER VI

### OF HOW SIGNY SENT THE CHILDREN OF HER AND SIGGEIR TO SIGMUND

Now whenas Sigmund is loosed and the stocks are broken, he dwells in the woods and holds himself there; but Signy sends yet again to wot of the tidings, whether Sigmund were alive or no; but when those who were sent came to him, he told them all as it had betid, and how things had

[1] See note, p. 286.

gone betwixt him and the wolf; so they went home and tell Signy the tidings; but she goes and finds her brother, and they take counsel in such wise as to make a house underground in the wild-wood; and so things go on a while, Signy hiding him there, and sending him such things as he needed; but King Siggeir deemed that all the Volsungs were dead.

Now Siggeir had two sons by his wife, whereof it is told that when the eldest was ten winters old, Signy sends him to Sigmund, so that he might give him help, if he would in any wise strive to avenge his father; so the youngling goes to the wood, and comes late in evening-tide to Sigmund's earth-house; and Sigmund welcomed him in seemly fashion, and said that he should make ready their bread; "but I," said he, "will go seek firewood."

Therewith he gives the meal-bag into his hands while he himself went to fetch firing; but when he came back the youngling had done naught at the bread-making. Then asks Sigmund if the bread be ready—

Says the youngling, "I durst not set hand to the mealsack, because somewhat quick lay in the meal."

Now Sigmund deemed he wotted that the lad was of no such heart as that he would be fain to have him for his fellow; and when he met his sister, Sigmund said that he had come no nigher to the aid of a man though the youngling were with him.

Then said Signy, "Take him and kill him then: for why should such an one live longer?" and even so he did.

So this winter wears, and the next winter Signy sent her next son to Sigmund; and there is no need to make a long tale thereof, for in like wise went all things, and he slew the child by the counsel of Signy.

## CHAPTER VII

### OF THE BIRTH OF SINFJOTLI THE SON OF SIGMUND

So on a tide it befell as Signy sat in her bower, that there came to her a witch-wife exceeding cunning, and Signy talked with her in such wise, 'Fain am I," says she, " that we should change semblances together."

She says, " Even as thou wilt then."

And so by her wiles she brought it about that they changed semblances, and now the witch-wife sits in Signy's place according to her rede, and goes to bed by the king that night, and he knows not that he has other than Signy beside him.

But the tale tells of Signy, that she fared to the earth-house of her brother, and prayed him give her harbouring for the night; " For I have gone astray abroad in the woods, and know not whither I am going."

So he said she might abide, and that he would not refuse harbour to one lone woman, deeming that she would scarce pay back his good cheer by tale-bearing: so she came into the house, and they sat down to meat, and his eyes were often on her, and a goodly and fair woman she seemed to him; but when they are full, then he says to her, that he is right fain that they should have but one bed that night; she nowise turned away therefrom, and so for three nights together he laid her in bed by him.

Thereafter she fared home, and found the witch-wife, and bade her change semblances again, and she did so.

Now as time wears, Signy brings forth a man-child, who was named Sinfjotli, and when he grew up he was both big and strong, and fair of face, and much like unto the kin of the Volsungs, and he was hardly yet ten winters old when she sent him to Sigmund's earth-house; but this trial she had made of her other sons or ever she had sent them to Sigmund, that she had sewed gloves on to their hands through flesh and skin, and they had borne it ill and cried out thereat; and this she now did to Sinfjotli, and he changed countenance in nowise thereat. Then she flayed off the kirtle so that the skin came off with the sleeves, and said that this would be torment enough for him; but he said—

" Full little would Volsung have felt such a smart as this."

So the lad came to Sigmund, and Sigmund bade him

knead their meal up, while he goes to fetch firing; so he
gave him the meal-sack, and then went after the wood, and
by then he came back had Sinfjotli made an end of his
baking. Then asked Sigmund if he had found nothing in
the meal.

"I misdoubted me that there was something quick in the
meal when I first fell to kneading of it, but I have kneaded
it all up together, both the meal and that which was therein,
whatsoever it was."

Then Sigmund laughed out, he said—

"Naught wilt thou eat of this bread to-night, for the
most deadly of worms[1] hast thou kneaded up therewith."

Now Sigmund was so mighty a man that he might eat
venom and have no hurt therefrom; but Sinfjotli might
abide whatso venom came on the outside of him, but might
neither eat nor drink thereof.

## CHAPTER VIII

### The Death of King Siggeir and of Signy

The tale tells that Sigmund thought Sinfjotli over young
to help him to his revenge, and will first of all harden
him with manly deeds; so in summer-tide they fare wide
through the woods and slay men for their wealth; Sigmund
deems him to take much after the kin of the Volsungs,
though he thinks that he is Siggeir's son, and deems him to
have the evil heart of his father, with the might and daring
of the Volsungs; withal he must needs think him in nowise a kinsome man, for full oft would he bring Sigmund's
wrongs to his memory, and prick him on to slay King
Siggeir.

Now on a time as they fare abroad in the woods for
the getting of wealth, they find a certain house, and two
men with great gold rings asleep therein: now these twain
were spell-bound skin-changers,[1] and wolf-skins were hang-

---

[1] Serpents.

[1] "Skin-changers" were universally believed in once, in Iceland no less
than elsewhere, as see Ari in several places of his history, especially the
episode of Dufthach and Storwolf o' Whale. Men possessing the power of
becoming wolves at intervals, in the present case compelled to so become,

ing up over them in the house; and every tenth day might they come out of those skins; and they were kings' sons: so Sigmund and Sinfjotli do the wolf-skins on them, and then might they nowise come out of them, though forsooth the same nature went with them as heretofore; they howled as wolves howl, but both knew the meaning of that howling; they lay out in the wild-wood, and each went his way; and a word they made betwixt them, that they should risk the onset of seven men, but no more, and that he who was first to be set on should howl in wolfish wise: "Let us not depart from this," says Sigmund, "for thou art young and over-bold, and men will deem the quarry good, when they take thee."

Now each goes his way, and when they were parted, Sigmund meets certain men, and gives forth a wolf's howl; and when Sinfjotli heard it, he went straightway thereto, and slew them all, and once more they parted. But ere Sinfjotli has fared long through the woods, eleven men meet him, and he wrought in such wise that he slew them all, and was awearied therewith, and crawls under an oak, and there takes his rest. Then came Sigmund thither, and said—

"Why didst thou not call on me?"

Sinfjotli said, "I was loth to call for thy help for the slaying of eleven men."

Then Sigmund rushed at him so hard that he staggered and fell, and Sigmund bit him in the throat. Now that day they might not come out of their wolf-skins: but Sigmund lay the other on his back, and bears him home to the house, and cursed the wolf-gears and gave them to the trolls. Now on a day he saw where two weasels went, and how that one bit the other in the throat, and then ran straightway into the thicket, and took up a leaf and laid it

wer-wolves or *loupsgarou*, find large place in medieval story, but were equally well-known in classic times. Belief in them still lingers in parts of Europe where wolves are to be found. Herodotus tells of the Neuri, who assumed once a year the shape of wolves; Pliny says that one of the family of Antæus, chosen by lot annually, became a wolf, and so remained for nine years; Giraldus Cambrensis will have it that Irishmen may become wolves; and Nennius asserts point-blank that "the descendants of wolves are still in Ossory;" they retransform themselves into wolves when they bite. Apuleius, Petronius, and Lucian have similar stories. The Emperor Sigismund convoked a council of theologians in the fifteenth century, who decided that wer-wolves did exist.

on the wound, and thereon his fellow sprang up quite and clean whole; so Sigmund went out and saw a raven flying with a blade of that same herb to him; so he took it and drew it over Sinfjotli's hurt, and he straightway sprang up as whole as though he had never been hurt. Thereafter they went home to their earth-house, and abode there till the time came for them to put off the wolf-shapes; then they burnt them up with fire, and prayed that no more hurt might come to any one from them; but in that uncouth guise they wrought many famous deeds in the kingdom and lordship of King Siggeir.

Now when Sinfjotli was come to man's estate, Sigmund deemed he had tried him fully, and or ever a long time has gone by he turns his mind to the avenging of his father, if so it may be brought about; so on a certain day the twain get them gone from their earth-house, and come to the abode of King Siggeir late in the evening, and go into the porch before the hall, wherein were tuns of ale, and there they lie hid: now the queen is ware of them, where they are, and is fain to meet them; and when they met they took counsel and were of one mind that Volsung should be revenged that same night.

Now Signy and the king had two children of tender age, who played with a golden toy on the floor, and bowled it along the pavement of the hall, running along with it; but therewith a golden ring from off it trundles away into the place where Sigmund and Sinfjotli lay, and off runs the little one to search for the same, and beholds withal where two men are sitting, big and grimly to look on, with overhanging helms and bright white byrnies;[2] so he runs up the hall to his father, and tells him of the sight he has seen, and thereat the king misdoubts of some guile abiding him; but Signy heard their speech, and arose and took both the children, and went out into the porch to them and said—

"Lo ye! these younglings have bewrayed you; come now therefore and slay them!"

Sigmund says, "Never will I slay thy children for telling of where I lay hid."

[2] Corslet, cuirass.

But Sinfjotli made little enow of it, but drew his sword and slew them both, and cast them in to the hall at King Siggeir's feet.

Then up stood the king and cried on his men to take those who had lain privily in the porch through the night. So they ran thither and would lay hands on them, but they stood on their defence well and manly, and long he remembered it who was the nighest to them; but in the end they were borne down by many men and taken, and bonds were set upon them, and they were cast into fetters wherein they sit night long.

Then the king ponders what longest and worst of deaths he shall mete out to them; and when morning came he let make a great barrow of stones and turf; and when it was done, let set a great flat stone midmost inside thereof, so that one edge was aloft, the other alow; and so great it was that it went from wall to wall, so that none might pass it.

Now he bids folk take Sigmund and Sinfjotli and set them in the barrow, on either side of the stone, for the worse for them he deemed it, that they might hear each the other's speech, and yet that neither might pass one to the other. But now, while they were covering in the barrow with the turf-slips, thither came Signy, bearing straw with her, and cast it down to Sinfjotli, and bade the thralls hide this thing from the king; they said yea thereto, and therewithal was the barrow closed in.

But when night fell, Sinfjotli said to Sigmund, "Belike we shall scarce need meat for a while, for here has the queen cast swine's flesh into the barrow, and wrapped it round about on the outer side with straw."

Therewith he handles the flesh and finds that therein was thrust Sigmund's sword; and he knew it by the hilts, as mirk as it might be in the barrow, and tells Sigmund thereof, and of that were they both fain enow.

Now Sinfjotli drave the point of the sword up into the big stone, and drew it hard along, and the sword bit on the stone. With that Sigmund caught the sword by the point, and in this wise they sawed the stone between them, and let not or all the sawing was done that need be done, even as the song sings:

" Sinfjotli sawed
And Sigmund sawed,
Atwain with main
The stone was done."

Now are they both together loose in the barrow, and
soon they cut both through stone and through iron, and
bring themselves out thereof. Then they go home to the
hall, whenas all men slept there, and bear wood to the hall,
and lay fire therein; and withal the folk therein are waked
by the smoke, and by the hall burning over their heads.

Then the king cries out, " Who kindled this fire, I burn
withal? "

" Here am I," says Sigmund, " with Sinfjotli, my sister's
son; and we are minded that thou shalt wot well that all
the Volsungs are not yet dead."

Then he bade his sister come out, and take all good
things at his hands, and great honour, and fair atonement
in that wise, for all her griefs.

But she answered, " Take heed now, and consider, if
I have kept King Siggeir in memory, and his slaying of
Volsung the king! I let slay both my children, whom I
deemed worthless for the revenging of our father, and I
went into the wood to thee in a witch-wife's shape; and
now behold, Sinfjotli is the son of thee and of me both!
and therefore has he this so great hardihood and fierceness,
in that he is the son both of Volsung's son and Volsung's
daughter; and for this, and for naught else, have I so
wrought, that Siggeir might get his bane at last; and all
these things have I done that vengeance might fall on him,
and that I too might not live long; and merrily now will I
die with King Siggeir, though I was naught merry to wed
him."

Therewith she kissed Sigmund her brother, and Sinfjotli,
and went back again into the fire, and there she died with
King Siggeir and all his good men.

But the two kinsmen gathered together folk and ships,
and Sigmund went back to his father's land, and drave
away thence the king, who had set himself down there in
the room of king Volsung.

So Sigmund became a mighty King and far-famed, wise and high-minded: he had to wife one named Borghild, and two sons they had between them, one named Helgi and the other Hamund; and when Helgi was born, Norns came to him,[3] and spake over him, and said that he should be in time to come the most renowned of all kings. Even therewith was Sigmund come home from the wars, and so therewith he gives him the name of Helgi, and these matters as tokens thereof, Land of Rings, Sun-litten Hill, and Sharp-shearing Sword, and withal prayed that he might grow of great fame, and like unto the kin of the Volsungs.

And so it was that he grew up high-minded, and well-beloved, and above all other men in all prowess; and the story tells that he went to the wars when he was fifteen winters old. Helgi was lord and ruler over the army, but Sinfjotli was gotten to be his fellow herein; and so the twain bare sway thereover.

## CHAPTER IX

### How Helgi the son of Sigmund, won King Hodbrod and his Realm, and wedded Sigrun

Now the tale tells that Helgi in his warring met a king hight Hunding, a mighty king, and lord of many men and many lands; they fell to battle together, and Helgi went forth mightily, and such was the end of that fight that Helgi had the victory, but King Hunding fell and many of his men with him; but Helgi is deemed to have grown greatly in fame because he had slain so mighty a king.

Then the sons of Hunding draw together a great army to avenge their father. Hard was the fight betwixt them; but Helgi goes through the folk of those brothers unto their banner, and there slays these sons of Hunding, Alf and Eyolf, Herward and Hagbard, and wins there a great victory.

[3] "Norns came to him." Nornir are the fates of the northern mythology. They are three—*Urd*, the past; *Verdandi*, the present; and *Skuld*, the future. They sit beside the fountain of Urd (*Urdarbrunur*), which is below one of the roots of *Yggdrasil*, the world-tree, which tree their office it is to nourish by sprinkling it with the waters of the fountain.

Now as Helgi fared from the fight, he met a many women right fair and worthy to look on, who rode in exceeding noble array; but one far excelled them all; then Helgi asked them the name of that their lady and queen, and she named herself Sigrun, and said she was daughter of King Hogni.

Then said Helgi, "Fare home with us: good welcome shall ye have!"

Then said the king's daughter, "Other work lies before us than to drink with thee."

"Yea, and what work, king's daughter?" said Helgi.

She answers, "King Hogni has promised me to Hodbrod, the son of King Granmar, but I have vowed a vow that I will have him to my husband no more than if he were a crow's son and not a king's; and yet will the thing come to pass, but and if thou standest in the way thereof, and goest against him with an army, and takest me away withal; for verily with no king would I rather bide on bolster than with thee."

"Be of good cheer, king's daughter," says he, "for certes he and I shall try the matter, or ever thou be given to him; yea, we shall behold which may prevail against the other; and hereto I pledge my life."

Thereafter, Helgi sent men with money in their hands to summon his folk to him, and all his power is called together to Red-Berg: and there Helgi abode till such time as a great company came to him from Hedinsey; and therewithal came mighty powers from Norvi Sound aboard great and fair ships. Then King Helgi called to him the captain of his ships, who was hight Leif, and asked him if he had told over the tale of his army.

"A thing not easy to tell, lord," says he, "on the ships that came out of Norvi Sound are twelve thousand men, and otherwhere are half as many again."

Then bade King Helgi turn into the firth, called Varin's-firth, and they did so: but now there fell on them so fierce a storm and so huge a sea, that the beat of the waves on board and bow was to hearken to like as the clashing together of high hills broken.

But Helgi bade men fear naught, nor take in any sail,

but rather hoist every rag higher than heretofore; but little did they miss of foundering or ever they made land; then came Sigrun, daughter of King Hogni, down on to the beach with a great army, and turned them away thence to a good haven called Gnipalund; but the landsmen see what has befallen and come down to the sea-shore. The brother of King Hodbrod, lord of a land called Swarin's Cairn, cried out to them, and asked them who was captain over that mighty army. Then up stands Sinfjotli, with a helm on his head, bright shining as glass, and a byrny as white as snow; a spear in his hand, and thereon a banner of renown, and a gold-rimmed shield hanging before him; and well he knew with what words to speak to kings—

"Go thou and say, when thou hast made an end of feeding thy swine and thy dogs, and when thou beholdest thy wife again, that here are come the Volsungs, and in this company may King Helgi be found, if Hodbrod be fain of finding him, for his game and his joy it is to fight and win fame, while thou art kissing the handmaids by the fire-side."

Then answered Granmar, "In nowise knowest thou how to speak seemly things, and to tell of matters remembered from of old, whereas thou layest lies on chiefs and lords; most like it is that thou must have long been nourished with wolf-meat abroad in the wild-woods, and has slain thy brethren; and a marvel it is to behold that thou darest to join thyself to the company of good men and true, thou, who hast sucked the blood of many a cold corpse."

Sinfjotli answered, "Dim belike is grown thy memory now, of how thou wert a witch-wife on Varinsey, and wouldst fain have a man to thee, and choose me to that same office of all the world; and how thereafter thou wert a Valkyria[1] in Asgarth, and it well-nigh came to this, that for thy sweet sake should all men fight; and nine wolf-whelps I begat on thy body in Lowness, and was the father to them all."

Granmar answers, "Great skill of lying hast thou; yet

[1] Valkyrja, "Chooser of the elected." The women were so called whom Odin sent to choose those for death in battle who were to join the *Einherjar* in the hall of the elected, "*Val-holl.*"

belike the father of naught at all mayst thou be, since thou wert gelded by the giant's daughters of Thrasness; and lo thou art the stepson of King Siggeir, and were wont to lie abroad in wilds and woods with the kin of wolves; and unlucky was the hand wherewith thou slewest thy brethren, making for thyself an exceeding evil name."

Said Sinfjotli, "Mindest thou not then, when thou were stallion Grani's mare, and how I rode thee an amble on Bravoll, and that afterwards thou wert giant Golnir's goat-herd?"

Granmar says, "Rather would I feed fowls with the flesh of thee than wraggle any longer with thee."

Then spake King Helgi, "Better were it for ye, and a more manly deed, to fight, rather than to speak such things as it is a shame even to hearken to; Granmar's sons are no friends of me and of mine, yet are they hardy men none the less."

So Granmar rode away to meet King Hodbrod, at a stead called Sunfells, and the horses of the twain were named Sveipud and Sveggjud. The brothers met in the castle-porch, and Granmar told Hodbrod of the war-news. King Hodbrod was clad in a byrny, and had his helm on his head; he asked—

"What men are anigh, why look ye so wrathful?"

Granmar says, "Here are come the Volsungs, and twelve thousand men of them are afloat off the coast, and seven thousand are at the island called Sok, but at the stead called Grindur is the greatest company of all, and now I deem withal that Helgi and his fellowship have good will to give battle."

Then said the king, "Let us send a message through all our realm, and go against them, neither let any who is fain of fight sit idle at home; let us send word to the sons of Ring, and to King Hogni, and to Alf the Old, for they are mighty warriors."

So the hosts met at Wolfstone, and fierce fight befell there; Helgi rushed forth through the host of his foes, and many a man fell there; at last folk saw a great company of shield-maidens, like burning flames to look on, and there was come Sigrun, the king's daughter. Then King Helgi

fell on King Hodbrod, and smote him, and slew him even
under his very banner; and Sigrun cried out—

"Have thou thanks for thy so manly deed! now shall we
share the land between us, and a day of great good hap
this is to me, and for this deed shalt thou get honour and
renown, in that thou hast felled to earth so mighty a king."

So Helgi took to him that realm and dwelt there long,
when he had wedded Sigrun, and became a king of great
honour and renown, though he has naught more to do with
this story.

## CHAPTER X

### THE ENDING OF SINFJOTLI, SIGMUND'S SON

Now the Volsungs fare back home, and have gained great
renown by these deeds. But Sinfjotli betook himself to
warfare anew; and therewith he had sight of an exceeding fair woman, and yearned above all things for her;
but that same woman was wooed also of the brother of
Borghild, the king's wife: and this matter they fought out
betwixt them and Sinfjotli slew that king; and thereafter
he harried far and wide, and had many a battle and ever
gained the day; and he became hereby honoured and renowned above all men; but in autumn tide he came home
with many ships and abundant wealth.

Then he told his tidings to the king his father, and he
again to the queen, and she for her part bids him get him
gone from the realm, and made as if she would in nowise
see him. But Sigmund said he would not drive him away,
and offered her atonement of gold and great wealth for her
brother's life, albeit he said he had never erst given weregild[1] to any for the slaying of a man, but no fame it was to
uphold wrong against a woman.

So seeing she might not get her own way herein, she
said, "Have thy will in this matter, O my lord, for it is
seemly so to be."

And now she holds the funeral feast for her brother by
the aid and counsel of the king, and makes ready all things

[1] Fine for man-slaying.

therefor in the best of wise, and bade thither many great men.

At that feast, Borghild the queen bare the drink to folk, and she came over against Sinfjotli with a great horn, and said—

"Fall to now and drink, fair stepson!"

Then he took the horn to him, and looked therein, and said—

"Nay, for the drink is charmed drink."

Then said Sigmund, "Give it unto me then;" and therewith he took the horn and drank it off.

But the queen said to Sinfjotli, "Why must other men needs drink thine ale for thee?" And she came again the second time with the horn, and said, "Come now and drink!" and goaded him with many words.

And he took the horn, and said—

"Guile is in the drink."

And thereon, Sigmund cried out—

"Give it then unto me!"

Again, the third time, she came to him, and bade him drink off his drink, if he had the heart of a Volsung; then he laid hand on the horn, but said—

"Venom is therein."

"Nay, let the lip strain it out then, O son," quoth Sigmund; and by then was he exceeding drunk with drink, and therefore spake he in that wise.

So Sinfjotli drank, and straightway fell down dead to the ground.

Sigmund rose up, and sorrowed nigh to death over him; then he took the corpse in his arms and fared away to the wood, and went till he came to a certain firth; and there he saw a man in a little boat; and that man asked if he would be wafted by him over the firth, and he said yea thereto; but so little was the boat, that they might not all go in it at once, so the corpse was first laid therein, while Sigmund went by the firth-side. But therewith the boat and the man therein vanished away from before Sigmund's eyes.[2]

So thereafter Sigmund turned back home, and drave

[2] The man in the boat is Odin, doubtless.

away the queen, and a little after she died. But Sigmund the king yet ruled his realm, and is deemed ever the greatest champion and king of the old law.


## CHAPTER XI

### Of King Sigmund's last Battle, and of how he must yield up his Sword again

There was a king called Eylimi, mighty and of great fame, and his daughter was called Hjordis, the fairest and wisest of womankind; and Sigmund hears it told of her that she was meet to be his wife, yea if none else were. So he goes to the house of King Eylimi, who would make a great feast for him, if so be he comes not thither in the guise of a foe. So messages were sent from one to the other that this present journey was a peaceful one, and not for war; so the feast was held in the best of wise and with many a man thereat; fairs were in every place established for King Sigmund, and all things else were done to the aid and comfort of his journey: so he came to the feast, and both kings hold their state in one hall; thither also was come King Lyngi, son of King Hunding, and he also is a-wooing the daughter of King Eylimi.

Now the king deemed he knew that the twain had come thither but for one errand, and thought withal that war and trouble might be looked for from the hands of him who brought not his end about; so he spake to his daughter, and said—

"Thou art a wise woman, and I have spoken it, that thou alone shalt choose a husband for thyself; choose therefore between these two kings, and my rede shall be even as thine."

"A hard and troublous matter," says she; "yet will I choose him who is of greatest fame, King Sigmund to wit, albeit he is well stricken in years."

So to him was she betrothed, and King Lyngi gat him gone. Then was Sigmund wedded to Hjordis, and now each day was the feast better and more glorious than on the day before it. But thereafter Sigmund went back home to Hunland, and King Eylimi, his father-in-law, with him, and King Sigmund betakes himself to the due ruling of his realm.

But King Lyngi and his brethren gather an army together to fall on Sigmund, for as in all matters they were wont to have the worser lot, so did this bite the sorest of all; and they would fain prevail over the might and pride of the Volsungs. So they came to Hunland, and sent King Sigmund word how that they would not steal upon him, and that they deemed he would scarce slink away from them. So Sigmund said he would come and meet them in battle, and drew his power together; but Hjordis was borne into the wood with a certain bondmaid, and mighty wealth went with them; and there she abode the while they fought.

Now the vikings rushed from their ships in numbers not to be borne up against, but Sigmund the King, and Eylimi, set up their banners, and the horns blew up to battle; but King Sigmund let blow the horn his father erst had had, and cheered on his men to the fight, but his army was far the fewest.

Now was that battle fierce and fell, and though Sigmund were old, yet most hardily he fought, and was ever the foremost of his men; no shield or byrny might hold against him, and he went ever through the ranks of his foemen on that day, and no man might see how things would fare between them; many an arrow and many a spear was aloft in air that day, and so his spae-wrights wrought for him that he got no wound, and none can tell over the tale of those who fell before him, and both his arms were red with blood, even to the shoulders.

But now whenas the battle had dured a while, there came a man into the fight clad in a blue cloak, and with a slouched hat on his head, one-eyed he was,[1] and bare a bill in his hand; and he came against Sigmund the King, and have up his bill against him, and as Sigmund smote fiercely with the sword it fell upon the bill and burst asunder in the midst; thenceforth the slaughter and dismay turned to his side, for the good-hap of King Sigmund had departed from him,

[1] Odin coming to change the ownership of the sword he had given Sigmund.

and his men fell fast about him; naught did the king spare himself, but the rather cheered on his men; but even as the saw says, *No might 'gainst many,* so was it now proven; and in this fight fell Sigmund the King, and King Eylimi, his father-in-law, in the fore-front of their battle, and therewith the more part of their folk.

## CHAPTER XII

### OF THE SHARDS OF THE SWORD GRAM, AND HOW HJORDIS WENT TO KING ALF

Now King Lyngi made for the king's abode, and was minded to take the king's daughter there, but failed herein, for there he found neither wife nor wealth: so he fared through all the realm, and gave his men rule thereover, and now deemed that he had slain all the kin of the Volsungs, and that he need dread them no more from henceforth.

Now Hjordis went amidst the slain that night of the battle, and came whereas lay King Sigmund, and asked if he might be healed; but he answered—

" Many a man lives after hope has grown little; but my good-hap has departed from me, nor will I suffer myself to be healed, nor wills Odin that I should ever draw sword again, since this my sword and his is broken; lo now, I have waged war while it was his will."

" Naught ill would I deem matters," said she, " if thou mightest be healed and avenge my father."

The king said, " That is fated for another man; behold now, thou art great with a man-child; nourish him well and with good heed, and the child shall be the noblest and most famed of all our kin: and keep well withal the shards of the sword: thereof shall a goodly sword be made, and it shall be called Gram, and our son shall bear it, and shall work many a great work therewith, even such as eld shall never minish; for his name shall abide and flourish as long as the world shall endure: and let this be enow for thee. But now I grow weary with my wounds, and I will go see our kin that have gone before me."

So Hjordis sat over him till he died at the day-dawning; and then she looked, and behold, there came many ships sailing to the land: then she spake to the handmaid—

" Let us now change raiment, and be thou called by my name, and say that thou art the king's daughter."

And thus they did; but now the vikings behold the great slaughter of men there, and see where two women fare away thence into the wood; and they deem that some great tidings must have befallen, and they leaped ashore from out their ships.  Now the captain of these folks was Alf, son of Hjalprek, king of Denmark, who was sailing with his power along the land.  So they came into the field among the slain, and saw how many men lay dead there; then the king bade go seek for the women and bring them thither, and they did so.  He asked them what women they were; and, little as the thing seems like to be, the bondmaid answered for the twain, telling of the fall of King Sigmund and King Eylimi, and many another great man, and who they were withal who had wrought the deed.  Then the king asks if they wotted where the wealth of the king was bestowed; and then says the bondmaid—

" It may well be deemed that we know full surely thereof."

And therewith she guides them to the place where the treasure lay; and there they found exceeding great wealth; so that men deem they have never seen so many things of price heaped up together in one place.  All this they bore to the ships of King Alf, and Hjordis and the bondmaid went with them.  Therewith these sail away to their own realm, and talk how that surely on that field had fallen the most renowned of kings.

So the king sits by the tiller, but the women abide in the forecastle; but talk he had with the women and held their counsels of much account.

In such wise the king came home to his realm with great wealth, and he himself was a man exceeding goodly to look on.  But when he had been but a little while at home, the queen, his mother, asked him why the fairest of the two women had the fewer rings and the less worthy attire.

"I deem," she said, "that she whom ye have held of least account is the noblest of the twain."

He answered: "I too have misdoubted me, that she is little like a bondwoman, and when we first met, in seemly wise she greated noble men. Lo now, we will make a trial of the thing."

So on a time as men sat at the drink, the king sat down to talk with the women, and said—

"In what wise do ye note the wearing of the hours, whenas night grows old, if ye may not see the lights of heaven?"

Then says the bondwoman, "This sign have I, that whenas in my youth I was wont to drink much in the dawn, so now when I no longer use that manner, I am yet wont to wake up at that very same tide, and by that token do I know thereof."

Then the king laughed and said, "Ill manners for a king's daughter!" And therewith he turned to Hjordis, and asked her even the same question; but she answered—

"My father erst gave me a little gold ring of such nature, that it groweth cold on my finger in the day-dawning; and that is the sign that I have to know thereof."

The king answered: "Enow of gold there, where a very bondmaid bore it! but come now, thou hast been long enow hid from me; yet if thou hadst told me all from the beginning, I would have done to thee as though we had both been one king's children: but better than thy deeds will I deal with thee, for thou shalt be my wife, and due jointure will I pay thee whenas thou hast borne me a child."

She spake therewith and told out the whole truth about herself: so there was she held in great honour, and deemed the worthiest of women.

## CHAPTER XIII

### OF THE BIRTH AND WAXING OF SIGURD FAFNIR'S-BANE

THE tale tells that Hjordis brought forth a man-child, who was straightly borne before King Hjalprek, and then was the king glad thereof, when he saw the keen eyes in the head of him, and he said that few men would be equal to him or like unto him in any wise. So he was sprinkled with water, and had to name Sigurd, of whom all men speak with one speech and say that none was ever his like for growth and goodliness. He was brought up in the house of King Hjalprek in great love and honour; and so it is, that whenso all the noblest men and greatest kings are named in the olden tales, Sigurd is ever put before them all, for might and prowess, for high mind and stout heart, wherewith he was far more abundantly gifted than any man of the northern parts of the wide world.

So Sigurd waxed in King Hjalprek's house, and there was no child but loved him; through him was Hjordis betrothed to King Alf, and jointure meted to her.

Now Sigurd's foster-father was hight Regin, the son of Hreidmar; he taught him all manner of arts, the chess play, and the lore of runes, and the talking of many tongues, even as the wont was with kings' sons in those days. But on a day when they were together, Regin asked Sigurd, if he knew how much wealth his father had owned, and who had the ward thereof; Sigurd answered, and said that the kings kept the ward thereof.

Said Regin, "Dost thou trust them all utterly?"

Sigurd said, "It is seemly that they keep it till I may do somewhat therewith, for better they wot how to guard it than I do."

Another time came Regin to talk to Sigurd, and said—

"A marvellous thing truly that thou must needs be a horse-boy to the kings, and go about like a running knave."

"Nay," said Sigurd, "it is not so, for in all things I have my will, and whatso thing I desire is granted me with good will."

"Well, then," said Regin, "ask for a horse of them."

"Yea," quoth Sigurd, "and that shall I have, whenso I have need thereof."

Thereafter Sigurd went to the king, and the king said—

"What wilt thou have of us?"

Then said Sigurd, "I would even a horse of thee for my disport."

Then said the king, "Choose for thyself a horse, and whatso thing else thou desirest among my matters."

So the next day went Sigurd to the wood, and met on the way an old man, long-bearded, that he knew not, who asked him whither away.

Sigurd said, "I am minded to choose me a horse; come thou, and counsel me thereon."

"Well then," said he, "go we and drive them to the river which is called Busil-tarn."

They did so, and drave the horses down into the deeps of the river, and all swam back to land but one horse; and that horse Sigurd chose for himself; grey he was of hue, and young of years, great of growth, and fair to look on, nor had any man yet crossed his back.

Then spake the grey-beard, "From Sleipnir's kin is this horse come, and he must be nourished heedfully, for it will be the best of all horses;" and therewithal he vanished away.

So Sigurd called the horse Grani, the best of all the horses of the world; nor was the man he met other than Odin himself.

Now yet again spake Regin to Sigurd, and said—

"Not enough is thy wealth, and I grieve right sore that thou must needs run here and there like a churl's son; but I can tell thee where there is much wealth for the winning, and great name and honour to be won in the getting of it."

Sigurd asked where that might be, and who had watch and ward over it.

Regin answered, "Fafnir is his name, and but a little way hence he lies, on the waste of Gnita-heath; and when thou comest there thou mayest well say that thou hast never seen more gold heaped together in one place, and that none might desire more treasure, though he were the most ancient and famed of all kings."

"Young am I," says Sigurd,, "yet know I the fashion of this worm, and how that none durst go against him, so huge and evil is he."

Regin said, "Nay it is not so, the fashion and the growth of him is even as of other lingworms,[1] and an over great

---

[1] Lingworm—longworm, dragon.

tale men make of it; and even so would thy forefathers have
deemed; but thou, though thou be of the kin of the Volsungs,
shalt scarce have the heart and mind of those, who are told
of as the first in all deeds of fame."

Sigurd said, "Yea, belike I have little of their hardihood
and prowess, but thou hast naught to do, to lay a coward's
name upon me, when I am scarce out of my childish years.
Why dost thou egg me on hereto so busily?"

Regin said, "Therein lies a tale which I must needs tell
thee."

"Let me hear the same," said Sigurd.

## CHAPTER XIV

### Regin's tale of his Brothers, and of the Gold called Andvari's Hoard

"Thus the tale begins," said Regin. "Hreidmar was my
father's name, a mighty man and a wealthy: and his first
son was named Fafnir, his second Otter, and I was the third,
and the least of them all both for prowess and good con-
ditions, but I was cunning to work in iron, and silver, and
gold, whereof I could make matters that availed somewhat.
Other skill my brother Otter followed, and had another
nature withal, for he was a great fisher, and above other
men herein; in that he had the likeness of an otter by day,
and dwelt ever in the river, and bare fish to bank in his
mouth, and his prey would he ever bring to our father, and
that availed him much: for the most part he kept him in his
otter-gear, and then he would come home, and eat alone,
and slumbering, for on the dry land he might see naught.
But Fafnir was by far the greatest and grimmest, and would
have all things about called his.

"Now," says Regin, "there was a dwarf called Andvari,
who ever abode in that force,[1] which was called Andvari's
force, in the likeness of a pike, and got meat for himself,
for many fish there were in the force; now Otter, my
brother, was ever wont to enter into the force, and bring

[1] Waterfall.

fish aland, and lay them one by one on the bank. And so it befell that Odin, Loki, and Hœnir, as they went their ways, came to Andvari's force, and Otter had taken a salmon, and ate it slumbering upon the river bank; then Loki took a stone and cast it at Otter, so that he gat his death thereby; the gods were well content with their prey, and fell to flaying off the otter's skin; and in the evening they came to Hreidmar's house, and showed him what they had taken: thereon he laid hands on them, and doomed them to such ransom, as that they should fill the otter skin with gold, and cover it over without with red gold; so they sent Loki to gather gold together for them; he came to Ran,[2] and got her net, and went therewith to Andvari's force, and cast the net before the pike, and the pike ran into the net and was taken. Then said Loki—

> " ' What fish of all fishes,
>    Swims strong in the flood,
> But hath learnt little wit to beware?
>    Thine head must thou buy,
>    From abiding in hell,
> And find me the wan waters flame.'

He answered—

> " ' Andvari folk call me,
>    Call Oinn my father,
> Over many a force have I fared;
>    For a Norn of ill-luck,
>    This life on me lay
> Through wet ways ever to wade.'

" So Loki beheld the gold of Andvari, and when he had given up the gold, he had but one ring left, and that also Loki took from him; then the dwarf went into a hollow of the rocks, and cried out, that that gold-ring, yea

---

[2] Ran is the goddess of the sea, wife of Ægir. The otter was held sacred by Norsefolk and figures in the myth and legend of most races besides; to this day its killing is held a great crime by the Parsees (Haug. *Religion of the Parsees*, page 212). Compare penalty above with that for killing the Welsh king's cat (*Ancient Laws and Institutes of Wales.* Ed., Aneurin Owen. *Longman, London,* 1841, 2 vols., 8vo.).

and all the gold withal, should be the bane of every man who should own it thereafter.

"Now the gods rode with the treasure to Hreidmar, and fulfilled the otter-skin, and set it on its feet, and they must cover it over utterly with gold: but when this was done then Hreidmar came forth, and beheld yet one of the muzzle hairs, and bade them cover that withal; then Odin drew the ring, Andvari's loom, from his hand, and covered up the hair therewith; then sang Loki—

"'Gold enow, gold enow,
A great weregild, thou hast,
That my head in good hap I may hold;
But thou and thy son
Are naught fated to thrive,
The bane shall it be of you both.'

"Thereafter," says Regin, "Fafnir slew his father and murdered him, nor got I aught of the treasure, and so evil he grew, that he fell to lying abroad, and begrudged any share in the wealth of any man, and so became the worst of all worms, and ever now lies brooding upon that treasure: but for me, I went to the king and became his mastersmith; and thus is the tale of how I lost the heritage of my father, and the weregild for my brother."

So spake Regin; but since that time gold is called Ottergild, and for no other cause than this.

But Sigurd answered, "Much hast thou lost, and exceeding evil have thy kinsmen been! but now, make a sword by thy craft, such a sword as that none can be made like unto it; so that I may do great deeds therewith, if my heart avail thereto, and thou wouldst have me slay this mighty dragon."

Regin says, "Trust me well herein; and with that same sword shalt thou slay Fafnir."

## CHAPTER XV

### OF THE WELDING TOGETHER OF THE SHARDS OF THE SWORD GRAM

So Regin makes a sword, and gives it into Sigurd's hands. He took the sword, and said—

"Behold thy smithying, Regin!" and therewith smote it into the anvil, and the sword brake; so he cast down the brand, and bade him forge a better.

Then Regin forged another sword, and brought it to Sigurd, who looked thereon.

Then said Regin, "Belike thou art well content therewith, hard master though thou be in smithying."

So Sigurd proved the sword, and brake it even as the first; then he said to Regin—

"Ah, art thou, mayhappen, a traitor and a liar like to those former kin of thine?"

Therewith he went to his mother, and she welcomed him in seemly wise, and they taked and drank together.

Then spake Sigurd, "Have I heard aright, that King Sigmund gave thee the good sword Gram in two pieces?"

"True enough," she said.

So Sigurd said, "Deliver them into my hands, for I would have them."

She said he looked like to win great fame, and gave him the sword. Therewith went Sigurd to Regin, and bade him make a good sword thereof as he best might; Regin grew wroth thereat, but went into the smithy with the pieces of the sword, thinking well meanwhile that Sigurd pushed his head far enow into the matter of smithying. So he made a sword, and as he bore it forth from the forge, it seemed to the smiths as though fire burned along the edges thereof. Now he bade Sigurd take the sword, and said he knew not how to make a sword if this one failed. Then Sigurd smote it into the anvil, and cleft it down to the stock thereof, and neither burst the sword nor brake it. Then he praised the sword much, and thereafter went to the river with a lock of wool, and threw it up against the stream, and it fell asunder when it met the sword. Then was Sigurd glad, and went home.

But Regin said, "Now whereas I have made the sword for thee, belike thou wilt hold to thy troth given, and wilt go meet Fafnir?"

"Surely will I hold thereto," said Sigurd, "yet first must I avenge my father."

Now Sigurd the older he grew, the more he grew in the love of all men, so that every child loved him well.

## CHAPTER XVI

### The Prophecy of Grifir

THERE was a man hight Grifir,[1] who was Sigurd's mother's brother, and a little after the forging of the sword Sigurd went to Grifir, because he was a man who knew things to come, and what was fated to men: of him Sigurd asked diligently how his life should go; but Grifir was long or he spake, yet at the last, by reason of Sigurd's exceeding great prayers, he told him all his life and the fate thereof, even as afterwards came to pass. So when Grifir had told him all even as he would, he went back home; and a little after he and Regin met.

Then said Regin, "Go thou and slay Fafnir, even as thou hast given thy word."

Sigurd said, "That work shall be wrought; but another is first to be done, the avenging of Sigmund the king and the other of my kinsmen who fell in that their last fight."

## CHAPTER XVII

### Of Sigurd's Avenging of Sigmund his Father

Now Sigurd went to the kings, and spake thus—

"Here have I abode a space with you, and I owe you thanks and reward, for great love and many gifts and all due honour; but now will I away from the land and go meet the sons of Hunding, and do them to wit that the

---

[1] Called "Grípir" in the Edda.

Volsungs are not all dead; and your might would I have to strengthen me therein."

So the kings said that they would give him all things soever that he desired, and therewith was a great army got ready, and all things wrought in the most heedful wise, ships and all war-gear, so that his journey might be of the stateliest: but Sigurd himself steered the dragon-keel which was the greatest and noblest; richly wrought were their sails, and glorious to look on.

So they sail and have wind at will; but when a few days were overpast, there arose a great storm on the sea, and the waves were to behold even as the foam of men's blood; but Sigurd bade take in no sail, howsoever they might be riven, but rather to lay on higher than heretofore. But as they sailed past the rocks of a ness, a certain man hailed the ships, and asked who was captain over that navy; then was it told him that the chief and lord was Sigurd, the son of Sigmund, the most famed of all the young men who now are.

Then said the man, "Naught but one thing, certes, do all say of him, that none among the sons of kings may be likened unto him; now fain were I that ye would shorten sail on some of the ships, and take me aboard."

Then they asked him of his name, and he sang—

> Hnikar I hight,
> When I gladdened Huginn,
> And went to battle,
> Bright son of Volsung;
> Now may ye call
> The carl on the cliff top,
> Feng or Fjolnir:
> Fain would I with you.

They made for land therewith, and took that man aboard. Then quoth Sigurd,[1] as the song says—

> Tell me this, O Hnikar,
> Since full well thou knowest

[1] This and verses following were inserted from the *Reginsmál* by the

Fate of Gods, good and ill of mankind,
  What best our hap foresheweth,
  When amid the battle
About us sweeps the sword edge.

Quoth Hnikar—

  Good are many tokens
  If thereof men wotted
When the swords are sweeping:
  Fair fellow deem I
  The dark-winged raven,
In war, to weapon-wielder.

  The second good thing:
  When abroad thou goest
For the long road well arrayed,
  Good if thou seest
  Two men standing,
Fain of fame within the forecourt.

  A third thing:
  Good hearing,
  The wolf a howling
Abroad under ash boughs;
  Good hap shalt thou have
  Dealing with helm-staves,
If thou seest these fare before thee.

  No man in fight
  His face shall turn
  Against the moon's sister
  Low, late-shining,
  For he winneth battle
  Who best beholdeth
  Through the midmost sword-play,
And the sloping ranks best shapeth.

  Great is the trouble
  Of foot ill-tripping,
When arrayed for light thou farest,

For on both sides about
Are the Dísir[2] by thee,
Guileful, wishful of thy wounding,

Fair-combed, well washen
Let each warrior be,
Nor lack meat in the morning,
For who can rule
The eve's returning,
And base to fall before fate grovelling.

Then the storm abated, and on they fared till they came aland in the realm of Hunding's sons, and then Fjolnir vanished away.

Then they let loose fire and sword, and slew men and burnt their abodes, and did waste all before them: a great company of folk fled before the face of them to Lyngi the King, and tell him that men of war are in the land, and are faring with such rage and fury that the like has never been heard of; and that the sons of King Hunding had no great forecast in that they said they would never fear the Volsungs more, for here was come Sigurd, the son of Sigmund, as captain over this army.

So King Lyngi let send the war-message all throughout his realm, and has no will to flee, but summons to him all such as would give him aid. So he came against Sigurd with a great army, he and his brothers with him, and an exceeding fierce fight befell; many a spear and many an arrow might men see there raised aloft, axes hard driven, shields cleft and byrnies torn, helmets were shivered, skulls split atwain, and many a man felled to the cold earth.

And now when the fight has long dured in such wise, Sigurd goes forth before the banners, and has the good sword Gram in his hand, and smites down both men and horses, and goes through the thickest of the throng with both arms red with blood to the shoulder; and folk shrank aback before him wheresoever he went, nor would either helm or byrny hold before him, and no man deemed he

---

[2] Dísir, *sing.* Dís. These are the guardian beings who follow a man from his birth to his death. The word originally means sister, and is used throughout the Eddaic poems as a dignified synonym for woman, lady.

had ever seen his like. So a long while the battle lasted, and many a man was slain, and furious was the onset; till at last it befell, even as seldom comes to hand, when a land army falls on, that, do whatso they might, naught was brought about; but so many men fell of the sons of Hunding that the tale of them may not be told, and now whenas Sigurd was among the foremost, came the sons of Hunding against him, and Sigurd smote therewith at Lyngi the king, and clave him down, both helm and head, and mail-clad body, and thereafter he smote Hjorward his brother atwain, and then slew all the other sons of Hunding who were yet alive, and the more part of their folk withal.

Now home goes Sigurd with fair victory won, and plenteous wealth and great honour, which he had gotten to him in this journey, and feasts were made for him against he came back to the realm.

But when Sigurd had been at home but a little, came Regin to talk with him, and said—

"Belike thou wilt now have good will to bow down Fafnir's crest according to thy word plighted, since thou hast thus revenged thy father and the others of thy kin."

Sigurd answered, "That will we hold to, even as we have promised, nor did it ever fall from our memory."

## CHAPTER XVIII

### Of the Slaying of the Worm Fafnir

Now Sigurd and Regin ride up the heath along that same way wherein Fafnir was wont to creep when he fared to the water; and folk say that thirty fathoms was the height of that cliff along which he lay when he drank of the water below. Then Sigurd spake:

"How sayedst thou, Regin, that this drake[1] was no greater than other lingworms; methinks the track of him is marvellous great?"

Then said Regin, "Make thee a hole, and sit down therein,

[1] Lat. *draco,* a dragon.

and whenas the worm comes to the water, smite him into the heart, and so do him to death, and win for thee great fame thereby."

But Sigurd said, "What will betide me if I be before the blood of the worm?"

Says Regin, "Of what avail to counsel thee if thou art still afeard of everything? Little art thou like thy kin in stoutness of heart."

Then Sigurd rides right over the heath; but Regin gets him gone, sore afeard.

But Sigurd fell to digging him a pit, and whiles he was at that work, there came to him an old man with a long beard, and asked what he wrought there, and he told him.

Then answered the old man and said, "Thou doest after sorry counsel: rather dig thee many pits, and let the blood run therein; but sit thee down in one thereof, and so thrust the worm's heart through."

And therewithal he vanished away; but Sigurd made the pits even as it was shown to him.

Now crept the worm down to his place of watering, and the earth shook all about him, and he snorted forth venom on all the way before him as he went; but Sigurd neither trembled nor was adrad at the roaring of him. So whenas the worm crept over the pits, Sigurd thrust his sword under his left shoulder, so that it sank in up to the hilts, then up leapt Sigurd from the pit and drew the sword back again unto him, and therewith was his arm all bloody, up to the very shoulder.

Now when that mighty worm was ware that he had his death-wound, then he lashed out head and tail, so that all things soever that were before him were broken to pieces.

So whenas Fafnir had his death-wound, he asked "Who art thou? and who is thy father? and what thy kin, that thou wert so hardy as to bear weapons against me?"

Sigurd answered, "Unknown to men is my kin. I am called a noble beast:[2] neither father have I nor mother, and all alone have I fared hither."

Said Fafnir, "Whereas thou hast neither father nor

[2] "Unknown to men is my kin." Sigurd refusing to tell his name is to be referred to the superstition that a dying man could throw a curse on his enemy.

mother, of what wonder wert thou born then? But now, though thou tellest me not thy name on this my death-day, yet thou knowest verily that thou liest unto me."

He answered, "Sigurd am I called, and my father was Sigmund."

Says Fafnir, "Who egged thee on to this deed, and why wouldst thou be driven to it? Hadst thou never heard how that all folk were adrad of me, and of the awe of my countenance? But an eager father thou hadst, O bright-eyed swain!"

Sigurd answered, "A hardy heart urged me on hereto; and a strong hand and this sharp sword, which well thou knowest now, stood me in stead in the doing of the deed; *Seldom hath hardy eld a faint-heart youth.*"

Fafnir said, "Well, I wot that hadst thou waxed amid thy kin, thou mightest have good skill to slay folk in thine anger; but more of a marvel is it, that thou, a bondsman taken in war, shouldst have the heart to set on me, *for few among bondsmen have heart for the fight.*"

Said Sigurd, "Wilt thou then cast it in my teeth that I am far away from my kin? Albeit I was a bondsman, yet was I never shackled. God wot thou hast found me free enow."

Fafnir answered, "In angry wise dost thou take my speech; but hearken, for that same gold which I have owned shall be thy bane too."

Quoth Sigurd, "Fain would we keep all our wealth till that day of days; yet shall each man die once for all."

Said Fafnir, "Few things wilt thou do after my counsel; but take heed that thou shalt be drowned if thou farest unwarily over the sea; so bide thou rather on the dry land, for the coming of the calm tide."

Then said Sigurd, "Speak, Fafnir, and say, if thou art so exceeding wise, who are the Norns who rule the lot of all mothers' sons."

Fafnir answers, "Many there be and wide apart; for some are of the kin of the Æsir, and some are of Elfin kin, and some there are who are daughters of Dvalin."

Said Sigurd, " How namest thou the holm whereon Surt,[3] and the Æsir mix and mingle the water of the sword? "

" Unshapen is that holm hight," said Fafnir.

And yet again he said, " Regin, my brother, has brought about my end, and it gladdens my heart that thine too he bringeth about; for thus will things be according to his will."

And once again he spake, " A countenance of terror I bore up before all folk, after that I brooded over the heritage of my brother, and on every side did I spout out poison, so that none durst come anigh me, and of no weapon was I adrad, nor ever had I so many men before me, as that I deemed myself not stronger than all; for all men were sore afeard of me."

Sigurd answered and said, " Few may have victory by means of that same countenance of terror, for whoso comes amongst many shall one day find that no one man is by so far the mightiest of all."

Then says Fafnir, " Such counsel I give thee, that thou take thy horse and ride away at thy speediest, for ofttimes it falls out so, that he who gets a death-wound avenges himself none the less."

Sigurd answered, " Such as thy redes are I will nowise do after them; nay, I will ride now to thy lair and take to me that great treasure of thy kin."

" Ride there then," said Fafnir, " and thou shalt find gold enow to suffice thee for all thy life-days; yet shall that gold be thy bane, and the bane of every one soever who owns it."

Then up stood Sigurd, and said, " Home would I ride and lose all that wealth, if I deemed that by the losing thereof I should never die; but every brave and true man will fain have his hand on wealth till that last day; but thou, Fafnir, wallow in the death-pain till Death and Hell have thee."

And therewithal Fafnir died.

[3] Surt; a fire-giant, who will destroy the world at the Ragnarok, or destruction of all things. Æsir; the gods.

## CHAPTER XIX

### OF THE SLAYING OF REGIN, SON OF HREIDMAR

THEREAFTER came Regin to Sigurd, and said, " Hail, lord and master, a noble victory hast thou won in the slaying of Fafnir, whereas none durst heretofore abide in the path of him; and now shall this deed of fame be of renown while the world stands fast."

Then stood Regin staring on the earth a long while, and presently thereafter spake from heavy mood: "Mine own brother hast thou slain, and scarce may I be called sackless of the deed."

Then Sigurd took his sword Gram and dried it on the earth, and spake to Regin—

"Afar thou faredst when I wrought this deed and tried this sharp sword with the hand and the might of me; with all the might and main of a dragon must I strive, while thou wert laid alow in the heather-bush, wotting not if it were earth or heaven."

Said Regin, "Long might this worm have lain in his lair, if the sharp sword I forged with my hand had not been good at need to thee; had that not been, neither thou nor any man would have prevailed against him as at this time."

Sigurd answers, "Whenas men meet foes in fight, better is stout heart than sharp sword."

Then said Regin, exceeding heavily, "Thou hast slain my brother, and scarce may I be sackless of the deed."

Therewith Sigurd cut out the heart of the worm with the sword called Ridil; but Regin drank of Fafnir's blood, and spake, "Grant me a boon, and do a thing little for thee to do. Bear the heart to the fire, and roast it, and give me thereof to eat."

Then Sigurd went his ways and roasted it on a rod; and when the blood bubbled out he laid his finger thereon to essay it, if it were fully done; and then he set his finger in his mouth, and lo, when the heart-blood of the worm touched his tongue, straightway he knew the voice of all fowls, and heard withal how the wood-peckers chattered in the brake beside him—

"There sittest thou, Sigurd, roasting Fafnir's heart for another, that thou shouldest eat thine ownself, and then thou shouldest become the wisest of all men."

And another spake: "There lies Regin, minded to beguile the man who trusts in him."

But yet again said the third, "Let him smite the head from off him then, and be only lord of all that gold."

And once more the fourth spake and said, "Ah, the wiser were he if he followed after that good counsel, and rode thereafter to Fafnir's lair, and took to him that mighty treasure that lieth there, and then rode over Hindfell, whereas sleeps Brynhild; for there would he get great wisdom. Ah, wise he were, if he did after your redes, and bethought him of his own weal; *for where wolf's ears are, wolf's teeth are near.*"

Then cried the fifth: "Yea, yea, not so wise is he as I deem him, if he spareth him, whose brother he hath slain already."

At last spake the sixth: "Handy and good rede to slay him, and be lord of the treasure!"

Then said Sigurd, "The time is unborn wherein Regin shall be my bane; nay, rather oné road shall both these brothers fare."

And therewith he drew his sword Gram and struck off Regin's head.

Then heard Sigurd the wood-peckers a-singing, even as the song says.[1]

For the first sang:

> Bind thou, Sigurd,
> The bright red rings!
> Not meet it is
> Many things to fear.
> A fair may know I,
> Fair of all the fairest
> Girt about with gold,
> Good for thy getting.

[1] The Songs of the Birds were inserted from *Reginsmál* by the translators.

And the second:

> Green go the ways
> Toward the hall of Giuki
> That the fates show forth
> To those who fare thither;
> There the rich king
> Reareth a daughter;
> Thou shalt deal, Sigurd,
> With gold for thy sweetling.

And the third:

> A high hall is there
> Reared upon Hindfell,
> Without all around it
> Sweeps the red flame aloft
> Wise men wrought
> That wonder of halls
> With the unhidden gleam
> Of the glory of gold.

Then the fourth sang:

> Soft on the fell
> A shield-may sleepeth
> The lime-trees' red plague
> Playing about her:
> The sleep-thorn set Odin
> Into that maiden
> For her choosing in war
> The one he willed not.

> Go, son, behold
> That may under helm
> Whom from battle
> Vinskornir bore,
> From her may not turn
> The torment of sleep.
> Dear offspring of kings
> In the dread Norns' despite.

Then Sigurd ate some deal of Fafnir's heart, and the remnant he kept. Then he leapt on his horse and rode along the trail of the worm Fafnir, and so right unto his abiding-place; and he found it open, and beheld all the doors and the gear of them that they were wrought of iron: yea, and all the beams of the house; and it was dug down deep into the earth: there found Sigurd gold exceeding plenteous, and the sword Rotti; and thence he took the Helm of Awe, and the Gold Byrny, and many things fair and good. So much gold he found there, that he thought verily that scarce might two horses, or three belike, bear it thence. So he took all the gold and laid it in two great chests, and set them on the horse Grani, and took the reins of him, but nowise will he stir, neither will he abide smiting. Then Sigurd knows the mind of the horse, and leaps on the back of him, and smites and spurs into him, and off the horse goes even as if he were unladen.

## CHAPTER XX

### Of Sigurd's Meeting with Brynhild on the Mountain

By long roads rides Sigurd, till he comes at the last up on to Hindfell, and wends his way south to the land of the Franks; and he sees before him on the fell a great light, as of fire burning, and flaming up even unto the heavens; and when he came thereto, lo a shield-hung castle before him, and a banner on the topmost thereof: into the castle went Sigurd, and saw one lying there asleep, and all-armed. Therewith he takes the helm from off the head of him, and sees that it no man, but a woman; and she was clad in a byrny as closely set on her as though it had grown to her flesh; so he rent it from the collar downwards; and then the sleeves thereof, and ever the sword bit on it as if it were cloth. Then said Sigurd that over-long had she lain asleep; but she asked—

"What thing of great might is it that has prevailed to rend my byrny, and draw me from my sleep?"

Even as sings the song[1]—

> What bit on the byrny,
> Why breaks my sleep away,
> Who has turned from me
> My wan tormenting?

"Ah, is it so, that here is come Sigurd Sigmundson, bearing Fafnir's helm on his head and Fafnir's bane in his hand?"

Then answered Sigurd—

> Sigmund's son
> With Sigurd's sword
> E'en now rent down
> The raven's wall.

"Of the Volsung's kin is he who has done the deed; but now I have heard that thou art daughter of a mighty king, and folk have told us that thou wert lovely and full of lore, and now I will try the same."

Then Brynhild sang—

> Long have I slept
> And slumbered long,
> Many and long are the woes of mankind,
> By the might of Odin
> Must I bide helpless
> To shake from off me the spells of slumber.

> Hail to the day come back!
> Hail, sons of the daylight!
> Hail to thee, dark night, and thy daughter!
> Look with kind eyes a-down,
> On us sitting here lonely,
> And give unto us the gain that we long for.

[1] The stanzas on the two following pages were inserted here from *Sigdrifasmál* by the translators.

   Hail to the Æsir,
   And the sweet Asyniur![2]
  Hail to the fair earth fulfilled of plenty!
   Fair words, wise hearts,
   Would we win from you,
  And healing hands while life we hold."


Then Brynhild speaks again and says, "Two kings fought, one hight Helm Gunnar, an old man, and the greatest of warriors, and Odin had promised the victory unto him; but his foe was Agnar, or Audi's brother: and so I smote down Helm Gunnar in the fight; and Odin, in vengeance for that deed, struck the sleep-thorn into me, and said that I should never again have the victory, but should be given away in marriage; but there-against I vowed a vow, that never would I wed one who knew the name of fear."

Then said Sigurd, "Teach us the lore of mighty matters!"

She said, "Belike thou cannest more skill in all than I; yet will I teach thee; yea, and with thanks, if there be aught of my cunning that will in anywise pleasure thee, either of runes or of other matters that are the root of things; but now let us drink together, and may the Gods give to us twain a good day, that thou mayst win good help and fame from my wisdom, and that thou mayst hereafter mind thee of that which we twain speak together."

Then Brynhild filled a beaker and bore it to Sigurd, and gave him the drink of love, and spake—


   "Beer bring I to thee,
    Fair fruit of the byrnies' clash,
    Mixed is it mightily,
    Mingled with fame,
    Brimming with bright lays
    And pitiful runes,
    Wise words, sweet words,
    Speech of great game.

      [2] Goddesses.

Runes of war know thou,
If great thou wilt be!
Cut them on hilt of hardened sword,
  Some on the brand's back,
  Some on its shining side,
Twice name Tyr therein.


Sea-runes good at need,
Learnt for ship's saving,
For the good health of the swimming norse;
  On the stern cut them,
  Cut them on the rudder-blade
And set flame to shaven oar:
  Howso big be the sea-hills,
  Howso blue beneath,
Hail from the main then comest thou home.


Word-runes learn well
If thou wilt that no man
Pay back grief for the grief thou gavest;
  Wind thou these,
  Weave thou these,
  Cast thou these all about thee,
  At the Thing,
  Where folk throng,
Unto the full doom faring.


Of ale-runes know the wisdom
If thou wilt that another's wife
Should not bewray thine heart that trusteth:
  Cut them on the mead-horn,
  On the back of each hand,
And nick an N upon thy nail.


Ale have thou heed
To sign from all harm
Leek lay thou in the liquor,
  Then I know for sure
  Never cometh to thee,
Mead with hurtful matters mingled.

Help-runes shalt thou gather
  If skill thou wouldst gain
To loosen child from low-laid mother;
  Cut be they in hands hollow,
  Wrapped the joints round about;
Call for the Good-folks' gainsome helping.


Learn the bough-runes wisdom
  If leech-lore thou lovest;
And wilt wot about wounds' searching
  On the bark be they scored;
  On the buds of trees
Whose boughs look eastward ever.


Thought-runes shalt thou deal with
  If thou wilt be of all men
Fairest-souled wight, and wisest,
  These areded
  These first cut
These first took to heart high Hropt.


On the shield were they scored
  That stands before the shining God,
  On Early-waking's ear,
  On All-knowing's hoof,
  On the wheel which runneth
  Under Rognir's chariot;
  On Sleipnir's jaw-teeth,
  On the sleigh's traces.


On the rough bear's paws,
  And on Bragi's tongue,
  On the wolf's claws,
  And on eagle's bill,
  On bloody wings,
  And bridge's end;
  On loosing palms,
  And pity's path:

On glass, and on gold,
And on goodly silver,
In wine and in wort,
And the seat of the witch-wife;
On Gungnir's point,
And Grani's bosom;
On the Norn's nail,
And the neb of the night-owl.

All these so cut,
Were shaven and sheared,
And mingled in with holy mead,
And sent upon wide ways enow;
Some abide with the Elves,
Some abide with the Æsir,
Or with the wise Vanir,
Some still hold the sons of mankind.

These be the book-runes,
And the runes of good help,
And all the ale-runes,
And the runes of much might;
To whomso they may avail,
Unbewildered unspoilt;
They are wholesome to have:
Thrive thou with these then.
When thou hast learnt their lore,
Till the Gods end thy life-days.

Now shalt thou choose thee
E'en as choice is bidden,
Sharp steel's root and stem,
Choose song or silence;
See to each in thy heart,
All hurt has been heeded."

Then answered Sigurd—

"Ne'er shall I flee,
Though thou wottest me fey;

Never was I born for blenching,
Thy loved rede will I
    Hold aright in my heart
Even as long as I may live."


## CHAPTER XXI

### MORE WISE WORDS OF BRYNHILD

SIGURD spake now, " Sure no wiser woman than thou art one may be found in the wide world; yea, yea, teach me more yet of thy wisdom!"

She answers, " Seemly is it that I do according to thy will, and show thee forth more redes of great avail, for thy prayer's sake and thy wisdom;" and she spake withal—

" Be kindly to friend and kin, and reward not their trespasses against thee; bear and forbear, and win for thee thereby long enduring praise of men.

" Take good heed of evil things: a may's love, and a man's wife; full oft thereof doth ill befall!

" Let not thy mind be overmuch crossed by unwise men at thronged meetings of folk; for oft these speak worse than they wot of; lest thou be called a dastard, and art minded to think that thou art even as is said; slay such an one on another day, and so reward his ugly talk.

" If thou farest by the way whereas bide evil things, be well ware of thyself; take not harbour near the highway, though thou be benighted, for oft abide there ill wights for men's bewilderment.

"Let not fair women beguile thee, such as thou mayst meet at the feast, so that the thought thereof stand thee in stead of sleep, and a quite mind; yea, draw them not to thee with kisses or other sweet things of love.

" If thou hearest the fool's word of a drunken man, strive not with him being drunk with drink and witless; many a grief, yea, and the very death, groweth from out such things.

" Fight thy foes in the field, nor be burnt in thine house.

" Never swear thou wrongsome oath; great and grim is the reward for the breaking of plighted troth.

"Give kind heed to dead men,—sick-dead, sea-dead, or sword-dead; deal heedfully with their dead corpses.

"Trow never in him for whom thou hast slain father, brother, or whatso near kin, yea, though young he be; *for oft waxes wolf in youngling.*

"Look thou with good heed to the wiles of thy friends; but little skill is given to me, that I should foresee the ways of thy life; yet good it were that hate fell not on thee from those of thy wife's house."

Sigurd spake, "None among the sons of men can be found wiser than thou; and thereby swear I, that thee will I have as my own, for near to my heart thou liest."

She answers, "Thee would I fainest choose, though I had all men's sons to choose from."

And thereto they plighted troth both of them.

## CHAPTER XXII

### OF THE SEMBLANCE AND ARRAY OF SIGURD FAFNIR'S-BANE[1]

Now Sigurd rides away; many-folded is his shield, and blazing with red gold, and the image of a dragon is drawn thereon; and this same was dark brown above, and bright red below; and with even such-like image was adorned helm, and saddle, and coat-armour; and he was clad in the golden byrny, and all his weapons were gold-wrought.

Now for this cause was the drake drawn on all his weapons, that when he was seen of men, all folk might know who went there; yea, all those who had heard of his slaying of that great dragon, that the Vœrings call Fafnir; and for that cause are his weapons gold-wrought, and brown of hue, and that he was by far above other men in courtesy and goodly manners, and well-nigh in all things else; and whenas folk tell of all the mightiest champions, and the noblest chiefs, then ever is he named the foremost, and his name goes wide about on all tongues north of the sea of the Greek-lands, and even so shall it be while the world endures.

[1] This chapter is nearly literally the same as chapter 166 of the *Wilkina-saga;* Ed.: Perinskiold, Stockholm, 1715.

Now the hair of this Sigurd was golden-red of hue, fair of fashion, and falling down in great locks; thick and short was his beard, and of no other colour; high-nosed he was, broad and high-boned of face; so keen were his eyes, that few durst gaze up under the brows of him; his shoulders were as broad to look on as the shoulders of two; most duly was his body fashioned betwixt height and breadth, and in such wise as was seemliest; and this is the sign told of his height, that when he was girt with his sword Gram, which same was seven spans long, as he went through the full-gown rye-fields, the dew-shoe of the said sword smote the ears of the standing corn; and, for all that, greater was his strength than his growth: well could he wield sword, and cast forth spear, shoot shaft, and hold shield, bend bow, back horse, and do all the goodly deeds that he learned in his youth's days.

Wise he was to know things yet undone; and the voice of all fowls he knew, wherefore few things fell on him unawares.

Of many words he was, and so fair of speech withal, that whensoever he made it his business to speak, he never left speaking before that to all men it seemed full sure, that no otherwise must the matter be than as he said.

His sport and pleasure it was to give aid to his own folk, and to prove himself in mighty matters, to take wealth from his unfriends, and give the same to his friends.

Never did he lose heart, and of naught was he adrad.

## CHAPTER XXIII

### Sigurd comes to Hlymdale

Forth Sigurd rides till he comes to a great and goodly dwelling, the lord whereof was a mighty chief called Heimir; he had to wife a sister of Brynhild, who was hight Bekkhild, because she had bidden at home, and learned handicraft, whereas Brynhild fared with helm and byrny unto the wars, wherefore was she called Brynhild.

Heimir and Bekkhild had a son called Alswid, the most courteous of men.

Now at this stead were men disporting them abroad, but when they see the man riding thereto, they leave their play to wonder at him, for none such had they ever seen erst; so they went to meet him, and gave him good welcome; Alswid bade him abide and have such things at his hands as he would; and he takes his bidding blithesomely; due service withal was established for him; four men bore the treasure of gold from off the horse, and the fifth took it to him to guard the same; therein were many things to behold, things of great price, and seldom seen; and great game and joy men had to look on byrnies and helms, and mighty rings, and wondrous great golden stoups, and all kinds of war weapons.

So there dwelt Sigurd long in great honour holden; and tidings of that deed of fame spread wide through all lands, of how he had slain that hideous and fearful dragon. So good joyance had they there together, and each was leal to other; and their sport was in the arraying of their weapons, and the shafting of their arrows, and the flying of their falcons.

## CHAPTER XXIV

### Sigurd sees Brynhild at Hlymdale

In those days came home to Heimir, Brynhild, his foster-daughter, and she sat in her bower with her maidens, and could more skill in handicraft than other women; she sat, overlaying cloth with gold, and sewing therein the great deeds which Sigurd had wrought, the slaying of the Worm, and the taking of the wealth of him, and the death of Regin withal.

Now tells the tale, that on a day Sigurd rode into the wood with hawk, and hound, and men thronging; and whenas he came home his hawk flew up to a high tower, and sat him down on a certain window. Then fared Sigurd after his hawk, and he saw where sat a fair woman, and knew that it was Brynhild, and he deems all things he sees there to be worthy together, both her fairness, and the fair things she wrought: and therewith he goes into the hall, but has no more joyance in the games of the men folk.

Then spake Alswid, "Why art thou so bare of bliss? this manner of thine grieveth us thy friends; why then wilt thou not hold to thy gleesome ways? Lo, thy hawks pine now, and thy horse Grani droops; and long will it be ere we are booted thereof?"

Sigurd answered, "Good friend, hearken to what lies on my mind; for my hawk flew up into a certain tower; and when I came thereto and took him, lo there I saw a fair woman, and she sat by a needlework of gold, and did thereon my deeds that are passed, and my deeds that are to come."

Then said Alswid, "Thou hast seen Brynhild, Budli's daughter, the greatest of great women."

"Yea, verily," said Sigurd; "but how came she hither?

Alswid answered, "Short space there was betwixt the coming hither of the twain of you."

Says Sigurd, "Yea, but a few days agone I knew her for the best of the world's women."

Alswid said, "Give not all thine heed to one woman, being such a man as thou art; ill life to sit lamenting for what we may not have."

"I shall go meet her," says Sigurd, "and get from her love like my love, and give her a gold ring in token thereof."

Alswid answered, "None has ever yet been known whom she would let sit beside her, or to whom she would give drink; for ever will she hold to warfare and to the winning of all kinds of fame."

Sigurd said, "We know not for sure whether she will give us answer or not, or grant us a seat beside her."

So the next day after, Sigurd went to the bower, but Alswid stood outside the bower door, fitting shafts to his arrows.

Now Sigurd spake, "Abide, fair and hale lady,—how farest thou?"

She answered, "Well it fares; my kin and my friends live yet: but who shall say what goodhap folk may bear to their life's end?"

He sat him down by her, and there came in four damsels

with great golden beakers, and the best of wine therein; and these stood before the twain.

Then said Brynhild, "This seat is for few, but and if my father come."

He answered, "Yet is it granted to one that likes me well."

Now that chamber was hung with the best and fairest of hangings, and the floor thereof was all covered with cloth.

Sigurd spake, "Now has it come to pass even as thou didst promise."

"O be thou welcome here!" said she, and arose therewith, and the four damsels with her, and bore the golden beaker to him, and bade him drink; he stretched out his hand to the beaker, and took it, and her hand withal, and drew her down beside him; and cast his arms round about her neck and kissed her, and said—

"Thou art the fairest that was ever born!"

But Brynhild said, "Ah, wiser is it not to cast faith and troth into a woman's power, for ever shall they break that they have promised."

He said, "That day would dawn the best of days over our heads whereon each of each should be made happy."

Brynhild answered, "It is not fated that we should abide together; I am a shield-may, and wear helm on head even as the kings of war, and them full oft I help, neither is the battle become loathsome to me."

Sigurd answered, "What fruit shall be of our life, if we live not together: harder to bear this pain that lies hereunder, than the stroke of sharp sword."

Brynhild answers, "I shall gaze on the hosts of the war-kings, but thou shalt wed Gudrun, the daughter of Giuki."

Sigurd answered, "What king's daughter lives to beguile me? neither am I double-hearted herein; and now I swear by the Gods that thee shall I have for mine own, or no woman else."

And even suchlike wise spake she.

Sigurd thanked her for her speech, and gave her a gold ring, and now they swore oath anew, and so he went his ways to his men, and is with them awhile in great bliss.

## CHAPTER XXV

### Of the Dream of Gudrun, Giuki's daughter

There was a king hight Giuki, who ruled a realm south of the Rhine; three sons he had, thus named: Gunnar, Hogni, and Guttorm, and Gudrun was the name of his daughter, the fairest of maidens; and all these children were far before all other king's children in all prowess, and in goodliness and growth withal; ever were his sons at the wars and wrought many a deed of fame. But Giuki had wedded Grimhild, the Wise-wife.

Now Budli was the name of a king mightier than Giuki, mighty though they both were: and Atli was the brother of Brynhild: Atli was a fierce man and a grim, great and black to look on, yet noble of mien withal, and the greatest of warriors. Grimhild was a fierce-hearted woman.

Now the days of the Giukings bloomed fair, and chiefly because of those children, so far before the sons of men.

On a day Gudrun says to her mays that she may have no joy of heart; then a certain woman asked her wherefore her joy was departed.

She answered, "Grief came to me in my dreams, therefore is there sorrow in my heart, since thou must needs ask thereof."

"Tell it me, then, thy dream," said the woman, "for dreams oft forecast but the weather."

Gudrun answers, "Nay, nay, no weather, is this; I dreamed that I had a fair hawk on my wrist, feathered with feathers of gold."

Says the woman, "Many have heard tell of thy beauty, thy wisdom, and thy courtesy; some king's son abides thee, then."

Gudrun answers, "I dreamed that naught was so dear to me as this hawk, and all my wealth had I cast aside rather than him."

The woman said, "Well, then, the man thou shalt have will be of the goodliest, and well shalt thou love him."

Gudrun answered, "It grieves me that I know not who

he shall be; let us go seek Brynhild, for she belike will wot thereof."

So they arrayed them in gold and many a fair thing, and she went with her damsels till they came to the hall of Brynhild, and that hall was dight with gold, and stood on a high hill; and whenas their goings were seen, it was told Brynhild, that a company of women drove toward the burg in gilded waggons.

"That shall be Gudrun, Giuki's daughter," says she: "I dreamed of her last night; let us go meet her! no fairer woman may come to our house."

So they went abroad to meet them, and gave them good greeting, and they went into the goodly hall together; fairly painted it was within, and well adorned with silver vessel; cloths were spread under the feet of them, and all folk served them, and in many wise they sported.

But Gudrun was somewhat silent.

Then said Brynhild, "Ill to abash folk of their mirth; prithee do not so; let us talk together for our disport of mighty kings and their great deeds."

"Good talk," says Gudrun, "let us do even so; what kings deemest thou to have been the first of all men?"

Brynhild says, "The sons of Haki, and Hagbard withal; they brought to pass many a deed of fame in their warfare."

Gudrun answers, "Great men certes, and of noble fame! Yet Sigar took their one sister, and burned the other, house and all; and they may be called slow to revenge the deed; why didst thou not name my brethren, who are held to be the first of men as at this time?"

Brynhild says, "Men of good hope are they surely, though but little proven hitherto; but one I know far before them, Sigurd, the son of Sigmund the king; a youngling was he in the days when he slew the sons of Hunding, and revenged his father, and Eylimi, his mother's father."

Said Gudrun, "By what token tellest thou that?"

Brynhild answered, "His mother went amid the dead, and found Sigmund the king sore wounded, and would bind up his hurts; but he said he grew over old for war, and bade her lay this comfort to her heart, that she should bear the most famed of sons; and wise was the wise man's word therein: for after the death of King Sigmund, she went to King Alf, and there was Sigurd nourished in great honour, and day by day he wrought some deed of fame, and is the man most renowned of all the wide world."

Gudrun says, "From love hast thou gained these tidings of him; but for this cause came I here, to tell thee dreams of mine which have brought me great grief."

Says Brynhild, "Let not such matters sadden thee; abide with thy friends who wish thee blithsome, all of them!"

"This I dreamed," said Gudrun, "that we went, a many of us in company, from the bower, and we saw an exceeding great hart, that far excelled all other deer ever seen, and the hair of him was golden; and this deer we were all fain to take, but I alone got him; and he seemed to me better than all things else; but sithence thou, Brynhild, didst shoot and slay my deer even at my very knees, and such grief was that to me that scarce might I bear it; and then afterwards thou gavest me a wolf-cub, which besprinkled me with the blood of my brethren."

Brynhild answers, "I will arede thy dream, even as things shall come to pass hereafter; for Sigurd shall come to thee, even he whom I have chosen for my well-beloved; and Grimhild shall give him mead mingled with hurtful things, which shall cast us all into mighty strife. Him shalt thou have, and him shalt thou quickly miss; and Atli the king shalt thou wed; and thy brethren shalt thou lose, and slay Atli withal in the end."

Gudrun answers, "Grief and woe to know that such things shall be!"

And therewith she and hers get them gone home to King Giuki.

## CHAPTER XXVI

### SIGURD COMES TO THE GIUKINGS AND IS WEDDED TO GUDRUN

Now Sigurd goes his ways with all that great treasure, and in friendly wise he departs from them; and on Grani he rides with all his war-gear and the burden withal; and thus he rides until he comes to the hall of King Giuki; there he rides into the burg, and that sees one of the king's men, and he spake withal—

" Sure it may be deemed that here is come one of the Gods, for his array is all done with gold, and his horse is far mightier than other horses, and the manner of his weapons is most exceeding goodly, and most of all the man himself far excels all other men ever seen."

So the king goes out with his court and greets the man, and asks—

" Who art thou who thus ridest into my burg, as none has durst hitherto without the leave of my sons? "

He answered, " I am called Sigurd, son of King Sigmund."

Then said King Giuki, " Be thou welcome here then, and take at our hands whatso thou willest."

So he went into the king's hall, and all men seemed little beside him, and all men served him, and there he abode in great joyance.

Now oft they all ride abroad together, Sigurd and Gunnar and Hogni, and ever is Sigurd far the foremost of them, mighty men of their hands though they were.

But Grimhild finds how heartily Sigurd loved Brynhild, and how oft he talks of her; and she falls to thinking how well it were, if he might abide there and wed the daughter of King Giuki, for she saw that none might come anigh to his goodliness, and what faith and goodhelp there was in him, and how that he had more wealth withal than folk might tell of any man; and the king did to him even as unto his own sons, and they for their parts held him of more worth than themselves.

So on a night as they sat at the drink, the queen arose, and went before Sigurd, and said—

" Great joy we have in thine abiding here, and all good things will we put before thee to take of us; lo now, take this horn and drink thereof."

So he took it and drank, and therewithal she said, " Thy father shall be Giuki the king, and I shall be thy mother, and Gunnar and Hogni shall be thy brethren, and all this shall be sworn with oaths each to each; and then surely shall the like of you never be found on earth."

Sigurd took her speech well, for with the drinking of that drink all memory of Brynhild departed from him. So there he abode awhile.

And on a day went Grimhild to Giuki the king, and cast her arms about his neck, and spake—

"Behold, there has now come to us the greatest of great hearts that the world holds; and needs must he be trusty and of great avail; give him thy daughter then, with plenteous wealth, and as much of rule as he will; perchance thereby he will be well content to abide here ever."

The king answered, "Seldom does it befall that kings offer their daughters to any; yet in higher wise will it be done to offer her to this man, than to take lowly prayers for her from others."

On a night Gudrun pours out the drink, and Sigurd beholds her how fair she is and how full of all courtesy.

Five seasons Sigurd abode there, and ever they passed their days together in good honour and friendship.

And so it befell that the kings held talk together, and Giuki said—

"Great good thou givest us, Sigurd, and with exceeding strength thou strengthenest our realm."

Then Gunnar said, "All things that may be will we do for thee, so thou abidest here long; both dominion shalt thou have, and our sister freely and unprayed for, whom another man would not get for all his prayers."

Sigurd says, "Thanks have ye for this wherewith ye honour me, and gladly will I take the same."

Therewith they swore brotherhood together, and to be even as if they were children of one father and one mother; and a noble feast was holden, and endured many days, and Sigurd drank at the wedding of him and Gudrun; and there might men behold all manner of game and glee, and each day the feast better and better.

Now fare these folk wide over the world, and do many great deeds, and slay many kings' sons, and no man has ever done such works of prowess as did they; then home they come again with much wealth won in war.

Sigurd gave of the serpent's heart to Gudrun, and she ate thereof, and became greater-hearted, and wiser than ere before: and the son of these twain was called Sigmund.

Now on a time went Grimhild to Gunnar her son, and spake—

"Fair blooms the life and fortune of thee, but for one thing only, and namely whereas thou art unwedded; go woo Brynhild; good rede is this, and Sigurd will ride with thee."

Gunnar answered, "Fair is she certes, and I am fain enow to win her;" and therewith he tells his father, and his brethren, and Sigurd, and they all prick him on to that wooing.

## CHAPTER XXVII

### The Wooing of Brynhild

Now they array them joyously for their journey, and ride over hill and dale to the house of King Budli, and woo his daughter of him; in a good wise he took their speech, if so be that she herself would not deny them; but he said withal that so high-minded was she, that that man only might wed her whom she would.

Then they ride to Hlymdale, and there Heimir gave them good welcome; so Gunnar tells his errand; Heimir says, that she must needs wed but him whom she herself chose freely; and tells them how her abode was but a little way thence, and that he deemed that him only would she have who should ride through the flaming fire that was drawn around about her hall; so they depart and come to the hall and the fire, and see there a castle with a golden roof-ridge, and all round about a fire roaring up.

Now Gunnar rode on Goti, but Hogni on Holkvi, and Gunnar smote his horse to face the fire, but he shrank aback.

Then said Sigurd, "Why givest thou back, Gunnar?"

He answered, "The horse will not tread this fire; but lend me thy horse Grani."

"Yea, with all my good will," says Sigurd.

Then Gunnar rides him at the fire, and yet nowise will

Grani stir, nor may Gunnar any the more ride through that fire. So now they change semblance, Gunnar and Sigurd, even as Grimhild had taught them; then Sigurd in the likeness of Gunnar mounts and rides, Gram in his hand, and golden spurs on his heels; then leapt Grani into the fire when he felt the spurs; and the mighty roar arose as the fire burned ever madder, and the earth trembled, and the flames went up even unto the heavens, nor had any dared to ride as he rode, even as it were through the deep mirk.

But now the fire sank withal, and he leapt from his horse and went into the hall, even as the song says—

> The flame flared at its maddest,
> Earth's fields fell a-quaking
> As the red flame aloft
> Licked the lowest of heaven.
> Few had been fain,
> Of the rulers of folk,
> To ride through that flame,
> Or athwart it to tread.

> Then Sigurd smote
> Grani with sword,
> And the flame was slaked
> Before the king;
> Low lay the flames
> Before the fain of fame;
> Bright gleamed the array
> That Regin erst owned.

Now when Sigurd had passed through the fire, he came into a certain fair dwelling, and therein sat Brynhild.

She asked, " What man is it? "

Then he named himself Gunnar, son of Giuki, and said— " Thou art awarded to me as my wife, by the good-will and word of thy father and thy foster-father, and I have ridden through the flames of thy fire, according to thy word that thou hast set forth."

" I wot not clearly," said she, " how I shall answer thee."

Now Sigurd stood upright on the hall floor, and leaned on the hilt of his sword, and he spake to Brynhild—

"In reward thereof, shall I pay thee a great dower in gold and goodly things?"

She answered in heavy mood from her seat, whereas she sat like unto swan on billow, having a sword in her hand, and a helm on her head, and being clad in a byrny, "O Gunnar," she says, "speak not to me of such things; unless thou be the first and best of all men; for then shalt thou slay those my wooers, if thou hast heart thereto; I have been in battles with the king of the Greeks, and our weapons were stained with red blood, and for such things still I yearn."

He answered, "Yea, certes many great deeds hast thou done; but yet call thou to mind thine oath, concerning the riding through of this fire, wherein thou didst swear that thou wouldst go with the man who should do this deed."

So she found that he spake but the sooth, and she paid heed to his words, and arose, and greeted him meetly, and he abode there three nights, and they lay in one bed together; but he took the sword Gram and laid it betwixt them: then she asked him why he laid it there; and he answered, that in that wise must he needs wed his wife or else get his bane.

Then she took from off her the ring Andvari's-loom, which he had given her aforetime, and gave it to him, but he gave her another ring out of Fafnir's hoard.

Thereafter he rode away through the same fire unto his fellows, and he and Gunnar changed semblances again, and rode unto Hlymdale, and told how it had gone with them.

That same day went Brynhild home to her foster-father, and tells him as one whom she trusted, how that there had come a king to her; "And he rode through my flaming fire and said he was come to woo me, and named himself Gunnar; but I said that such a deed might Sigurd alone have done, with whom I plighted troth on the mountain; and he is my first troth-plight, and my well-beloved."

Heimir said that things must needs abide even as now they had now come to pass.

Brynhild said, "Aslaugh the daughter of me and Sigurd shall be nourished here with thee."

Now the kings fare home, but Brynhild goes to her father; Grimhild welcomes the kings meetly, and thanks Sigurd for his fellowship; and withal is a great feast made, and many were the guests thereat; and thither came Budli the King with his daughter Brynhild, and his son Atli, and for many days did the feast endure: and at that feast was Gunnar wedded to Brynhild: but when it was brought to an end, once more has Sigurd memory of all the oaths that he sware unto Brynhild, yet withal he let all things abide in rest and peace."

Brynhild and Gunnar sat together in great game and glee, and drank goodly wine.

## CHAPTER XXVIII

### How the Queens Held Angry Converse Together at the Bathing

On a day as the Queens went to the river to bathe them, Brynhild waded the farthest out into the river; then asked Gudrun what that deed might signify.

Brynhild said, "Yea, and why then should I be equal to thee in this matter more than in others? I am minded to think that my father is mightier than thine, and my true-love has wrought many wondrous works of fame, and hath ridden the flaming fire withal, while thy husband was but the thrall of King Hjalprek."

Gudrun answered full of wrath, "Thou wouldst be wise if thou shouldst hold thy peace rather than revile my husband: lo now, the talk of all men it is, that none has ever abode in this world like unto him in all matters soever; and little it beseems thee of all folk to mock him who was thy first beloved: and Fafnir he slew, yea, and he rode thy flaming fire, whereas thou didst deem that he was Gunnar the King, and by thy side he lay, and took from thine hand the ring Andvari's-loom;—here mayst thou well behold it!"

Then Brynhild saw the ring and knew it, and waxed as wan as a dead woman, and she went home and spake no word the evening long.

So when Sigurd came to bed to Gudrun she asked him why Brynhild's joy was so departed.

He answered, "I know not, but sore I misdoubt me that soon we shall know thereof overwell."

Gudrun said, "Why may she not love her life, having wealth and bliss, and the praise of all men, and the man withal that she would have?"

"Ah, yea!" said Sigurd, "and where in all the world was she then, when she said that she deemed she had the noblest of all men, and the dearest to her heart of all?"

Gudrun answers, "Tomorn will I ask her concerning this, who is the liefest to her of all men for a husband."

Sigurd said, "Needs must I forbid thee this, and full surely wilt thou rue the deed if thou doest it."

Now the next morning they sat in the bower, and Brynhild was silent; then spake Gudrun—

"Be merry, Brynhild! Grievest thou because of that speech of ours together, or what other thing slayeth thy bliss?"

Brynhild answers, "With naught but evil intent thou sayest this, for a cruel heart thou hast."

"Say not so," said Gudrun; "but rather tell me all the tale."

Brynhild answers, "Ask such things only as are good for thee to know—matters meet for mighty dames. Good to love good things when all goes according to thy heart's desire!"

Gudrun says, "Early days for me to glory in that; but this word of thine looketh toward some foreseeing. What ill dost thou thrust at us? I did naught to grieve thee."

Brynhild answers, "For this shalt thou pay, in that thou hast got Sigurd to thee,—nowise can I see thee living in the bliss thereof, whereas thou hast him, and the wealth and the might of him."

But Gudrun answered, "Naught knew I of your words

and vows together; and well might my father look to the mating of me without dealing with thee first."

"No secret speech had we," quoth Brynhild, "though we swore oath together; and full well didst thou know that thou wentest about to beguile me; verily thou shalt have thy reward!"

Says Gudrun, "Thou art mated better than thou art worthy of; but thy pride and rage shall be hard to slake belike, and therefor shall many a man pay."

"Ah, I should be well content," said Brynhild, "if thou hadst not the nobler man!"

Gudrun answers, "So noble a husband hast thou, that who knows of a greater king or a lord of more wealth and might?"

Says Brynhild, "Sigurd slew Fafnir, and that only deed is of more worth than all the might of King Gunnar."

(Even as the song says):

> The worm Sigurd slew,
> Nor ere shall that deed
> Be worsened by age
> While the world is alive:
> But thy brother the King
> Never durst, never bore
> The flame to ride down
> Through the fire to fare.

Gudrun answers, "Grani would not abide the fire under Gunnar the King, but Sigurd durst the deed, and thy heart may well abide without mocking him."

Brynhild answers, "Nowise will I hide from thee that I deem no good of Grimhild."

Says Gudrun, "Nay, lay no ill words on her, for in all things she is to thee as to her own daughter."

"Ah," says Brynhild, "she is the beginning of all this bale that biteth so; an evil drink she bare to Sigurd, so that he had no more memory of my very name."

"All wrong thou talkest; a lie without measure is this," quoth Gudrun.

Brynhild answered, "Have thou joy of Sigurd according

to the measure of the wiles wherewith ye have beguiled me!
unworthily have ye conspired against me; may all things go
with you as my heart hopes!"

Gudrun says, "More joy shall I have of him than thy
wish would give unto me: but to no man's mind it came,
that he had aforetime his pleasure of me; nay not once."

"Evil speech thou speakest," says Brynhild; "when thy
wrath runs off thou wilt rue it; but come now, let us no
more cast angry words one at the other!"

Says Gudrun, "Thou wert the first to cast such words at
me, and now thou makest as if thou wouldst amend it, but
a cruel and hard heart abides behind."

"Let us lay aside vain babble," says Brynhild. "Long
did I hold my peace concerning my sorrow of heart, and, lo
now, thy brother alone do I love; let us fall to other talk."
Gudrun said, "Far beyond all this doth thine heart look."

And so ugly ill befell from that going to the river,
and that knowing of the ring, wherefrom did all their talk
arise.

## CHAPTER XXIX

### OF BRYNHILD'S GREAT GRIEF AND MOURNING

AFTER this talk Brynhild lay a-bed, and tidings were
brought to King Gunnar that Brynhild was sick; he goes
to see her thereon, and asks what ails her; but she answered
him naught, but lay there as one dead: and when he was
hard on her for an answer, she said—

"What didst thou with that ring that I gave thee, even
the one which King Budli gave me at our last parting, when
thou and King Giuki came to him and threatened fire and
the sword, unless ye had me to wife? Yea, at that time
he led me apart, and asked me which I had chosen of those
who were come; but I prayed him that I might abide to
ward the land and be chief over the third part of his men;
then were there two choices for me to deal betwixt, either
that I should be wedded to him whom he would, or lose
all my weal and friendship at his hands; and he said withal
that his friendship would be better to me than his wrath:
then I bethought me whether I should yield to his will, or

slay many a man; and therewithal I deemed that it would avail little to strive with him, and so it fell out, that I promised to wed whomsoever should ride the horse Grani with Fafnir's Hoard, and ride through my flaming fire, and slay those men whom I called on him to slay, and now so it was, that none durst ride, save Sigurd only, because he lacked no heart thereto; yea, and the Worm he slew, and Regin, and five kings beside; but thou, Gunnar, durst do naught; as pale as a dead man didst thou wax, and no king thou art, and no champion; so whereas I made a vow unto my father, that him alone would I love who was the noblest man alive, and that this is none save Sigurd, lo, now have I broken my oath and brought it to naught, since he is none of mine, and for this cause shall I compass thy death; and a great reward of evil things have I wherewith to reward Grimhild;—never, I wot, has woman lived eviler or of lesser heart than she."

Gunnar answered in such wise that few might hear him, "Many a vile word hast thou spoken, and an evil-hearted woman art thou, whereas thou revilest a woman far better than thou; never would she curse her life as thou dost; nay, nor has she tormented dead folk, or murdered any; but lives her life well praised of all."

Brynhild answered, "Never have I dwelt with evil things privily, or done loathsome deeds;—yet most fain I am to slay thee."

And therewith would she slay King Gunnar, but Hogni laid her in fetters; but then Gunnar spake withal—

"Nay, I will not that she abide in fetters."

Then said she, "Heed it not! for never again seest thou me glad in thine hall, never drinking, never at the chessplay, never speaking the words of kindness, never overlaying the fair cloths with gold, never giving thee good counsel;—ah, my sorrow of heart that I might not get Sigurd to me!"

Then she sat up and smote her needlework, and rent it asunder, and bade set open her bower doors, that far away might the wailings of her sorrow be heard; then great mourning and lamentation there was, so that folk heard it far and wide through that abode.

Now Gudrun asked her bower-maidens why they sat so joyless and downcast. "What has come to you, that ye fare ye as witless women, or what unheard-of wonders have befallen you?"

Then answered a waiting lady, hight Swaflod, "An untimely, an evil day it is, and our hall is fulfilled of lamentation."

Then spake Gudrun to one of her handmaids, "Arise, for we have slept long; go, wake Brynhild, and let us fall to our needlework and be merry."

"Nay, nay," she says, "nowise may I wake her, or talk with her; for many days has she drunk neither mead nor wine; surely the wrath of the Gods has fallen upon her."

Then spake Gudrun to Gunnar, "Go and see her," she says, "and bid her know that I am grieved with her grief."

"Nay," says Gunnar, "I am forbid to go see her or to share her weal."

Nevertheless he went unto her, and strives in many wise to have speech of her, but gets no answer whatsoever: therefore he gets him gone and finds Hogni, and bids him go see her: he said he was loth thereto, but went, and gat no more of her.

Then they go and find Sigurd, and pray him to visit her; he answered naught thereto, and so matters abode for that night.

But the next day, when he came home from hunting, Sigurd went to Gudrun, and spake—

"In such wise do matters show to me, as though great and evil things will betide from this trouble and upheaving, and that Brynhild will surely die."

Gudrun answers, "O my lord, by great wonders is she encompassed, seven days and seven nights has she slept, and none has dared wake her."

"Nay, she sleeps not," said Sigurd, "her heart is dealing rather with dreadful intent against me."

Then said Gudrun, weeping, "Woe worth the while for thy death! go and see her; and wot if her fury may not be abated; give her gold, and smother up her grief and anger therewith!"

Then Sigurd went out, and found the door of Brynhild's

chamber open; he deemed she slept, and drew the clothes from off her, and said—

"Awake, Brynhild! the sun shineth now over all the house, and thou hast slept enough; cast off grief from thee, and take up gladness!"

She said, "And how then hast thou dared to come to me? in this treason none was worse to me than thou."

Said Sigurd, "Why wilt thou not speak to folk? for what cause sorrowest thou?"

Brynhild answers, "Ah, to thee will I tell of my wrath!"

Sigurd said, "As one under a spell art thou, if thou deemest that there is aught cruel in my heart against thee; but thou hast him for husband whom thou didst choose."

"Ah, nay," she said, "never did Gunnar ride through the fire to me, nor did he give me to dower the host of the slain: I wondered at the man who came into my hall; for I deemed indeed that I knew thine eyes; but I might not see clearly, or divide the good from the evil, because of the veil that lay heavy on my fortune."

Says Sigurd, "No nobler men are there than the sons of Giuki, they slew the king of the Danes, and that great chief, the brother of King Budli."

Brynhild answered, "Surely for many an ill-deed must I reward them; mind me not of my griefs against them! But thou, Sigurd, slewest the Worm, and rodest the fire through; yea, and for my sake, and not one of the sons of King Giuki."

Sigurd answers, "I am not thy husband, and thou art not my wife; yet did a farfamed king pay dower to thee."

Says Brynhild, "Never looked I at Gunnar in such a wise that my heart smiled on him; and hard and fell am I to him, though I hide it from others."

"A marvellous thing," says Sigurd, "not to love such a king; what angers thee most? for surely his love should be better to thee than gold."

"This is the sorest sorrow to me," she said, "that the bitter sword is not reddened in thy blood."

"Have no fear thereof!" says he, "no long while to wait or the bitter sword stand deep in my heart; and no worse needest thou to pray for thyself, for thou wilt not live when I am dead; the days of our two lives shall be few enough from henceforth."

Brynhild answers, "Enough and to spare of bale is in thy speech, since thou bewrayedst me, and didst twin[1] me and all bliss;—naught do I heed my life or death."

Sigurd answers, "Ah, live, and love King Gunnar and me withal! and all my wealth will I give thee if thou die not."

Brynhild answers, 'Thou knowest me not, nor the heart that is in me; for thou art the first and best of all men, and I am become the most loathsome of all women to thee."

"This is truer," says Sigurd, "that I loved thee better than myself, though I fell into the wiles from whence our lives may not escape; for whenso my own heart and mind availed me, then I sorrowed sore that thou wert not my wife; but as I might put my trouble from me, for in a king's dwelling was I; and withal and in spite of all I was well content that we were all together. Well may it be, that that shall come to pass which is foretold; neither shall I fear the fulfilment thereof."

Brynhild answered, and said, "Too late thou tellest me that my grief grieved thee: little pity shall I find now."

Sigurd said, "This my heart would, that thou and I should go into one bed together; even so wouldst thou be my wife."

Said Brynhild, "Such words may nowise be spoken, nor will I have two kings in one hall; I will lay my life down rather than beguile Gunnar the King."

And therewith she call to mind how they met, they two, on the mountain, and swore oath each to each.

"But now is all changed, and I will not live."

"I might not call to mind thy name," said Sigurd, "or know thee again, before the time of thy wedding; the greatest of all griefs is that."

Then said Brynhild, "I swore an oath to wed the man who should ride my flaming fire, and that oath will I hold to, or die."

"Rather than thou die, I will wed thee, and put away Gudrun," said Sigurd.

[1] Sunder.

But therewithal so swelled the heart betwixt the sides of him, that the rings of his byrny burst asunder.

"I will not have thee," says Brynhild, "nay, nor any other!"

Then Sigurd got him gone.

So saith the song of Sigurd—

> "Out then went Sigurd,
>     The great kings' well-loved,
>     From the speech and the sorrow,
>     Sore drooping, so grieving,
>     That the shirt round about him
>     Of iron rings woven,
>     From the sides brake asunder
>     Of the brave in the battle."

So when Sigurd came into the hall, Gunnar asked if he had come to a knowledge of what great grief lay heavy on her, or if she had power of speech: and Sigurd said that she lacked it not. So now Gunnar goes to her again, and asked her, what wrought her woe, or if there were anything that might amend it.

"I will not live," says Brynhild, "for Sigurd has bewrayed me, yea, and thee no less, whereas thou didst suffer him to come into my bed: lo thou, two men in one dwelling I will not have; and this shall be Sigurd's death, or thy death, or my death;—for now has he told Gudrun all, and she is mocking me even now!"


## CHAPTER XXX

### Of the Slaying of Sigurd Fafnir's-bane

Thereafter Brynhild went out, and sat under her bower-wall, and had many words of wailing to say, and still she cried that all things were loathsome to her, both land and lordship alike, so she might not have Sigurd.

But therewith came Gunnar to her yet again, and Brynhild spake, "Thou shalt lose both realm and wealth, and thy life and me, for I shall fare home to my kin, and abide there in sorrow, unless thou slayest Sigurd and his son; never nourish thou a wolfcub."

Gunnar grew sick at heart thereat, and might nowise see what fearful thing lay beneath it all; he was bound to Sigurd by oath, and this way and that way swung the heart within him; but at the last he bethought him of the measureless shame if his wife went from him, and he said within himself, "Brynhild is better to me than all things else, and the fairest woman of all women, and I will lay down my life rather than lose the love of her." And herewith he called to him his brother and spake,—

"Trouble is heavy on me," and he tells him that he must needs slay Sigurd, for that he has failed him where in he trusted him; "so let us be lords of the gold and the realm withal."

Hogni answers, "Ill it behoves us to break our oaths with wrack and wrong, and withal great aid we have in him; no kings shall be as great as we, if so be the King of the Hun-folk may live; such another brother-in-law never may we get again; bethink thee how good it is to have such a brother-in-law, and such sons to our sister! But well I see how things stand, for this has Brynhild stirred thee up to, and surely shall her counsel drag us into huge shame and scathe."

Gunnar says, "Yet shall it be brought about: and, lo, a rede thereto;—let us egg on our brother Guttorm to the deed; he is young, and of little knowledge, and is clean out of all the oaths moreover."

"Ah, set about in ill wise," says Hogni, "and though indeed it may well be compassed, a due reward shall we gain for the bewrayal of such a man as is Sigurd."

Gunnar says, "Sigurd shall die, or I shall die."

And therewith he bids Brynhild arise and be glad at heart: so she arose, and still ever she said that Gunnar should come no more into her bed till the deed was done.

So the brothers fall to talk, and Gunnar says that it is a deed well worthy of death, that taking of Brynhild's maidenhead; "So come now, let us prick on Guttorm to do the deed."

Therewith they call him to them, and offer him gold

and great dominion, as they well have might to do. Yea,
and they took a certain worm and somewhat of wolf's
flesh and let seethe them together, and gave him to eat of
the same, even as the singer sings—

> Fish of the wild-wood,
> Worm smooth crawling,
> With wolf-meat mingled,
> They minced for Guttorm;
> Then in the beaker,
> In the wine his mouth knew,
> They set it, still doing
> More deeds of wizards.

Wherefore with the eating of this meat he grew so wild
and eager, and with all things about him, and with the
heavy words of Grimhild, that he gave his word to do the
deed; and mighty honour they promised him in reward
thereof.

But of these evil wiles naught at all knew Sigurd, for
he might not deal with his shapen fate, nor the measure
of his life-days, neither deemed he that he was worthy of
such things at their hands.

So Guttorm went in to Sigurd the next morning as he
lay upon his bed, yet durst he not do aught against him,
but shrank back out again; yea, and even so he fared a
second time, for so bright and eager were the eyes of
Sigurd that few durst look upon him. But the third time he
went in, and there lay Sigurd asleep; then Guttorm drew
his sword and thrust Sigurd through in such wise that the
sword point smote into the bed beneath him; then Sigurd
awoke with that wound, and Guttorm gat him unto the
door; but therewith Sigurd caught up the sword Gram, and
cast it after him, and it smote him on the back, and
struck him asunder in the midst, so that the feet of
him fell one way, and the head and hands back into the
chamber.

Now Gudrun lay asleep on Sigurd's bosom, but she woke
up unto woe that may not be told of, all swimming in the
blood of him, and in such wise did she bewail her with

weeping and words of sorrow, that Sigurd rose up on the bolster, and spake.

"Weep not," said he, "for thy brothers live for thy delight; but a young son have I, too young to be ware of his foes; and an ill turn have these played against their own fortune; for never will they get a mightier brother-in-law to ride abroad with them; nay, nor a better son to their sister, than this one, if he may grow to man's estate. Lo, now is that come to pass which was foretold me long ago, but from mine eyes has it been hidden, for none may fight against his fate and prevail. Behold this has Brynhild brought to pass, even she who loves me before all men; but this may I swear, that never have I wrought ill to Gunnar, but rather have ever held fast to my oath with him, nor was I ever too much a friend to his wife. And now if I had been forewarned, and had been afoot with my weapons, then should many a man have lost his life or ever I had fallen, and all those brethren should have been slain, and a harder work would the slaying of me have been than the slaying of the mightiest bull or the mightiest boar of the wild-wood."

And even therewithal life left the King; but Gudrun moaned and drew a weary breath, and Brynhild heard it, and laughed when she heard her moaning.

Then said Gunnar, "Thou laughest not because thy heart-roots are gladdened, or else why doth thy visage wax so wan? Sure an evil creature thou art; most like thou art nigh to thy death! Lo now, how meet would it be for thee to behold thy brother Atli slain before thine eyes, and that thou shouldst stand over him dead; whereas we must needs now stand over our brother-in-law in such a case—our brother-in-law and our brother's bane."

She answered, "None need mock at the measure of slaughter being unfulfilled; yet heedeth not Atli your wrath or your threats; yea, he shall live longer than ye, and be a mightier man."

Hogni spake and said, "Now hath come to pass the sooth-saying of Brynhild; an ill work not to be atoned for."

And Gudrun said, "My kinsmen have slain my husband; but ye, when ye next ride to the war and are come into the

battle, then shall ye look about and see that Sigurd is neither
on the right hand nor the left, and ye shall know that he
was your good-hap and your strength; and if he had lived
and had sons, then should ye have been strengthened by
his offspring and his kin."

## CHAPTER XXXI

### Of the Lamentation of Gudrun Over Sigurd Dead, as it is Told in the Ancient Songs[1]

> Gudrun of old days
> Drew near to dying
> As she sat in sorrow
> Over Sigurd;
> Yet she sighed not
> Nor smote hand on hand,
> Nor wailed she aught
> As other women.
>
> Then went earls to her,
> Full of all wisdom,
> Fain help to deal
> To her dreadful heart:
> Hushed was Gudrun
> Of wail, or greeting,
> But with a heavy woe
> Was her heart a-breaking.
>
> Bright and fair
> Sat the great earls' brides,
> Gold arrayed
> Before Gudrun;
> Each told the tale
> Of her great trouble,
> The bitterest bale
> She erst abode.

[1] This chapter is the Eddaic poem, called the first Lay of Gudrun, inserted here by the translators.

Then spake Giaflaug,
Guiki's sister:
" Lo upon earth
I live most loveless
Who of five mates
Must see the ending,
Of daughters twain
And three sisters,
Of brethren eight,
And abide behind lonely."

Naught gat Gudrun
Of wail and greeting,
So heavy was she
For her dead husband,
So dreadful-hearted
For the King laid dead there.

Then spake Herborg
Queen of Hunland—
" Crueller tale
Have I to tell of,
Of my seven sons
Down in the Southlands,
And the eighth man, my mate,
Felled in the death-mead.

" Father and mother,
And four brothers,
On the wide sea
The winds and death played with;
The billows beat
On the bulwark boards.

" Alone must I sing o'er them,
Alone must I array them,
Alone must my hands deal with
Their departing;
And all this was
In one season's wearing,

And none was left
For love or solace.

" Then was I bound
A prey of the battle,
When that same season
Wore to its ending;
As a tiring may
Must I bind the shoon
Of the duke's high dame,
Every day at dawning.

" From her jealous hate
Gat I heavy mocking,
Cruel lashes
She laid upon me,
Never met I
Better master
Or mistress worser
In all the wide world."

Naught gat Gudrun
Of wail or greeting,
So heavy was she
For her dead husband,
So dreadful-hearted
For the King laid dead there.

Then spake Gullrond,
Guiki's daughter—
" O foster-mother,
Wise as thou mayst be,
Naught canst thou better
The young wife's bale."
And she bade uncover
The dead King's corpse.

She swept the sheet
Away from Sigurd,
And turned his cheek

Towards his wife's knees—
"Look on thy loved one
Lay lips to his lips,
E'en as thou wert clinging
To thy king alive yet!"

Once looked Gudrun—
One look only,
And saw her lord's locks
Lying all bloody,
The great man's eyes
Glazed and deadly,
And his heart's bulwark
Broken by sword-edge.

Back then sank Gudrun,
Back on the bolster,
Loosed was her head array,
Red did her cheeks grow,
And the rain-drops ran
Down over her knees.

Then wept Gudrun,
Giuki's daughter,
So that the tears flowed
Through the pillow;
As the geese withal
That were in the homefield,
The fair fowls the may owned,
Fell a-screaming.

Then spake Gullrond,
Giuki's daughter—
"Surely knew I
No love like your love
Among all men,
On the mould abiding;
Naught wouldst thou joy in
Without or within doors,

O my sister,
Save beside Sigurd."

Then spake Gudrun,
Giuki's daughter—
" Such was my Sigurd
Among the sons of Giuki,
As is the king leek
O'er the low grass waxing,
Or a bright stone
Strung on band,
Or a pearl of price
On a prince's brow.

" Once was I counted
By the king's warriors
Higher than any
Of Herjan's mays;
Now am I as little
As the leaf may be,
Amid wind-swept wood
Now when dead he lieth.

" I miss from my seat,
I miss from my bed,
My darling of sweet speech.
Wrought the sons of Giuki,
Wrought the sons of Giuki,
This sore sorrow,
Yea, for their sister,
Most sore sorrow.

" So may your lands
Lie waste on all sides,
As ye have broken
Your bounden oaths!
Ne'er shalt thou, Gunnar,
The gold have joy of,
The dear-bought rings
Shall drag thee to death,

Whereon thou swarest
Oath unto Sigurd.

" Ah, in the days by-gone
Great mirth in the homefield
When my Sigurd
Set saddle on Grani,
And they went their ways
For the wooing of Brynhild!
An ill day, an ill woman,
And most ill hap!"

Then spake Brynhild,
Budli's daughter—
" May the woman lack
Both love and children,
Who gained greeting
For thee, O Gudrun!
Who gave thee this morning
Many words!"

Then spake Gullrond,
Giuki's daughter—
" Hold peace of such words
Thou hated of all folk!
The bane of brave men
Hast thou been ever,
All waves of ill
Wash over thy mind,
To seven great kings
Hast thou been a sore sorrow,
And the death of good will
To wives and women."

Then spake Brynhild,
Budli's daughter—
" None but Atli
Brought bale upon us,
My very brother
Born of Budli.

" When we saw in the hall
Of the Hunnish people
The gold a-gleaming
On the kingly Giukings;
I have paid for that faring
Oft and full,
And for the sight
That then I saw."


By a pillar she stood
And strained its wood to her;
From the eyes of Brynhild,
Budli's daughter,
Flashed out fire,
And she snorted forth venom,
As the sore wounds she gazed on
Of the dead-slain Sigurd.


## CHAPTER XXXII

### OF THE ENDING OF BRYNHILD

AND now none might know for what cause Brynhild must
bewail with weeping for what she had prayed for with
laughter: but she spake—

" Such a dream I had, Gunnar, as that my bed was acold,
and that thou didst ride into the hands of thy foes: lo
now, ill shall it go with thee and all thy kin, O ye breakers
of oaths; for on the day thou slayedst him, dimly didst
thou remember how thou didst blend thy blood with the
blood of Sigurd, and with an ill reward hast thou rewarded
him for all that he did well to thee; whereas he gave unto
thee to be the mightiest of men; and well was it proven
how fast he held to his oath sworn, when he came to me
and laid betwixt us the sharp edged sword that in venom
had been made hard. All too soon did ye fall to working
wrong against him and against me, whenas I abode at
home with my father, and had all that I would, and had no
will that any one of you should be any of mine, as ye rode

into our garth, ye three kings together; but then Atli led
me apart privily, and asked me if I would not have him
who rode Grani;—yea, a man nowise like unto you; but
in those days I plighted myself to the son of King Sigmund
and no other; and lo, now, no better shall ye fare for the
death of me."

Then rose up Gunnar, and laid his arms about her neck,
and besought her to live and have wealth from him; and
all others in likewise letted her from dying; but she thrust
them all from her, and said that it was not the part of any
to let her in that which was her will.

Then Gunnar called to Hogni, and prayed him for counsel, and bade him go to her, and see if he might perchance
soften her dreadful heart, saying withal, that now they
had need enough on their hands in the slaking of her
grief, till time might get over.

But Hogni answered, "Nay, let no man hinder her from
dying; for no gain will she be to us, nor has she been
gainsome since she came hither!"

Now she bade bring forth much gold, and bade all those
come thither who would have wealth: then she caught up
a sword, and thrust it under her armpit, and sank aside
upon the pillows, and said, "Come, take gold whoso
will!"

But all held their peace, and she said, "Take the gold,
and be glad thereof!"

And therewith she spake unto Gunnar, "Now for a little
while will I tell of that which shall come to pass hereafter;
for speedily shall ye be at one again with Gudrun by the
rede of Grimhild the Wise-wife; and the daughter of Gudrun and Sigurd shall be called Swanhild, the fairest of all
women born. Gudrun shall be given to Atli, yet not with her
good will. Thou shalt be fain to get Oddrun, but that shall
Atli forbid thee; but privily shall ye meet, and much shall
she love thee. Atli shall bewray thee, and cast thee into
a worm-close, and thereafter shall Atli and his sons be slain,
and Gudrun shall be their slayer; and afterwards shall the
great waves bear her to the burg of King Jonakr, to whom
she shall bear sons of great fame: Swanhild shall be sent
from the land and given to King Jormunrek; and her shall

bite the rede of Bikki, and therewithal is the kin of you clean gone; and more sorrows therewith for Gudrun.

"And now I pray thee, Gunnar, one last boon.—Let make a great bale on the plain meads for all of us; for me, and for Sigurd, and for those who were slain with him, and let that be covered over with cloth dyed red by the folk of the Gauls,[1] and burn me thereon on one side of the King of the Huns, and on the other those men of mine, two at the head and two at the feet, and two hawks withal; and even so is all shared equally; and lay there betwixt us a drawn sword, as in the other days when we twain stepped into one bed together; and then may we have the name of man and wife, nor shall the door swing to at the heel of him as I go behind him. Nor shall that be a niggard company if there follow him those five bond-women and eight bondmen, whom my father gave me, and those burn there withal who were slain with Sigurd.

"Now more yet would I say, but for my wounds, but my life-breath flits; the wounds open,—yet have I said sooth."

Now is the dead corpse of Sigurd arrayed in olden wise, and a mighty bale is raised, and when it was somewhat kindled, there was laid thereon the dead corpse of Sigurd Fafnir's-bane, and his son of three winters whom Brynhild had let slay, and Guttorm withal; and when the bale was all ablaze, thereunto was Brynhild borne out, when she had spoken with her bower-maidens, and bid them take the gold that she would give; and then died Brynhild, and was burned there by the side of Sigurd, and thus their life-days ended.

## CHAPTER XXXIII

### GUDRUN WEDDED TO ATLI

Now so it is, that whoso heareth these tidings sayeth, that no such an one as was Sigurd was left behind him in the world, nor ever was such a man brought forth because of all the worth of him, nor may his name ever minish

[1] The original has *raudu manna blodi,* red-dyed in the blood of men; the Sagaman's original error in dealing with the word *Valaript* in the corresponding passage of the short lay of Sigurd.—*Tr.*

by eld in the Dutch Tongue nor in all the Northern Lands, while the world standeth fast.

The story tells that, on a day, as Gudrun sat in her bower, she fell to saying, "Better was life in those days when I had Sigurd; he who was far above other men as gold is above iron, or the leek over other grass of the field, or the hart over other wild things; until my brethren begrudged me such a man, the first and best of all men; and so they might not sleep or they had slain him. Huge clamour made Grani when he saw his master and lord sore wounded, and then I spoke to him even as with a man, but he fell drooping down to the earth, for he knew that Sigurd was slain."

Thereafter Gudrun gat her gone into the wild woods, and heard on all ways round about her the howling of wolves, and deemed death a merrier thing than life. Then she went till she came to the hall of King Alf, and sat there in Denmark with Thora, the daughter of Hakon, for seven seasons, and abode with good welcome. And she set forth her needlework before her, and did thereinto many deeds and great, and fair plays after the fashion of those days, swords and byrnies, and all the gear of kings, and the ship of King Sigmund sailing along the land; yea, and they wrought there, how they fought, Sigar and Siggeir, south in Fion. Such was their disport; and now Gudrun was somewhat solaced of her grief.

So Grimhild comes to hear where Gudrun has take up her abode, and she calls her sons to talk with her, and asks whether they will make atonement to Gudrun for her son and her husband, and said that it was but meet and right to do so.

Then Gunnar spake, and said that he would atone for her sorrows with gold.

So they send for their friends, and array their horses, their helms, and their shields, and their byrnes, and all their war-gear; and their journey was furnished forth in the noblest wise, and no champion who was of the great men might abide at home; and their horses were clad in mailcoats, and every knight of them had his helm done over with gold or with silver.

Grimhild was of their company, for she said that their errand would never be brought fairly to pass if she sat at home.

There were well five hundred men, and noble men rode with them. There was Waldemar of Denmark, and Eymod and Jarisleif withal. So they went into the hall of King Alf, and there abode them the Longbeards, and Franks, and Saxons; they fared with all their war-gear, and had over them red fur-coats. Even as the song says—

> Byrnies short cut,
> Strong helms hammered,
> Girt with good swords,
> Red hair gleaming.

They were fain to choose good gifts for their sister, and spake softly to her, but in none of them would she trow. Then Gunnar brought unto her a drink mingled with hurtful things, and this she must needs drink, and with the drinking thereof she had no more memory of their guilt against her.

But in that drink was blended the might of the earth and the sea with the blood of her son; and in that horn were all letters cut and reddened with blood, as is said hereunder—

> On the horn's face were there
> All the kin of letters
> Cut aright and reddened,
> How should I rede them rightly?
> The ling-fish long
> Of the land of Hadding,
> Wheat-ears unshorn,
> And wild things' inwards.

> In that beer were mingled
> Many ills together,
> Blood of all the wood
> And brown-burnt acorns,
> The black dew of the hearth,
> The God-doomed dead beast's inwards,

And the swine's liver sodden
Because all wrongs that deadens.

And so now, when their hearts are brought anigh to each other, great cheer they made: then came Grimhild to Gudrun, and spake—

"All hail to thee, daughter! I give thee gold and all kinds of good things to take to thee after thy father, dear-bought rings and bed-gear of the maids of the Huns, the most courteous and well dight of all women; and thus is thy husband atoned for: and thereafter shalt thou be given to Atli, the mighty king, and be mistress of all his might. Cast not all thy friends aside for one man's sake, but do according to our bidding."

Gudrun answers, "Never will I wed Atli the King; unseemly it is for us to get offspring betwixt us."

Grimhild says, "Nourish not thy wrath; it shall be to thee as if Sigurd and Sigmund were alive when thou hast borne sons."

Gudrun says, "I cannot take my heart from thoughts of him, for he was the first of all men."

Grimhild says, "So it is shapen that thou must have this king and none else."

Says Gudrun, "Give not this man to me, for an evil thing shall come upon thy kin from him, and to his own sons shall he deal evil, and be rewarded with a grim revenge thereafter."

Then waxed Grimhild fell at those words, and spake, "Do even as we bid thee, and take therefore great honour, and our friendship, and the steads withal called Vinbjorg and Valbjorg."

And such might was in the words of her, that even so must it come to pass.

Then Gudrun spake, "Thus then must it needs befall, howsoever against the will of me, and for little joy shall it be and for great grief."

Then men leaped on their horses, and their women were set in wains. So they fared four days a-riding and other four a-shipboard, and yet four more again by land and road, till at the last they came to a certain high-built hall; then came to meet Gudrun many folk thronging; and an exceedingly goodly feast was there made, even as the word had gone between either kin, and it passed forth in most proud and stately wise. And at that feast drinks Atli his bridal with Gudrun; but never did her heart laugh on him, and little sweet and kind was their life together.

## CHAPTER XXXIV

### ATLI BIDS THE GIUKINGS TO HIM

Now tells the tale that on a night King Atli woke from sleep and spake to Gudrun—

"Medreamed," said he, "that thou didst thrust me through with a sword."

Then Gudrun areded the dream, and said that it betokened fire, whenas folk dreamed of iron. "It befalls of thy pride belike, in that thou deemest thyself the first of men."

Atli said, "Moreover I dreamed that here waxed two sorb-tree[1] saplings, and fain I was that they should have no scathe of me; then these were riven up by the roots and reddened with blood, and borne to the bench, and I was bidden eat thereof.

"Yea, yet again I dreamed that two hawks flew from my hand hungry and unfed, and fared to hell, and meseemed their hearts were mingled with honey, and that I ate thereof.

"And then again I dreamed that two fair whelps lay before me yelling aloud, and that the flesh of them I ate, though my will went not with the eating."

Gudrun says, "Nowise good are these dreams, yet shall they come to pass; surely thy sons are nigh to death, and many heavy things shall fall upon us."

"Yet again I dreamed," said he, "and methought I lay in a bath, and folk took counsel to slay me."

Now these things wear away with time, but in nowise was their life together fond.

[1] Service-tree; *pyrus sorbus domestica,* or *p. s. tormentalis.*

Now falls Atli to thinking of where may be gotten that plenteous gold which Sigurd had owned, but King Gunnar and his brethren were lords thereof now.

Atli was a great king and mighty, wise, and a lord of many men; and now he falls to counsel with his folk as to the ways of them.   He wotted well that Gunnar and his brethren had more wealth than any others might have; and so he falls to the rede of sending men to them, and bidding them to a great feast, and honouring them in diverse wise, and the chief of those messengers was hight Vingi.

Now the queen wots of their conspiring, and misdoubts her that this would mean some beguiling of her brethren: so she cut runes, and took a gold ring, and knit therein a wolf's hair, and gave it into the hands of the king's messengers.

Thereafter they go their ways according to the king's bidding; and or ever they came aland Vingi beheld the runes, and turned them about in such a wise as if Gudrun prayed her brethren in her runes to go meet King Atli.

Thereafter they came to the hall of King Gunnar, and had good welcome at his hands, and great fires were made for them, and in great joyance they drank of the best of drink.

Then spake Vingi, "King Atli sends me hither, and in fain that ye go to his house and home in all glory, and take of him exceeding honours, helms and shields, swords and byrnies, gold and goodly raiment, horses, hosts of war, and great and wide lands, for, saith he, he is fainest of all things to bestow his realm and lordship upon you."

Then Gunnar turned his head aside, and spoke to Hogni—
"In what wise shall we take this bidding? might and wealth he bids us take; but no kings know I who have so much gold as we have, whereas we have all the hoard which lay once on Gnitaheath; and great are our chambers, and full of gold, and weapons for smiting, and all kinds of raiment of war, and well I wot that amidst all men my horse is the best, and my sword the sharpest, and my gold the most glorious."

Hogni answers, "A marvel is it to me of his bidding,

for seldom hath he done in such a wise, and ill-counselled will it be to wend to him; lo now, when I saw those dear-bought things the king sends us I wondered to behold a wolf's hair knit to a certain gold ring; belike Gudrun deems him to be minded as a wolf towards us, and will have naught of our faring."

But withal Vingi shows him the runes which he said Gudrun had sent.

Now the most of folk go to bed, but these drank on still with certain others; and Kostbera, the wife of Hogni, the fairest of women, came to them, and looked on the runes.

But the wife of Gunnar was Glaumvor, a great-hearted wife.

So these twain poured out, and the kings drank, and were exceeding drunken, and Vingi notes it, and says—

" Naught may I hide that King Atli is heavy of foot and over-old for the warding of his realm; but his sons are young and of no account: now will he give you rule over his realms while they are yet thus young, and most fain will he be that ye have the joy thereof before all others."

Now so it befell both that Gunnar was drunk, and that great dominion was held out to him, nor might he work against the fate shapen for him; so he gave his word to go, and tells Hogni his brother thereof.

But he answered, " Thy word given must even stand now, nor will I fail to follow thee, but most loth am I to this journey."

## CHAPTER XXXV

### The Dreams of the Wives of the Giukings

So when men had drunk their fill, they fared to sleep; then falls Kostbera to beholding the runes, and spelling over the letters, and sees that beneath were other things cut and that the runes are guileful; yet because of her wisdom she had skill to read them aright. So then she goes to bed by her husband; but when they awoke, she spake unto Hogni—

" Thou art minded to wend away from home—ill-coun-selled is that; abide till another time! Scarce a keen reader of runes art thou, if thou deemest thou hast beheld in them the bidding of thy sister to this journey: lo, I read the runes, and had marvel of so wise a woman as Gud-run is, that she should have miscut them; but that which lieth underneath beareth your bane with it,—yea, either she lacked a letter, or others have dealt guilefully with the runes.

"And now hearken to my dream; for therein methought there fell in upon us here a river exceeding strong, and brake up the timbers of the hall."

He answered, "Full oft are ye evil of mind, ye women, but for me, I was not made in such wise as to meet men with evil who deserve no evil; belike he will give us good welcome."

She answered, "Well, the thing must ye yourselves prove, but no friendship follows this bidding:—but yet again I dreamed that another river fell in here with a great and grimly rush, and tore up the dais of the hall, and brake the legs of both you brethren; surely that betokeneth some-what."

He answers, "Meadows along our way, whereas thou didst dream of the river; for when we go through the meadows, plentifully doth the seeds of the hay hang about our legs."

"Again I dreamed," she says, "that thy cloak was afire, and that the flame blazed up above the hall."

Says he, "Well, I wot what that shall betoken; here lieth my fair-dyed raiment, and it shall burn and blaze, whereas thou dreamedst of the cloak."

"Methought a bear came in," she says, "and brake up the king's high-seat, and shook his paws in such a wise that we were all adrad thereat, and he gat us all together into the mouth of him, so that we might avail us naught, and thereof fell great horror on us."

He answered, "Some great storm will befall, whereas thou hadst a white bear in thy mind."

"An erne methought came in," she says, "and swept adown the hall, and drenched me and all of us with blood, and ill shall that betoken, for methought it was the double of King Atli."

He answered, "Full oft do we slaughter beasts freely, and smite down great neat for our cheer, and the dream of the erne has but to do with oxen; yea, Atli is heart-whole toward us."

And therewithal they cease this talk.

## CHAPTER XXXVI

### Of the Journey of the Giukings to King Atli

Now tells the tale of Gunnar, that in the same wise it fared with him; for when they awoke, Glaumvor his wife told him many dreams which seemed to her like to betoken guile coming; but Gunnar areded them all in other wise.

"This was one of them," said she; "methought a bloody sword was borne into the hall here, wherewith thou wert thrust through, and at either end of that sword wolves howled."

The king answered, "Cur dogs shall bite me belike; blood-stained weapons oft betoken dogs' snappings."

She said, "Yet again I dreamed—that women came in, heavy and drooping, and chose thee for their mate; mayhappen these would be thy fateful women."

He answered, "Hard to arede is this, and none may set aside the fated measure of his days, nor is it unlike that my time is short."

So in the morning they arose, and were minded for the journey, but some letted them herein.

Then cried Gunnar to the man who is called Fjornir—

"Arise, and give us to drink goodly wine from great tuns, because mayhappen this shall be very last of all our feasts; for belike if we die the old wolf shall come by the gold, and that bear shall nowise spare the bite of his war-tusks."

Then all the folk of his household brought them on their way weeping.

The son of Hogni said—

"Fare ye well with merry tide."

The more part of their folk were left behind; Solar and

Gnœvar, the sons of Hogni, fared with them, and a certain great champion, named Orkning, who was the brother of Kostbera.

So folk followed them down to the ships, and all letted them of their journey, but attained to naught therein.

Then spake Glaumvor, and said—

"O Vingi, most like that great ill hap will come of thy coming and mighty and evil things shall betide in thy travelling."

He answered, "Hearken to my answer; that I lie not aught: and may the high gallows and all things of grame have me, if I lie one word!"

Then cried Kostbera, "Fare ye well with merry days."

And Hogni answered, "Be glad of heart, howsoever it may fare with us!"

And therewith they parted, each to their own fate. Then away they rowed, so hard and fast, that well-nigh the half of the keel slipped away from the ship, and so hard they laid on to the oars that thole and gunwale brake.

But when they came aland they made their ship fast, and then they rode awhile on their noble steeds through the murk wild-wood.

And now they behold the king's army, and huge uproar, and the clatter of weapons they hear from thence; and they see there a mighty host of men, and the manifold array of them, even as they wrought there: and all the gates of the burg were full of men.

So they rode up to the burg, and the gates thereof were shut; then Hogni brake open the gates, and therewith they ride into the burg.

Then spake Vingi, "Well might ye have left this deed undone; go to now, bide ye here while I go seek your gallows-tree! Softly and sweetly I bade you hither, but an evil thing abode thereunder; short while to bide ere ye are tied up to that same tree!"

Hogni answered, "None the more shall we waver for that cause; for little methinks have we shrunk aback whenas men fell to fight; and naught shall it avail thee to make us afeard, —and for an ill fate hast thou wrought."

And therewith they cast him down to earth, and smote him with their axe-hammers till he died.

## CHAPTER XXXVII

### The Battle in the Burg of King Atli

THEN they rode unto the king's hall, and King Atli arrayed his host for battle, and the ranks were so set forth that a certain wall there was betwixt them and the brethren.

"Welcome hither," said he. "Deliver unto me that plenteous gold which is mine of right; even the wealth which Sigurd once owned, and which is now Gudrun's of right."

Gunnar answered, "Never gettest thou that wealth; and men of might must thou meet here, or ever we lay by life if thou wilt deal with us in battle: ah, belike thou settest forth this feast like a great man, and wouldst not hold thine hand from erne and wolf!"

"Long ago I had it in my mind," said Atli, "to take the lives of you, and be lord of the gold, and reward you for that deed of shame, wherein ye beguiled the best of all your affinity; but now shall I revenge him."

Hogni answered, "Little will it avail to lie long brooding over that rede, leaving the work undone."

And therewith they fell to hard fighting, at the first brunt with shot.

But therewithal came the tidings to Gudrun, and when she heard thereof she grew exceeding wroth, and cast her mantle from her, and ran out and greeted those new-comers, and kissed her brethren, and showed them all love,—and the last of all greetings was that betwixt them.

Then said she, "I thought I had set forth counsels whereby ye should not come hither, but none may deal with his shapen fate." And withal she said, "Will it avail aught to seek for peace?"

But stoutly and grimly they said nay thereto. So she sees that the game goeth sorely against her brethren, and she gathers to her great stoutness of heart, and does on her a mail-coat and takes to her a sword, and fights by her brethren, and goes as far forward as the bravest of manfolk: and all spoke in one wise that never saw any fairer defence than in her.

Now the men fell thick, and far before all others was

the fighting of those brethren, and the battle endured a long while unto midday; Gunnar and Hogni went right through the folk of Atli, and so tells the tale that all the mead ran red with blood; the sons of Hogni withal set on stoutly.

Then spake Atli the king, " A fair host and a great have we, and mighty champions withal, and yet have many of us fallen, and but evil am I apaid in that nineteen of my champions are slain, and but six left alive."

And therewithal was there a lull in the battle.

Then spake Atli the king, " Four brethren were we, and now am I left alone; great affinity I gat to me, and deemed my fortune well sped thereby; a wife I had, fair and wise, high of mind, and great of heart; but no joyance may I have of her wisdom, for little peace is betwixt us,—but ye—ye have slain many of my kin, and beguiled me of realm and riches, and for the greatest of all woes have slain my sister withal."

Quoth Hogni, " Why babblest thou thus? thou wert the first to break the peace. Thou didst take my kinswoman and pine her to death by hunger, and didst murder her, and take her wealth; an ugly deed for a king!—meet for mocking and laughter I deem it, that thou must needs make long tale of thy woes; rather will I give thanks to the Gods that thou fallest into ill."


## CHAPTER XXXVIII

### Of the Slaying of the Giukings

Now King Atli eggs on his folk to set on fiercely, and eagerly they fight; but the Guikings fell on so hard that King Atli gave back into the hall, and within doors was the fight, and fierce beyond all fights.

That battle was the death of many a man, but such was the ending thereof, that there fell all the folk of those brethren, and they twain alone stood upon their feet, and yet many more must fare to hell first before their weapons.

And now they fell on Gunnar the king, and because of the host of men that set on him was hand laid on him, and he was cast into fetters; afterwards fought Hogni, with the stoutest heart and the greatest manlihood; and he felled to earth twenty of the stoutest of the champions of King Atli, and many he thrust into the fire that burnt amidst the hall, and all were of one accord that such a man might scarce be seen; yet in the end was he borne down by many and taken.

Then said King Atli, "A marvellous thing how many men have gone their ways before him! Cut the heart from out of him, and let that be his bane!"

Hogni said, "Do according to thy will; merrily will I abide whatso thou wilt do against me; and thou shalt see that my heart is not adrad, for hard matters have I made trial of ere now, and all things that may try a man was I fain to bear, whiles yet I was unhurt; but now sorely am I hurt, and thou alone henceforth will bear mastery in our dealings together."

Then spake a counsellor of King Atli, "Better rede I see thereto; take we the thrall Hjalli, and give respite to Hogni; for this thrall is made to die, since the longer he lives the less worth shall he be."

The thrall hearkened, and cried out aloft, and fled away anywhither where he might hope for shelter, crying out that a hard portion was his because of their strife and wild doings, and an ill day for him whereon he must be dragged to death from his sweet life and his swine-keeping. But they caught him, and turned a knife against him, and he yelled and screamed or ever he felt the point thereof.

Then in such wise spake Hogni as a man seldom speaketh who is fallen into hard need, for he prayed for the thrall's life, and said that these shrieks he could not away with, and that it were a lesser matter to him to play out the play to the end; and therewithal the thrall gat his life as for that time: but Gunnar and Hogni are both laid in fetters.

Then spake King Atli with Gunnar the king, and bade him tell out concerning the gold, and where it was, if he would have his life.

But he answered, "Nay, first will I behold the bloody heart of Hogni, my brother."

So now they caught hold of the thrall again, and cut the heart from out of him, and bore it unto King Gunnar, but he said—

"The faint heart of Hjalli may ye here behold, little like the proud heart of Hogni, for as much as it trembleth now, more by the half it trembled whenas it lay in the breast of him."

So now they fell on Hogni even as Atli urged them, and cut the heart from out of him, but such was the might of his manhood, that he laughed while he abode that torment, and all wondered at his worth, and in perpetual memory is it held sithence.

Then they showed it to Gunnar, and he said—

"The mighty heart of Hogni, little like the faint heart of Hjalli, for little as it trembleth now, less it trembled whenas in his breast it lay! But now, O Atli, even as we die so shalt thou die; and lo, I alone wot where the gold is, nor shall Hogni be to tell thereof now; to and fro played the matter in my mind whiles we both lived, but now have I myself determined for myself, and the Rhine river shall rule over the gold, rather than that the Huns shall bear it on the hands of them."

Then said King Atli, "Have away the bondsman;" and so they did.

But Gudrun called to her men, and came to Atli, and said—

"May it fare ill with thee now and from henceforth, even as thou hast ill held to thy word with me!"

So Gunnar was cast into a worm-close, and many worms abode him there, and his hands were fast bound; but Gudrun sent him a harp, and in such wise did he set forth his craft, that wisely he smote the harp, smiting it with his toes, and so excellently well he played, that few deemed they had heard such playing, even when the hand had done it. And with such might and power he played, that all the worms fell asleep in the end, save one adder only, great and evil of aspect, that crept unto him and thrust its sting into him until it smote his heart; and in such wise with great hardihood he ended his life days.

## CHAPTER XXXIX

### The End of Atli and his Kin and Folk

Now thought Atli the King that he had gained a mighty victory, and spake to Gudrun even as mocking her greatly, or as making himself great before her. "Gudrun," saith he, "thus hast thou lost thy brethren, and thy very self hast brought it about."

She answers, "In good liking livest thou, whereas thou thrustest these slayings before me, but mayhappen thou wilt rue it, when thou hast tried what is to come hereafter; and of all I have, the longest-lived matter shall be the memory of thy cruel heart, nor shall it go well with thee whiles I live."

He answered and said, "Let there be peace betwixt us; I will atone for thy brethren with gold and dear-bought things, even as thy heart may wish."

She answers, "Hard for a long while have I been in our dealings together, and now I say, that while Hogni was yet alive thou mightest have brought it to pass; but now mayest thou never atone for my brethren in my heart; yet oft must we women be overborne by the might of you men; and now are all my kindred dead and gone, and thou alone art left to rule over me: wherefore now this is my counsel that we make a great feast, wherein I will hold the funeral of my brother and of thy kindred withal."

In such wise did she make herself soft and kind in words, though far other things forsooth lay thereunder, but he hearkened to her gladly, and trusted in her words, whereas she made herself sweet of speech.

So Gudrun held the funeral feast for her brethren, and King Atli for his men, and exceeding proud and great was this feast.

But Gudrun forgat not her woe, but brooded over it, how she might work some mighty shame against the king; and at nightfall she took to her the sons of King Atli and her as they played about the floor; the younglings waxed heavy of cheer, and asked what she would with them.

"Ask me not," she said; "ye shall die, the twain of you!"

Then they answered, "Thou mayest do with thy children even as thou wilt, nor shall any hinder thee, but shame there is to thee in the doing of this deed."

Yet for all that she cut the throats of them.

Then the king asked where his sons were, and Gudrun answered, "I will tell thee, and gladden thine heart by the telling; lo now, thou didst make a great woe spring up for me in the slaying of my brethren; now hearken and hear my rede and my deed; thou hast lost thy sons, and their heads are become beakers on the board here, and thou thyself hast drunken the blood of them blended with wine; and their hearts I took and roasted them on a spit, and thou hast eaten thereof."

King Atli answered, "Grim art thou in that thou hast murdered thy sons, and given me their flesh to eat, and little space passes betwixt ill deed of thine and ill deed."

Gudrun said, "My heart is set on the doing to thee of as great shame as may be; never shall the measure of ill be full to such a king as thou art."

The king said: "Worser deeds hast thou done than men have to tell of, and great unwisdom is there in such fearful redes; most meet art thou to be burned on bale when thou hast first been smitten to death with stones, for in such wise wouldst thou have what thou hast gone a weary way to seek."

She answered, "Thine own death thou foretellest, but another death is fated for me."

And many other words they spake in their wrath.

Now Hogni had a son left alive, hight Niblung, and great wrath of heart he bare against King Atli; and he did Gudrun to wit that he would avenge his father. And she took his words well, and they fell to counsel together thereover, and she said it would be great goodhap if it might be brought about.

So on a night, when the king had drunken, he gat him to bed, and when he was laid asleep, thither to him came Gudrun and the son of Hogni.

Gudrun took a sword and thrust it through the breast of King Atli, and they both of them set their hands to the deed, both she and the son of Hogni.

Then Atli the king awoke with the wound, and cried out, "No need of binding or salving here!—who art thou who hast done the deed?"

Gudrun says, "Somewhat have I, Gudrun, wrought therein, and somewhat withal the son of Hogni."

Atli said, "Ill it beseemed to thee to do this, though somewhat of wrong was between us; for thou wert wedded to me by the rede of thy kin, and dower paid I for thee; yea, thirty goodly knights, and seemly maidens, and many men besides; and yet wert thou not content, but if thou shouldest rule over the lands King Budli owned: and thy mother-in-law full oft thou lettest sit a-weeping."

Gudrun said, "Many false words hast thou spoken, and of naught I account them; oft, indeed, was I fell of mood, but much didst thou add thereto. Full oft in this thy house did frays befall, and kin fought kin, and friend fought friend, and made themselves big one against the other; better days had I whenas I abode with Sigurd, when we slew kings, and took their wealth to us, but gave peace to whomso would, and the great men laid themselves under our hands, and might we gave to him of them who would have it; then I lost him, and a little thing was it that I should bear a widow's name, but the greatest of griefs that I should come to thee—I who had aforetime the noblest of all kings, while for thee, thou never barest out of the battle aught but the worser lot."

King Atli answered, "Naught true are thy words, nor will this our speech better the lot of either of us, for all is fallen now to naught; but now do to me in seemly wise, and array my dead corpse in noble fashion."

"Yea, that will I," she says, "and let make for thee a goodly grave, and build for thee a worthy abiding place of stone, and wrap thee in fair linen, and care for all that needful is."

So therewithal he died, and she did according to her word: and then they cast fire into the hall.

And when the folk and men of estate awoke amid that dread and trouble, naught would they abide the fire, but smote each the other down, and died in such wise; so there Atli the king, and all his folk, ended their life-days. But

Gudrun had no will to live longer after this deed so wrought, but nevertheless her ending day was not yet come upon her.

Now the Volsungs and the Giukings, as folk tell in tale, have been the greatest-hearted and the mightiest of all men, as ye may well behold written in the songs of old time.

But now with the tidings just told were these troubles stayed.

## CHAPTER XL

### How Gudrun cast herself into the Sea, but was brought ashore again

Gudrun had a daughter by Sigurd hight Swanhild; she was the fairest of all women, eager-eyed as her father, so that few durst look under the brows of her; and as far did she excel other woman-kind as the sun excels the other lights of heaven.

But on a day went Gudrun down to the sea, and caught up stones in her arms, and went out into the sea, for she had will to end her life. But mighty billows drave her forth along the sea, and by means of their upholding was she borne along till she came at the last to the burg of King Jonakr, a mighty king, and lord of many folk. And he took Gudrun to wife, and their children were Hamdir, and Sorli, and Erp; and there was Swanhild nourished withal.

## CHAPTER XLI

### Of the Wedding and Slaying of Swanhild

Jormunrek was the name of a mighty king of those days, and his son was called Randver. Now this king called his son to talk with him, and said, "Thou shalt fare on an errand of mine to King Jonakr, with my counsellor Bikki, for with King Jonakr is nourished Swanhild, the daughter of Sigurd Fafnir's-bane; and I know for sure that she is the fairest may dwelling under the sun of this world; her above all others would I have to my wife, and thou shalt go woo her for me."

Randver answered, "Meet and right, fair lord, that I should go on thine errands."

So the king set forth this journey in seemly wise, and they fare till they come to King Jonakr's abode, and behold Swanhild, and have many thoughts concerning the treasure of her goodliness.

But on a day Randver called the king to talk with him, and said, "Jormunrek the King would fain be thy brother-in-law, for he has heard tell of Swanhild, and his desire it is to have her to wife, nor may it be shown that she may be given to any mightier man than he is one."

The King says, "This is an alliance of great honour, for a man of fame he is."

Gudrun says, "A wavering trust, the trust in luck that it change not!"

Yet because of the king's furthering, and all the matters that went herewith, is the wooing accomplished; and Swanhild went to the ship with a goodly company, and sat in the stern beside the king's son.

Then spake Bikki to Randver, "How good and right it were if thou thyself had to wife so lovely a woman rather than the old man there."

Good seemed that word to the heart of the king's son, and he spake to her with sweet words, and she to him in like wise.

So they came aland and go unto the king, and Bikki said unto him, "Meet and right it is, lord, that thou shouldst know what is befallen, though hard it be to tell of, for the tale must be concerning thy beguiling, whereas thy son has gotten to him the full love of Swanhild, nor is she other than his harlot; but thou, let not the deed be unavenged."

Now many an ill rede had he given the king or this, but of all his ill redes did this sting home the most; and still would the king hearken to all his evil redes; wherefore he, who might nowise still the wrath within him, cried out that Randver should be taken and tied up to the gallows-tree.

And as he was led to the gallows he took his hawk and plucked the feathers from off it, and bade show it to his father; and when the king saw it, then he said, "Now may folk behold that he deemeth my honour to be gone away from me, even as the feathers of this hawk;" and therewith he bade deliver him from the gallows.

But in that while had Bikki wrought his will, and Randver was dead-slain.

And, moreover, Bikki spake, "Against none hast thou more wrongs to avenge thee of than against Swanhild; let her die a shameful death."

"Yea," said the king, "we will do after thy counsel."

So she was bound in the gate of the burg, and horses were driven at her to tread her down; but when she opened her eyes wide, then the horses durst not trample her; so when Bikki beheld that, he bade draw a bag over the head of her; and they did so, and therewith she lost her life.[1]

## CHAPTER XLII

### Gudrun sends her Sons to Avenge Swanhild

Now Gudrun heard of the slaying of Swanhild, and spake to her sons, "Why sit ye here in peace amid merry words, whereas Jormunrek hath slain your sister, and trodden her under foot of horses in shameful wise? No heart ye have in you like to Gunnar or Hogni; verily they would have avenged their kinswoman!"

Hamdir answered, "Little didst thou praise Gunnar and Hogni, whereas they slew Sigurd, and thou wert reddened in the blood of him, and ill were thy brethren avenged by the slaying of thine own sons: yet not so ill a deed were it for us to slay King Jormunrek, and so hard thou pushest us on to this that we may naught abide thy hard words."

Gudrun went about laughing now, and gave them to drink from mighty beakers, and thereafter she got for them great byrnies and good, and all other weed[1] of war.

Then spake Hamdir, "Lo now, this is our last parting, for thou shalt hear tidings of us, and drink one grave-ale[2] over us and over Swanhild."

---

[1] In the prose Edda the slaying of Swanhild is a spontaneous and sudden act on the part of the king. As he came back from hunting one day, there sat Swanhild washing her linen, and it came into the king's mind how that she was the cause of all his woe, so he and his men rode over her and slew ner.—*Tr.*    [1] Weed, clothing.    [2] Grave-ale, burial-feast.

So therewith they went their ways.

But Gudrun went unto her bower, with heart swollen with sorrow, and spake—

"To three men was I wedded, and first to Sigurd Fafnir's-bane, and he was bewrayed and slain, and of all griefs was that the greatest grief. Then was I given to King Atli, and so fell was my heart toward him that I slew in the fury of my grief his children and mine. Then gave I myself to the sea, but the billows thereof cast me out aland, and to this king then was I given; then gave I Swanhild away out of the land with mighty wealth; and lo my next greatest sorrow after Sigurd, for under horses' feet was she trodden and slain; but the grimmest and ugliest of woes was the casting of Gunnar into the Worm-close, and the hardest was the cutting of Hogni's heart from him.

"Ah, better would it be if Sigurd came to meet me, and I went my ways with him, for here bideth now behind with me neither son nor daughter to comfort me. Oh, mindest thou not, Sigurd, the words we spoke when we went into one bed together, that thou wouldst come and look on me; yea, even from thine abiding place among the dead?"

And thus had the words of her sorrow an end.

## CHAPTER XLIII

### The Latter End of all the Kin of the Giukings

Now telleth the tale concerning the sons of Gudrun, that she had arrayed their war-raiment in such wise, that no steel would bite thereon; and she bade them play not with stones, or other heavy matters, for that it would be to their scathe if they did so.

And now, as they went on their way, they met Erp, their brother, and asked him in what wise he would help them.

He answered, "Even as hand helps hand, or foot helps foot."

But that they deemed naught at all, and slew him there and then. Then they went their ways, nor was it long or ever Hamdir stumbled, and thrust down his hand to steady himself, and spake therewith—

"Naught but a true thing spake Erp, for now should I have fallen, had not hand been to steady me."

A little after Sorli stumbled, but turned about on his feet, and so stood, and spake—

"Yea now had I fallen, but that I steadied myself with both feet."

And they said they had done evilly with Erp their brother.

But on they fare till they come to the abode of King Jormunrek, and they went up to him and set on him forthwith, and Hamdir cut both hands from him and Sorli both feet. Then spake Hamdir—

"Off were the head if Erp were alive; our brother, whom we slew on the way, and found out our deed too late." Even as the Song says,—

> Off were the head
> If Erp were alive yet,
> Our brother the bold,
> Whom we slew by the way,
> The well-famed in warfare.

Now in this must they turn away from the words of their mother, whereas they had to deal with stones. For now men fell on them, and they defended themselves in good and manly wise, and were the scathe of many a man, nor would iron bite on them.

But there came thereto a certain man, old of aspect and one-eyed,[1] and he spake—

"No wise men are ye, whereas ye cannot bring these men to their end."

Then the king said, "Give us rede thereto, if thou canst."

He said, "Smite them to the death with stones."

In such wise was it done, for the stones flew thick and fast from every side, and that was the end of their life-days.

And now has come to an end the whole root and stem of the Giukings.[2]

---

[1] Odin; he ends the tale as he began it.
[2] "And now," etc., inserted by translators from the prose Edda; the stanza at the end from the Whetting of Gudrun.

Now may all earls
Be bettered in mind,
May the grief of all maidens
Ever be minished,
For this tale of trouble
So told to its ending.

CERTAIN SONGS
FROM
# THE ELDER EDDA
WHICH DEAL WITH
THE STORY OF THE VOLSUNGS

# CONTENTS

TRANSLATED BY EIRÍKR MAGNÚSSON AND WILLIAM MORRIS

# PART OF THE SECOND LAY
## OF
# HELGI  HUNDING'S-BANE[1]

HELGI wedded Sigrun, and they begat sons together, but Helgi lived not to be old; for Dag,[2] the son of Hogni, sacrificed to Odin, praying that he might avenge his father. So Odin lent Dag his spear, and Dag met Helgi, his brother-in-law, at a place called Fetter-grove, and thrust him through with that spear, and there fell Helgi dead, but Dag rode to Sevafell, and told Sigrun of the news.

> Loth am I, sister,
> Of sorrow to tell thee,
> For by hard need driven
> Have I drawn on thee greeting;
> This morning fell
> In Fetter-grove
> The king well deemed
> The best in the wide world,
> Yea, he who stood
> On the necks of the strong.

### SIGRUN

> All oaths once sworn
> Shall bite thee sore,
> The oaths that to Helgi
> Once thou swarest
> At the bright white
> Water of Lightening,[3]

[1] Only that part of the song is given which completes the episode of Helgi Hunding's-bane; the earlier part of the song differs little from the Saga.
[2] Hogni, the father of Dag and Sigrun, had been slain by Helgi in battle, and Helgi had given peace to, and taken oaths of Dag.
[3] One of the rivers of the under-world.

And at the cold rock
That the sea runneth over.

May the ship sweep not on
That should sweep at its swiftest,
Though the wind desired
Behind thee driveth!
May the horse never run
That should run at his most might
When from thy foe's face
Thou hast most need to flee!

May the sword never bite
That thou drawest from scabbard.
But if round thine head
In wrath it singeth!

Then should meet price be paid
For Helgi's slaying
When a wolf thou wert
Out in the wild-wood,
Empty of good things,
Empty of gladness,
With no meat for thy mouth
But dead men's corpses!

### Dag

With mad words thou ravest,
Thy wits are gone from thee,
When thou for thy brother
Such ill fate biddest;
Odin alone
Let all this bale loose,
Casting the strife-runes
'Twixt friends and kindred.

Rings of red gold
Will thy brother give thee,

And the stead of Vandil
And the lands of Vigdale;
Have half of the land
For thy sorrow's healing,
O ring-arrayed sweetling
For thee and thy sons!

### · SIGRUN

No more sit I happy
At Sevafell;
At day-dawn, at night
Naught love I my life
Till broad o'er the people
My lord's light breaketh;
Till his war-horse runneth
Beneath him hither,
Well wont to the gold bit—
Till my king I welcome.

In such wise did Helgi
Deal fear around
To all his foes
And all their friends
As when the goat runneth
Before the wolf's rage
Filled with mad fear
Down from the fell.

As high above all lords
Did Helgi bear him
As the ash-tree's glory
From the thorn ariseth,
Or as the fawn
With the dew-fall sprinkled
Is far above
All other wild things,
As his horns go gleaming
'Gainst the very heavens.

A barrow was raised above Helgi, but when he came to Valhall, then Odin bade him be lord of all things there, even as he; so Helgi sang—

> Now shalt thou, Hunding,
> For the help of each man
> Get ready the foot-bath,
> And kindle the fire;
> The hounds shalt thou bind
> And give heed to the horses,
> Give wash to the swine
> Ere to sleep thou goest.

A bondmaid of Sigrun went in the evening-tide by Helgi's mound, and there she saw how Helgi rode toward it with a great company; then she sang—

> It is vain things' beguiling
> That methinks I behold
> Or the ending of all things,
> As ye ride, O ye dead men,
> Smiting with spurs
> Your horses' sides?
> Or may dead warriors
> Wend their ways homeward?

### THE DEAD

> No vain things' beguiling
> Is that thou beholdest,
> Nor the ruin of all things;
> Though thou lookest upon us,
> Though we smite with spurs
> Our horses' sides;
> Rather dead warriors
> May wend their ways homeward.

Then went the bondmaid home, and told Sigrun, and sang—

Go out, Sigrun
From Sevafell,
If thou listest to look on
The lord of thy people!
For the mound is uncovered
Thither is Helgi come,
And his wounds are bleeding,
But the king thee biddeth
To come and stay
That stream of sorrow.

So Sigrun went into the mound to Helgi, and sang—

Now am I as fain
Of this fair meeting,
As are the hungry
Hawks of Odin,
When they wot of the slaying
Of the yet warm quarry,
Or bright with dew
See the day a-dawning.

Ah, I will kiss
My king laid lifeless,
Ere thou castest by
Thy blood-stained byrny.
O Helgi, thy hair
Is thick with death's rime,
With the dew of the dead
Is my love all dripping;
Dead-cold are the hands
Of the son of Hogni!
How for thee, O my king,
May I win healing?

HELGI

Thou alone, Sigrun
Of Sevafell,
Hast so done that Helgi

With grief's dew drippeth;
O clad in gold
Cruel tears thou weepest,
Bright May of the Southlands,
Or ever thou sleepest:
Each tear in blood falleth
On the breast of thy lord,
Cold-wet and bitter-sharp
Swollen with sorrow.

Ah, we shall drink
Dear draughts and lovely
Though we have lost
Both life and lands;
Neither shall any
Sing song of sorrow,
Though in my breast
Be wounds wide to behold:
For now are brides
In the mound abiding;
Kings' daughters sit
By us departed.

Now Sigrun arrayed a bed in the mound, and sang:

Here Helgi, for thee
A bed have I dight,
Kind without woe,
O kin of the Ylfings!
To thy bosom, O king,
Will I come and sleep soft,
As I was wont
When my lord was living.

HELGI

Now will I call
Naught not to be hoped for
Early or late
At Sevafell,

When thou in the arms
Of a dead man art laid,
White maiden of Hogni,
Here in the mound:
And thou yet quick,
O King's daughter!

Now needs must I ride
On the reddening ways;
My pale horse must tread
The highway aloft:
West must I go
To Windhelm's bridge
Ere the war-winning crowd
Hall-crower [4] waketh.

So Helgi rode his ways: and the others gat them gone home to the house. But the next night Sigrun bade the bondwoman have heed of the mound. So at nightfall, whenas Sigrun came to the mound, she sang:

Here now would he come,
If to come he were minded;
Sigmund's offspring
From the halls of Odin.
O me the hope waneth
Of Helgi's coming;
For high on the ash-boughs
Are the ernes abiding,
And all folk drift
Toward the Thing of the dreamland.

### THE BONDMAID

Be not foolish of heart,
And fare all alone
To the house of the dead,
O Hero's daughter!
For more strong and dreadful

[4] Hall-crower, *Salgofnir:* lit. Hall-gaper, the cock of Valhall.

In the night season
Are all dead warriors
Than in the daylight.

But a little while lived Sigrun, because of her sorrow and trouble. But in old time folk trowed that men should be born again, though their troth be now deemed but an old wife's doting. And so, as folk say, Helgi and Sigrun were born again, and at that tide was he called Helgi the Scathe of Hadding, and she Kara the daughter of Halfdan; and she was a Valkyria, even as is said in the Lay of Kara.

# PART OF
# THE LAY OF SIGRDRIFA[1]

NOW this is my first counsel,
That thou with thy kin
Be guiltless, guileless ever,
Nor hasty of wrath,
Despite of wrong done—
Unto the dead good that doeth.

Lo the second counsel,
That oath thou swearest never,
But trusty oath and true:
Grim tormenting
Gripes troth-breakers;
Cursed wretch is the wolf of vows.

This is my third rede,
That thou at the Thing
Deal not with the fools of folk;
For unwise man
From mouth lets fall
Worser word than well he wotteth.

Yet hard it is
That holding of peace
When men shall deem thee dastard,
Or deem the lie said soothly;
But woeful is home-witness,
Unless right good thou gettest it
Ah, on another day
Drive the life from out him,
And pay the liar back for his lying.

Now behold the fourth rede:
If ill witch thee bideth,

---

[1] This continues the first part of the lay given in Chap. xx. of the Saga; and is, in fact, the original verse of Chap. xxi.

Woe-begetting by the way,
 Good going further
 Rather than guesting,
Though thick night be on thee.

 Far-seeing eyes
 Need all sons of men
Who wend in wrath to war;
 For baleful women
 Bide oft by the highway,
Swords and hearts to soften.

 And now the fifth rede:
 As fair as thou seest
Brides on the bench abiding,
 Let not love's silver
 Rule over thy sleeping;
Draw no woman to kind kissing!

 For the sixth thing, I rede
 When men sit a-drinking
Amid ale-words and ill-words,
 Deal thou naught
 With the drunken fight-staves,
For wine stealeth wit from many.

 Brawling and drink
 Have brought unto men
Sorrow sore oft enow;
 Yea, bane unto some,
 And to some weary bale;
Many are the griefs of mankind.

 For the seventh, I rede thee,
 If strife thou raisest
With a man right high of heart,
 Better fight a-field
 Than burn in the fire
Within thine hall fair to behold.

 The eighth rede that I give thee:
 Unto all ill look thou,

And hold thine heart from all beguiling;
  Draw to thee no maiden,
  No man's wife bewray thou,
Urge them not unto unmeet pleasure.

  This is the ninth counsel:
   That thou have heed of dead folk
Whereso thou findest them a-field;
  Be they sick-dead,
  Be they sea-dead,
Or come to ending by war weapons.

  Let bath be made
  For such men fordone,
Wash thou hands and feet thereof,
  Comb their hair and dry them
  Ere the coffin has them;
Then bid them sleep full sweetly.

  This for the tenth counsel:
  That thou give trust never
Unto oaths of foeman's kin,
Be'st thou bane of his brother,
Or hast thou felled his father;
Wolf in young son waxes,
Though he with gold be gladdened.

  For wrong and hatred
  Shall rest them never,
Nay, nor sore sorrow.
  Both wit and weapons
  Well must the king have
Who is fain to be the foremost.

  The last rede and eleventh:
  Until all ill look thou,
And watch thy friends' ways ever.
  Scarce durst I look
  For long life for thee, king:
Strong trouble ariseth now already.

# THE LAY
# CALLED THE SHORT LAY
# OF SIGURD

SIGURD of yore,
  Sought the dwelling of Giuki,
  As he fared, the young Volsung,
After fight won;
Troth he took
From the two brethren;
Oath swore they betwixt them,
Those bold ones of deed.

A may they gave to him
And wealth manifold,
Gudrun the young,
Giuki's daughter:
They drank and gave doom
Many days together,
Sigurd the young,
And the sons of Giuki.

Until they wended
For Brynhild's wooing,
Sigurd a-riding
Amidst their rout;
The wise young Volsung
Who knew of all ways—
Ah! he had wed her,
Had fate so willed it.

Southlander Sigurd
A naked sword,
Bright, well grinded,
Laid betwixt them;

No kiss he won
From the fair woman,
Nor in arms of his
Did the Hun King hold her,
Since he gat the young maid
For the son of Giuki.

No lack in her life
She wotted of now,
And at her death-day
No dreadful thing
For a shame indeed
Or a shame in seeming;
But about and betwixt
Went baleful fate.

Alone, abroad,
She sat of an evening,
Of full many things
She fell a-talking:
"O for my Sigurd!
I shall have death,
Or my fair, my lovely,
Laid in mine arms.

"For the word once spoken,
I sorrow sorely—
His queen is Gudrun,
I am wed to Gunnar;
The dread Norns wrought for us
A long while of woe."

Oft with heart deep
In dreadful thoughts,
O'er ice-fields and ice-hills
She fared a-night time,
When he and Gudrun
Were gone to their fair bed,
And Sigurd wrapped
The bed-gear round her.

"Ah! now the Hun King
His queen in arms holdeth,
While love I go lacking,
And all things longed for
With no delight
But in dreadful thought."

These dreadful things
Thrust her toward murder:
—" Listen, Gunnar,
For thou shalt lose
My wide lands,
Yea, me myself!
Never love I my life,
With thee for my lord—

" I will fare back thither
From whence I came,
To my nighest kin
And those that know me
There shall I sit
Sleeping my life away,
Unless thou slayest
Sigurd the Hun King,
Making thy might more
E'en than his might was!

" Yea, let the son fare
After the father,
And no young wolf
A long while nourish!
For on each man lieth
Vengeance lighter,
And peace shall be surer
If the son live not."

Adrad was Gunnar,
Heavy-hearted was he,
And in doubtful mood
Day-long he sat,

For naught he wotted,
Nor might see clearly
What was the seemliest
Of deeds to set hand to;
What of all deeds
Was best to be done:
For he minded the vows
Sworn to the Volsung,
And the sore wrong
To be wrought against Sigurd.

Wavered his mind
A weary while,
No wont it was
Of those days worn by,
That queens should flee
From the realms of their kings.

" Brynhild to me
Is better than all,
The child of Budli
Is the best of women.
Yea, and my life
Will I lay down,
Ere I am twinned
From that woman's treasure."

He bade call Hogni
To the place where he bided;
With all the trust that might be,
Trowed he in him.

"Wilt thou bewray Sigurd
For his wealth's sake?
Good it is to rule
O'er the Rhine's metal;
And well content
Great wealth to wield,
Biding in peace
And blissful days."

One thing alone Hogni
Had for an answer:
" Such doings for us
Are naught seemly to do;
To rend with sword
Oaths once sworn,
Oaths once sworn,
And troth once plighted.

"Nor know we on mould,
Men of happier days,
The while we four
Rule over the folk;
While the bold in battle,
The Hun King, bides living.

"And no nobler kin
Shall be known afield,
If our five sons
We long may foster;
Yea, a goodly stem
Shall surely wax.
—But I clearly see
In what wise it standeth,
Brynhild's sore urging
O'ermuch on thee beareth.

" Guttorm shall we
Get for the slaying,
Our younger brother
Bare of wisdom;
For he was out of
All the oaths sworn,
All the oaths sworn,
And the plighted troth."

Easy to rouse him
Who of naught recketh!
—Deep stood the sword
In the heart of Sigurd.

There, in the hall,
Gat the high-hearted vengeance;
For he cast his sword
At the reckless slayer:
Out at Guttorm
Flew Gram the mighty,
The gleaming steel
From Sigurd's hand.

Down fell the slayer
Smitten asunder;
The heavy head
And the hands fell one way,
But the feet and such like
Aback where they stood.

Gudrun was sleeping
Soft in the bed,
Empty of sorrow
By the side of Sigurd:
When she awoke
With all pleasure gone,
Swimming in blood
Of Frey's beloved.

So sore her hands
She smote together,
That the great-hearted
Gat raised in bed;
—" O Gudrun, weep not
So woefully,
Sweet lovely bride,
For thy brethren live for thee!

" A young child have I
For heritor;
Too young to win forth
From the house of his foes.—
Black deeds and ill
Have they been a-doing,

Evil rede
Have they wrought at last.

"Late, late, rideth with them
Unto the Thing,
Such sister's son,
Though seven thou bear,—
—But well I wot
Which way all goeth;
Alone wrought Brynhild
This bale against us.

"That maiden loved me
Far before all men,
Yet wrong to Gunnar
I never wrought;
Brotherhood I heeded
And all bounden oaths,
That none should deem me
His queen's darling."

Weary sighed Gudrun,
As the king gat ending,
And so sore her hands
She smote together,
That the cups arow
Rang out therewith,
And the geese cried on high
That were in the homefield.

Then laughed Brynhild
Budli's daughter,
Once, once only,
From out her heart;
When to her bed
Was borne the sound
Of the sore greeting
Of Giuki's daughter.

Then, quoth Gunnar,
The king, the hawk-bearer,

" Whereas, thou laughest,
O hateful woman,
Glad on thy bed,
No good it betokeneth:
Why lackest thou else
Thy lovely hue?
Feeder of foul deeds,
Fey do I deem thee,

" Well worthy art thou
Before all women,
That thine eyes should see
Atli slain of us;
That thy brother's wounds
Thou shouldst see a-bleeding,
That his bloody hurts
Thine hands should bind."

" No man blameth thee, Gunnar,
Thou hast fulfilled death's measure
But naught Atli feareth
All thine ill will;
Life shall he lay down
Later than ye,
And still bear more might
Aloft than thy might.

" I shall tell thee, Gunnar,
Though well the tale thou knowest,
In what early days
Ye dealt abroad your wrong:
Young was I then,
Worn with no woe,
Good wealth I had
In the house of my brother!

" No mind had I
That a man should have me,
Or ever ye Giukings,
Rode into our garth;

There ye sat on your steeds
Three kings of the people—
—Ah! that that faring
Had never befallen!

" Then spake Atli
To me apart,
And said that no wealth
He would give unto me,
Neither gold nor lands
If I would not be wedded;
Nay, and no part
Of the wealth apportioned,
Which in my first days
He gave me duly;
Which in my first days
He counted down.

" Wavered the mind
Within me then,
If to fight I should fall
And the felling of folk,
Bold in byrny
Because of my brother;
A deed of fame
Had that been to all folk,
But to many a man
Sorrow of mind.

" So I let all sink
Into peace at the last:
More grew I minded
For the mighty treasure,
The red-shining rings
Of Sigmund's son;
For no man's wealth else
Would I take unto me.

" For myself had I given
To that great king

Who sat amid gold
On the back of Grani;
Nought were his eyen
Like to your eyen,
Nor in any wise
Went his visage with yours;
Though ye might deem you
Due kings of men.

"One I loved,
One, and none other,
The gold-decked may
Had no doubtful mind;
Thereof shall Atli
Wot full surely,
When he getteth to know
I am gone to the dead.

"Far be it from me,
Feeble and wavering,
Ever to love
Another's love—
—Yet shall my woe
Be well avenged."

Up rose Gunnar,
The great men's leader,
And cast his arms
About the queen's neck
And all went nigh
One after other,
With their whole hearts
Her heart to turn.

But then all these
From her neck she thrust,
Of her long journey
No man should let her.

Then called he Hogni
To have talk with him:

"Let all folk go
Forth into the hall,
Thine with mine—
—O need sore and mighty!—
To wot if we yet
My wife's parting may stay.
Till with time's wearing
Some hindrance wax."

One answer Hogni
Had for all;
"Nay, let hard need
Have rule thereover,
And no man let her
Of her long journey!
Never born again,
May she come back thence.

"Luckless she came
To the lap of her mother,
Born into the world
For utter woe,
To many a man
For heart-whole mourning."

Upraised he turned
From the talk and the trouble,
To where the gem-field
Dealt out goodly treasure;
As she looked and beheld
All the wealth that she had,
And the hungry bondmaids,
And maids of the hall.

With no good in her heart
She donned her gold byrny,
Ere she thrust the sword-point
Through the midst of her body:
On the bolster's far side
Sank she adown,

And, smitten with sword,
Still bethought her of redes.

"Let all come forth
Who are fain the red gold,
Or things less worthy
To win from my hands;
To each one I give
A necklace gilt over,
Wrought hangings and bed-gear
And bright woven weed."

All they kept silence,
And thought what to speak,
Then all at once
Answer gave:
"Full enow are death-doomed
Fain are we to live yet,
Maids of the hall
All meet work winning."

From her wise heart at last
The linen-clad damsel,
The one of few years
Gave forth the word:
"I will that none driven
By hand or by word,
For our sake should lose
Well-loved life.

"Thou on the bones of you
Surely shall burn,
Less dear treasure
At your departing
Nor with Menia's Meal[1]
Shall ye come to see me."

"Sit thee down, Gunnar,
A word must I say to thee

[1] " Menia's Meal—" periphrasis for gold.

Of the life's ruin
Of thy lightsome bride—
—Nor shall thy ship
Swim soft and sweetly
For all that I
Lay life adown.

" Sooner than ye might deem
Shall ye make peace with Gudrun.
For the wise woman
Shall lull in the young wife
The hard memory
Of her dead husband.

" There is a may born
Reared by her mother,
Whiter and brighter
Than is the bright day;
She shall be Swanhild,
She shall be Sunbeam.

" Thou shalt give Gudrun
Unto a great one,
Noble, well-praised
Of the world's folk;
Not with her goodwill,
Or love shalt thou give her;
Yet will Atli
Come to win her,
My very brother,
Born of Budli.

—" Ah ! many a memory
Of how ye dealt with me,
How sorely, how evilly
Ye ever beguiled me,
How all pleasure left me
The while my life lasted !—

" Fain wilt thou be
Oddrun to win,

But thy good liking
Shall Atli let;
But in secret wise
Shall ye win together,
And she shall love thee
As I had loved thee,
If in such wise
Fate had willed it.

" But with all ill
Shall Atli sting thee,
Into the strait worm-close
Shall he cast thee.

" But no long space
Shall slip away
Ere Atli too
All life shall lose.
Yea, all his weal
With the life of his sons,
For a dreadful bed
Dights Gudrun for him,
From a heart sore laden,
With the sword's sharp edge.

" More seemly for Gudrun,
Your very sister,
In death to wend after
Her love first wed;
Had but good rede
To her been given,
Or if her heart
Had been like to my heart.

—" Faint my speech groweth—
But for our sake
Ne'er shall she lose
Her life beloved;
The sea shall have her,
High billows bear her

Forth unto Jonakr's
Fair land of his fathers.

" There shall she bear sons,
Stays of a heritage,
Stays of a heritage,
Jonakr's sons;
And Swanhild shall she
Send from the land,
That may born of her,
The may born of Sigurd.

" Her shall bite
The rede of Bikki,
Whereas for no good
Wins Jormunrek life;
And so is clean perished
All the kin of Sigurd,
Yea, and more greeting,
And more for Gudrun.

" And now one prayer
Yet pray I of thee—
The last word of mine
Here in the world—
So broad on the field
Be the burg of the dead
That fair space may be left
For us all to lie down,
All those that died
At Sigurd's death!

"Hang round that burg
Fair hangings and shields,
Web by Gauls woven,
And folk of the Gauls:
There burn the Hun King
Lying beside me.

" But on the other side
Burn by the Hun King

Those who served me
Strewn with treasure;
Two at the head,
And two at the feet,
Two hounds therewith,
And two hawks moreover:
Then is all dealt
With even dealing.

"Lay there amidst us
The ring-dight metal,
The sharp-edged steel,
That so lay erst;
When we both together
Into one bed went,
And were called by the name
Of man and wife.

"Never, then, belike
Shall clash behind him
Valhall's bright door
With rings bedight:
And if my fellowship
Followeth after,
In no wretched wise
Then shall we wend.

"For him shall follow
My five bondmaids,
My eight bondsmen,
No borel folk:
Yea, and my fosterer,
And my father's dower
That Budli of old days
Gave to his dear child.

"Much have I spoken,
More would I speak,
If the sword would give me
Space for speech;

But my words are waning,
My wounds are swelling—
Naught but truth have I told—
—And now make I ending."

# THE HELL-RIDE OF BRYNHILD

AFTER the death of Brynhild were made two bales, one for Sigurd, and that was first burned; but Brynhild was burned on the other, and she was in a chariot hung about with goodly hangings.

And so folk say that Brynhild drave in her chariot down along the way to Hell, and passed by an abode where dwelt a certain giantess, and the giantess spake:—

"Nay, with my goodwill
Never goest thou
Through this stone-pillared
Stead of mine!
More seemly for thee
To sit sewing the cloth,
Than to go look on
The love of another.

"What dost thou, going
From the land of the Gauls,
O restless head,
To this mine house?
Golden girl, hast thou not,
If thou listest to hearken,
In sweet wise from thy hands
The blood of men washen?"

BRYNHILD

"Nay, blame me naught,
Bride of the rock-hall,
Though I roved a warring
In the days that were;

413

The higher of us twain
Shall I ever be holden
When of our kind
Men make account."

### THE GIANT-WOMAN

" Thou, O Brynhild,
Budli's daughter,
Wert the worst ever born
Into the world:
For Giuki's children
Death hast thou gotten,
And turned to destruction
Their goodly dwelling."

### BRYNHILD

" I shall tell thee
True tale from my chariot,
O thou who naught wottest,
If thou listest to wot;
How for me they have gotten
Those heirs of Giuki,
A loveless life,
A life of lies.

" Hild under helm,
The Hlymdale people,
E'en those who knew me,
Ever would call me.

" The changeful shapes
Of us eight sisters,
The wise king bade
Under oak-tree to bear:
Of twelve winters was I,
If thou listest to wot,
When I sware to the young lord
Oaths of love.

" Thereafter gat I
Mid the folk of the Goths,
For Helmgunnar the old,
Swift journey to Hell,
And gave to Aud's brother
The young, gain and glory;
Whereof overwrath
Waxed Odin with me.

" So he shut me in shield-wall
In Skata grove,
Red shields and white
Close set around me;
And bade him alone
My slumber to brake
Who in no land
Knew how to fear.

" He set round my hall,
Toward the south quarter,
The Bane of all trees
Burning aloft;
And ruled that he only
Thereover should ride
Who should bring me the gold
O'er which Fafnir brooded.

" Then upon Grani rode
The goodly gold-strewer
To where my fosterer
Ruled his fair dwelling.
He who alone there
Was deemed best of all,
The War-lord of the Danes,
Well worthy of men.

" In peace did we sleep
Soft in one bed,
As though he had been
Naught but my brother:

There as we lay
Through eight nights wearing,
No hand in love
On each other we laid.

" Yet thence blamed me, Gudrun,
Giuki's daughter,
That I had slept
In the arms of Sigurd;
And then I wotted
As I fain had not wotted,
That they had bewrayed me
In my betrothals.

" Ah! for unrest
All too long
Are men and women
Made alive!
Yet we twain together
Shall wear through the ages,
Sigurd and I.—
—Sink adown, O giant-wife!"

# FRAGMENTS OF
# THE LAY OF BRYNHILD

. . . . .

### Hogni said

What hath wrought Sigurd
Of any wrong-doing
That the life of the famed one
Thou art fain of taking?

### Gunnar said

To me has Sigurd
Sworn many oaths,
Sworn many oaths,
And sworn them lying,
And he bewrayed me
When it behoved him
Of all folk to his troth
To be the most trusty.

### Hogni said

Thee hath Brynhild
Unto all bale,
And all hate whetted,
And a work of sorrow;
For she grudges to Gudrun
All goodly life;
And to thee the bliss
Of her very body.

. . . . . .

Some the wolf roasted,
Some minced the worm,
Some unto Guttorm
Gave the wolf-meat,
Or ever they might
In their lust for murder
On the high king
Lay deadly hand.

Sigurd lay slain
On the south of the Rhine.
High from the fair tree
Croaked forth the raven,
"Ah, yet shall Atli
On you redden edges,
The old oaths shall weigh
On your souls, O warriors."

Without stood Gudrun,
Giuki's daughter,
And the first word she said
Was even this word:
"Where then is Sigurd,
Lord of the Warfolk,
Since my kin
Come riding the foremost?"

One word Hogni
Had for an answer:
"Our swords have smitten
Sigurd asunder,
And the grey horse hangs drooping
O'er his lord lying dead."

Then quoth Brynhild,
Budli's daughter;
"Good weal shall ye have
Of weapons and lands,
That Sigurd alone
Would surely have ruled

If he had lived
But a little longer.

" Ah, nothing seemly
For Sigurd to rule
Giuki's house
And the folk of the Goths,
When of him five sons
For the slaying of men,
Eager for battle
Should have been begotten! "

Then laughed Brynhild—
Loud rang the whole house—
One laugh only
From out her heart:
" Long shall your bliss be
Of lands and people,
Whereas the famed lord
You have felled to the earth! "

Then spake Gudrun,
Giuki's daughter;
" Much thou speakest,
Many things fearful,
All grame be on Gunnar
The bane of Sigurd!
From a heart full of hate
Shall come heavy vengeance."

Forth sped the even
Enow there was drunken,
Full enow was there
Of all soft speech;
And all men got sleep
When to bed they were gotten;
Gunnar only lay waking
Long after all men.

His feet fell he to moving,
Fell to speak to himself

The waster of men,
Still turned in his mind
What on the bough
Those twain would be saying,
The raven and erne,
As they rode their ways homeward.

But Brynhild awoke,
Budli's daughter,
May of the shield-folk,
A little ere morning:
" Thrust ye on, hold ye back,
—Now all harm is wrought,—
To tell of my sorrow,
Or to let all slip by me? "

All kept silence
After her speaking,
None might know
That woman's mind,
Or why she must weep
To tell of the work
That laughing once
Of men she prayed.

BRYNHILD SPAKE

In dreams, O Gunnar,
Grim things fell on me;
Dead-cold the hall was,
And my bed was a-cold,
And thou, lord, wert riding
Reft of all bliss,
Laden with fetters
'Mid the host of thy foemen.

So now all ye,
O House of the Niblungs,
Shall be brought to naught,
O ye oath-breakers!

Think'st thou not, Gunnar,
How that betid,
When ye let the blood run
Both in one footstep?
With ill reward
Hast thou rewarded
His heart so fain
To be the foremost!

As well was seen
When he rode his ways,
That king of all worth,
Unto my wooing;
How the host-destroyer
Held to the vows
Sworn beforetime,
Sworn to the young king.

For his wounding-wand
All wrought with gold,
The king beloved
Laid between us;
Without were its edges
Wrought with fire,
But with venom-drops
Deep dyed within.

Thus this song telleth of the death of Sigurd, and setteth forth how that they slew him without doors; but some say that they slew him within doors, sleeping in his bed. But the Dutch Folk say that they slew him out in the wood: and so sayeth the ancient song of Gudrun, that Sigurd and the sons of Giuki were riding to the Thing whenas he was slain. But all with one accord say that they bewrayed him in their troth with him, and fell on him as he lay unarrayed and unawares.

# THE SECOND OR ANCIENT LAY
# OF GUDRUN

**T**HIODREK the King was in Atli's house, and had lost there the more part of his men: so there Thiodrek and Gudrun bewailed their troubles one to the other, and she spake and said:—

A may of all mays
My mother reared me
Bright in bower;
Well loved I my brethren,
Until that Giuki
With gold arrayed me,
With gold arrayed me,
And gave me to Sigurd.

Such was my Sigurd,
Among the sons of Giuki
As is the green leek
O'er the low grass waxen,
Or a hart high-limbed
Over hurrying deer,
Or glede-red gold
Over grey silver.

Till me they begrudged,
Those my brethren,
The fate to have him,
Who was first of all men;
Nor might they sleep,
Nor sit a-dooming,
Ere they let slay
My well-loved Sigurd.

Grani ran to the Thing,
There was clatter to hear,
But never came Sigurd
Himself thereunto;
All the saddle-girt beasts
With blood were besprinkled,
As faint with the way
Neath the slayers they went.

Then greeting I went
With Grani to talk,
And with tear-furrowed cheeks
I bade him tell all;
But drooping laid Grani,
His head in the grass,
For the steed well wotted
Of his master's slaying.

A long while I wandered,
Long my mind wavered,
Ere the kings I might ask
Concerning my king.

Then Gunnar hung head,
But Hogni told
Of the cruel slaying
Of my Sigurd:
"On the water's far side
Lies, smitten to death,
The bane of Guttorm
To the wolves given over.

"Go, look on Sigurd,
On the ways that go southward,
There shalt thou hear
The ernes high screaming,
The ravens a-croaking
As their meat they crave for;
Thou shalt hear the wolves howling
Over thine husband."

" How hast thou, Hogni,
The heart to tell me,
Me of joy made empty,
Of such misery?
Thy wretched heart
May the ravens tear
Wide over the world,
With no men mayst thou wend."

One thing Hogni
Had for answer,
Fallen from his high heart,
Full of all trouble:
" More greeting yet,
O Gudrun, for thee,
If my heart the ravens
Should rend asunder ! "

Thence I turned
From the talk and the trouble
To go a leasing[1]
What the wolves had left me;
No sigh I made
No smote hands together,
Nor did I wail
As other women
When I sat over
My Sigurd slain.

Night methought it,
And the moonless dark,
When I sat in sorrow
Over Sigurd:
Better than all things
I deemed it would be
If they would let me
Cast my life by,
Or burn me up
As they burn the birch-wood.

[1] Gleaning.

From the fell I wandered
Five days together,
Until the high hall
Of Half lay before me;
Seven seasons there
I sat with Thora,
The daughter of Hacon,
Up in Denmark.

My heart to gladden
With gold she wrought
Southland halls
And swans of the Dane-folk;
There had we painted
The chiefs a-playing;
Fair our hands wrought
Folk of the kings.

Red shields we did,
Doughty knights of the Huns,
Hosts spear-dight, hosts helm-dight,
All a high king's fellows;
And the ships of Sigmund
From the land swift sailing;
Heads gilt over
And prows fair graven.

On the cloth we broidered
That tide of their battling,
Siggeir and Siggar,
South in Fion.

Then heard Grimhild,
The Queen of Gothland,
How I was abiding,
Weighed down with woe;
And she thrust the cloth from her
And called to her sons,
And oft and eagerly
Asked them thereof,

Who for her son
Would their sister atone,
Who for her lord slain
Would lay down weregild.

Fain was Gunnar
Gold to lay down
All wrongs to atone for,
And Hogni in likewise;
Then she asked who was **fain**
Of faring straightly,
The steed to saddle
To set forth the wain,
The horse to back,
And the hawk to fly,
To shoot forth the arrow
From out the yew-bow.

Valdarr the Dane-king
Came with Jarisleif
Eymod the third went
Then went Jarizskar;
In kingly wise
In they wended,
The hosts of the Longbeards;
Red cloaks had they,
Byrnies short-cut,
Helms strong hammered,
Girt with glaives,
And hair red-gleaming.

Each would **give me**
Gifts desired,
Gifts desired,
Speech dear to my **heart**,
If they might yet,
Despite my sorrow,
Win back my trust,
But in **them** nought **I trusted.**

Then brought me Grimhild
A beaker to drink of,
Cold and bitter,
Wrong's memory to quench;
Made great was that drink
With the might of the earth,
With the death-cold sea
And the blood that Son[2] holdeth.

On that horn's face were there
All the kin of letters
Cut aright and reddened,
How should I rede them rightly?
The ling-fish long
Of the land of Hadding,
Wheat-ears unshorn,
And wild things' inwards.

In that mead were mingled
Many ills together,
Blood of all the wood,
And brown-burnt acorns;
The black dew of the hearth,[3]
And god-doomed dead beasts' inwards,
And the swine's liver sodden,
For wrongs late done that deadens.

Then waned my memory
When that was within me,
Of my lord 'mid the hall
By the iron laid low.
Three kings came
Before my knees
Ere she herself
Fell to speech with me.

" I will give to thee, Gudrun,
Gold to be glad with,

[2] Son was the vessel into which was poured the blood of Quasir, the God of Poetry.     [3] This means soot.

All the great wealth
Of thy father gone from us,
Rings of red gold
And the great hall of Lodver,
And all fair hangings left
By the king late fallen.

"Maids of the Huns
Woven pictures to make,
And work fair in gold
Till thou deem'st thyself glad.
Alone shalt thou rule
O'er the riches of Budli,
Shalt be made great with gold,
And be given to Atli."

"Never will I
Wend to a husband,
Or wed the brother
Of Queen Brynhild;
Naught it beseems me
With the son of Budli
Kin to bring forth,
Or to live and be merry."

"Nay, the high chiefs
Reward not with hatred,
For take heed that I
Was the first in this tale!
To thy heart shall it be
As if both these had life,
Sigurd and Sigmund,
When thou hast borne sons."

"Naught may I, Grimhild,
Seek after gladness,
Nor deem aught hopeful
Of any high warrior,
Since wolf and raven
Were friends together,

The greedy, the cruel,
O'er great Sigurd's heart-blood."

"Of all men that can be
For the noblest of kin
This king have I found,
And the foremost of all;
Him shalt thou have
Till with eld thou art heavy⁓⁓
Be thou ever unwed,
If thou wilt naught of him!"

"Nay, nay, bid me not
With thy words long abiding
To take unto me
That balefullest kin;
This king shall bid Gunnar
Be stung to his bane,
And shall cut the heart
From out of Hogni.

"Nor shall I leave life
Ere the keen lord,
The eager in sword-play,
My hand shall make end of."

Grimhild a-weeping
Took up the word then,
When the sore bale she wotted
Awaiting her sons,
And the bane hanging over
Her offspring beloved.

"I will give thee, moreover,
Great lands, many men,
Wineberg and Valberg,
If thou wilt but have them;
Hold them lifelong,
And live happy, O daughter!"

" Then him must I take
From among kingly men,
'Gainst my heart's desire,
From the hands of my kinsfolk;
But no joy I look
To have from that lord:
Scarce may my brother's bane
Be a shield to my sons."

Soon was each warrior
Seen on his horse,
But the Gaulish women
Into wains were gotten;
Then seven days long
O'er a cold land we rode,
And for seven other
Clove we the sea-waves
But with the third seven
O'er dry land we wended.

There the gate-wardens
Of the burg, high and wide,
Unlocked the barriers
Ere the burg-garth we rode to.—

. . . . . .
. . . . .

Atli woke me
When meseemed I was
Full evil of heart
For my kin dead slain.

" In such wise did the Norns
Wake me or now."—
Fain was he to know
Of this ill foreshowing—
" That methought, O Gudrun,
Giuki's daughter,
That thou setst in my heart
A sword wrought for guile."

" For fires tokening I deem it
That dreaming of iron,
But for pride and for lust
The wrath of fair women
Against some bale
Belike, I shall burn thee
For thy solace and healing
Though hateful thou art."

" In the fair garth methought
Had saplings fallen
E'en such as I would
Should have waxen ever;
Uprooted were these,
And reddened with blood,
And borne to the bench,
And folk bade me eat of them.

" Methought from my hand then
Went hawks a-flying
Lacking their meat
To the land of all ill;
Methought that their hearts
Mingled with honey,
Swollen with blood
I ate amid sorrow.

" Lo, next two whelps
From my hands I loosened,
Joyless were both,
And both a-howling;
And now their flesh
Became naught but corpses,
Whereof must I eat
But sore against my will."

" O'er the prey of the fishers
Will folk give doom;
From the bright white fish
The heads will they take;

Within a few nights,
Fey as they are,
A little ere day
Of that draught will they eat."

Ne'er since lay I down,
Ne'er since would I sleep,
Hard of heart, in my bed:—
That deed have I to do.[4]

[4] The whole of this latter part is fragmentary and obscure; there seems wanting to two of the dreams some trivial interpretation by Gudrun, like those given by Hogni to Kostbera in the Saga, of which nature, of course, the interpretation contained in the last stanza but one is, as we have rendered it: another rendering, from the different reading of the earlier edition of Edda (Copenhagen, 1818) would make this refer much more directly to the slaying of her sons by Gudrun.

# THE SONG OF ATLI

GUDRUN, Giuki's daughter, avenged her brethren, as is told far and wide: first she slew the sons of Atli, and then Atli himself; and she burned the hall thereafter, and all the household with it: and about these matters is this song made:—

In days long gone
Sent Atli to Gunnar
A crafty one riding,
Knefrud men called him;
To Giuki's garth came he,
To the hall of Gunnar,
To the benches gay-dight,
And the gladsome drinking.

There drank the great folk
'Mid the guileful one's silence,
Drank wine in their fair hall:
The Huns' wrath they feared,
When Knefrud cried
In his cold voice,
As he sat on the high seat,
That man of the Southland:

"Atli has sent me
Riding swift on his errands
On the bit-griping steed
Through dark woodways unbeaten,
To bid thee, King Gunnar,
Come to his fair bench
With helm well-adorned,
To the home of King Atli.

" Shields shall ye have there
And spears ashen-shafted,
Helms ruddy with gold,
And hosts of the Huns;
Saddle-gear silver-gilt,
Shirts red as blood,
The hedge of the warwife,
And horses bit-griping.

" And he saith he will give you
Gnitaheath widespread,
And whistling spears
And prows well-gilded,
Mighty wealth
With the stead of Danpi,
And that noble wood
Men name the Murkwood."

Then Gunnar turned head
And spake unto Hogni:
" What rede from thee, high one,
Since such things we hear?
No gold know I
On Gnitaheath,
That we for our parts
Have not portion as great.

" Seven halls we have
Fulfilled of swords,
And hilts of gold
Each sword there has;
My horse is the best,
My blade is the keenest;
Fair my bow o'er the bench is,
Gleams my byrny with gold;
Brightest helm, brightest shield,
From Kiar's dwelling ere brought—
Better all things I have
Than all things of the Huns."

### Hogni said

"What mind has our sister
That a ring she hath sent us
In weed of wolves clad?
Bids she not to be wary?
For a wolf's hair I found
The fair ring wreathed about;
Wolf beset shall the way be
If we wend on this errand."

No sons whetted Gunnar,
Nor none of his kin,
Nor learned men nor wise men,
Nor such as were mighty.
Then spake Gunnar
E'en as a king should speak,
Glorious in mead-hall
From great heart and high:

"Rise up now, Fiornir,
Forth down the benches
Let the gold-cups of great ones
Pass in hands of my good-men!
Well shall we drink wine,
Draughts dear to our hearts,
Though the last of all feasts
In our fair house this be!

"For the wolves shall rule
O'er the wealth of the Niblungs,
With the pine-woods' wardens
If Gunnar perish:
And the black-felled bears
With fierce teeth shall bite
For the glee of the dog-kind,
If again comes not Gunnar."

Then good men never shamed,
Greeting aloud,

Led the great king of men
From the garth of his home;
And cried the fair son
Of Hogni the king:
"Fare happy, O Lords,
Whereso your hearts lead you!"

Then the bold knights
Let their bit-griping steeds
Wend swift o'er the fells,
Tread the murk-wood unknown,
All the Hunwood was shaking
As the hardy ones fared there;
O'er the green meads they urged
Their steeds shy of the goad.

Then Atli's land saw they;
Great towers and strong,
And the bold men of Bikki,
Aloft on the burg:
The Southland folks' hall
Set with benches about,
Dight with bucklers well bounden,
And bright white shining shields.

There drank Atli,
The awful Hun king,
Wine in his fair hall;
Without were the warders,
Gunnar's folk to have heed of,
Lest they had fared thither
With the whistling spear
War to wake 'gainst the king.

But first came their sister
As they came to the hall,
Both her brethren she met,
With beer little gladdened:
"Bewrayed art thou, Gunnar!
What dost thou great king

To deal war to the Huns?
Go thou swift from the hall!

" Better, brother, hadst thou
Fared here in thy byrny
Than with helm gaily dight
Looked on Atli's great house:
Thou hadst sat then in saddle
Through days bright with the sun
Fight to awaken
And fair fields to redden:

" O'er the folk fate makes pale
Should the Norn's tears have fallen,
The shield-mays of the Huns
Should have known of all sorrow;
And King Atli himself
To worm-close should be brought;
But now is the worm-close
Kept but for thee."

Then spake Gunnar
Great 'mid the people:
" Over-late sister
The Niblungs to summon;
A long way to seek
The helping of warriors,
The high lords unshamed,
From the hills of the Rhine !"

.     .     .     .

.     .     .     .

Seven Hogni beat down
With his sword sharp-grinded,
And the eighth man he thrust
Amidst of the fire.
Ever so shall famed warrior
Fight with his foemen,
As Hogni fought
For the hand of Gunnar.

But on Gunnar they fell,
And set him in fetters,
And bound hard and fast
That friend of Burgundians;
Then the warrior they asked
If he would buy life,
Buy life with gold
That king of the Goths.

Nobly spake Gunnar,
Great lord of the Niblungs;
"Hogni's bleeding heart first
Shall lie in mine hand,
Cut from the breast
Of the bold-riding lord,
With bitter-sharp knife
From the son of the king."

With guile the great one
Would they beguile,
On the wailing thrall
Laid they hand unwares,
And cut the heart
From out of Hjalli,
Laid it bleeding on trencher
And bare it to Gunnar.

"Here have I the heart
Of Hjalli the trembler,
Little like the heart
Of Hogni the hardy,
As much as it trembleth
Laid on the trencher,
By the half more it trembled
In the breast of him hidden."

Then laughed Hogni
When they cut the heart from him,
From the crest-smith yet quick,
Little thought he to quail

The hard acorn of thought
From the high king they took,
Laid it bleeding on trencher
And bare it Gunnar.

" Here have I the heart
Of Hogni the hardy,
Little like to the heart
Of Hjalli the trembler.
Howso little it quaketh
Laid here on the dish,
Yet far less it quaked
In the breast of him laid.

" So far mayst thou bide
From men's eyen, O Atli,
As from that treasure
Thou shalt abide!

" Behold in my heart
Is hidden for ever
That hoard of the Niblungs,
Now Hogni is dead.
Doubt threw me two ways
While the twain of us lived,
But all that is gone
Now I live on alone.

" The great Rhine shall rule
O'er the hate-raising treasure,
That gold of the Niblungs,
The seed of the gods:
In the weltering water
Shall that wealth lie a-gleaming,
Or it shine on the hands
Of the children of Huns!"

Then cried Atli,
King of the Hun-folk,
" Drive forth your wains now
The slave is fast bounden."

And straightly thence
The bit-shaking steeds
Drew the hoard-warden,
The war-god to his death.

Atli the great king,
Rode upon Glaum,
With shields set round about,
And sharp thorns of battle:
Gudrun, bound by wedlock
To these, victory made gods of,
Held back her tears
As the hall she ran into.

" Let it fare with thee, Atli,
E'en after thine oaths sworn
To Gunnar full often;
Yea, oaths sworn of old time,
By the sun sloping southward,
By the high burg of Sigty,
By the fair bed of rest,
By the red ring of Ull!"

Now a host of men
Cast the high king alive
Into a close
Crept o'er within
With most foul worms,
Fulfilled of all venom,
Ready grave to dig
In his doughty heart.

Wrathful-hearted he smote
The harp with his hand,
Gunnar laid there alone;
And loud rang the strings.—
In such wise ever
Should hardy ring-scatterer
Keep gold from all folk
In the garth of his foemen.

Then Atli would wend
About his wide land,
On his steed brazen-shod,
Back from the murder.
Din there was in the garth,
All thronged with the horses;
High the weapon-song rose
From men come from the heath.

Out then went Gudrun,
'Gainst Atli returning,
With a cup gilded over,
To greet the land's ruler;
"Come, then, and take it,
King glad in thine hall,
From Gudrun's hands,
For the hell-farers groan not!"

Clashed the beakers of Atli,
Wine-laden on bench,
As in hall there a-gathered,
The Huns fell a-talking,
And the long-bearded eager ones
Entered therein,
From a murk den new-come,
From the murder of Gunnar.

Then hastened the sweet-faced
Delight of the shield-folk,
Bright in the fair hall,
Wine to bear to them:
The dreadful woman
Gave dainties withal
To the lords pale with fate,
Laid strange word upon Atli:

"The hearts of thy sons
Hast thou eaten, sword-dealer,
All bloody with death
And drenched with honey:

In most heavy mood
Brood o'er venison of men!
Drink rich draughts therewith,
Down the high benches send it!


"Never callest thou now
From henceforth to thy knee
Fair Erp or fair Eitil,
Bright-faced with the drink;
Never seest thou them now
Amidmost the seat,
Scattering the gold,
Or shafting of spears;
Manes trimming duly,
Or driving steeds forth!"


Din arose from the benches,
Dread song of men was there,
Noise 'mid the fair hangings,
As all Hun's children wept;
All saving Gudrun,
Who never gat greeting,
For her brethren bear-hardy,
For her sweet sons and bright,
The young ones, the simple
Once gotten with Atli.

. . . .
. . . .
. . . .


The seed of gold
Sowed the swan-bright woman,
Rings of red gold
She gave to the house carls;
Fate let she wax,
Let the bright gold flow forth,
In naught spared that woman
The store-houses' wealth.

Atli unaware
Was a-weary with drink;
No weapon had he,
No heeding of Gudrun—
Ah, the play would be better,
When in soft wise they twain
Would full often embrace
Before the great lords!

To the bed with sword-point
Blood gave she to drink
With a hand fain of death,
And she let the dogs loose:
Then in from the hall-door—
—Up waked the house-carls—
Hot brands she cast,
Gat revenge for her brethren.

To the flame gave she all
Who therein might be found;
Fell adown the old timbers,
Reeked all treasure-houses;
There the shield-mays were burnt,
Their lives' span brought to naught;
In the fierce fire sank down
All the stead of the Budlungs.

Wide told of is this—
Ne'er sithence in the world,
Thus fared bride clad in byrny
For her brothers' avenging;
For behold, this fair woman
To three kings of the people,
Hath brought very death
Or ever she died!

# THE WHETTING OF GUDRUN

GUDRUN went down unto the sea whenas she had slain Atli, and she cast herself therein, for she was fain to end her life: but nowise might she drown. She drave over the firths to the land of King Jonakr, and he wedded her, and their sons were Sorli, and Erp, and Hamdir, and there was Swanhild, Sigurd's daughter, nourished: and she was given to Jormunrek the Mighty. Now Bikki was a man of his, and gave such counsel to Randver, the king's son, as that he should take her; and with that counsel were the young folk well content.

Then Bikki told the king, and the king let hang Randver, but bade Swanhild be trodden under horses' feet. But when Gudrun heard thereof, she spake to her sons—

Words of strife heard I,
Huger than any,
Woeful words spoken,
Sprung from all sorrow,
When Gudrun fierce-hearted
With the grimmest of words
Whetted her sons
Unto the slaying.

"Why are ye sitting here?
Why sleep ye life away?
Why doth it grieve you nought?
Glad words to speak,
Now when your sister—
Young of years was she—
Has Jormunrek trodden
With the treading of horses?—

444

"Black horses and white
In the highway of warriors:
Grey horses that know
The roads of the Goths.—

"Little like are ye grown
To that Gunnar of old days!
Nought are your hearts
As the heart of Hogni!
Well would ye seek
Vengeance to win
If your mood were in aught
As the mood of my brethren,
Or the hardy hearts
Of the Kings of the Huns!"

Then spake Hamdir,
The high-hearted—
"Little didst thou
Praise Hogni's doings,
When Sigurd woke
From out of sleep,
And the blue-white bed-gear
Upon thy bed
Grew red with man's blood—
With the blood of thy mate!

"Too baleful vengeance
Wroughtest thou for thy brethren
Most sore and evil
When thy sons thou slewedst,
Else all we together
On Jormunrek
Had wrought sore vengeance
For that our sister.

"Come, bring forth quickly
The Hun kings' bright gear,
Since thou hast urged us
Unto the sword-Thing!"

Laughing went Gudrun
To the bower of good gear,
Kings' crested helms
From chests she drew,
And wide-wrought byrnies
Bore to her sons:
Then on their horses
Load laid the heroes.

Then spake Hamdir,
The high-hearted—
"Never cometh again
His mother to see
The spear-god laid low
In the land of the Goths.
That one arvel mayst thou
For all of us drink
For sister Swanhild,
And us thy sons."

Greeted Gudrun,
Giuki's daughter;
Sorrowing she went
In the forecourt to sit,
That she might tell,
With cheeks tear-furrowed,
Her weary wail
In many a wise.

"Three fires I knew,
Three hearths I knew,
To three husbands' houses
Have I been carried;
And better than all
Had been Sigurd alone,
He whom my brethren
Brought to his bane.

"Such sore grief as that
Methought never should be,
Yet more indeed

Was left for my torment
Then, when the great ones
Gave me to Atli.

" My fair bright boys
I bade unto speech,
Nor yet might I win
Weregild for my bale,
Ere I had hewn off
Those Niblungs' heads.

" To the sea-strand I went
With the Norns sorely wroth,
For I would thrust from me
The storm of their torment;
But the high billows
Would not drown, but bore me
Forth, till I stepped a-land
Longer to live.

" Then I went a-bed——
——Ah, better in the old days,
This was the third time!——
To a king of the people;
Offspring I brought forth,
Props of a fair house,
Props of a fair house,
Jonakr's fair sons.

" But around Swanhild
Bond-maidens sat,
Her, that of all mine
Most to my heart was;
Such was my Swanhild,
In my hall's midmost,
As is the sunbeam
Fair to behold.

" In gold I arrayed her,
And goodly raiment,
Or ever I gave her

To the folk of the Goths.
That was the hardest
Of my heavy woes,
When the bright hair,—
O the bright hair of Swanhild!—
In the mire was trodden
By the treading of horses.

" This was the sorest,
When my love, my Sigurd,
Reft of glory
In his bed gat ending:
But this the grimmest
When glittering worms
Tore their way
Through the heart of Gunnar.

" But this the keenest
When they cut to the quick
Of the hardy heart
Of the unfeared Hogni.
Of much of bale I mind me,
Of many griefs I mind me;
Why should I sit abiding
Yet more bale and more?

" Thy coal-black horse,
O Sigurd, bridle,
The swift on the highway!
O let him speed hither!
Here sitteth no longer
Son or daughter,
More good gifts
To give to Gudrun!

" Mindst thou not, Sigurd,
Of the speech betwixt us,
When on one bed
We both sat together,
O my great king—

That thou wouldst come to me
E'en from the hall of Hell,
I to thee from the fair earth?

" Pile high, O earls,
The oaken pile,
Let it be the highest
That ever queen had!
Let the fire burn swift,
My breast with woe laden,
And thaw all my heart,
Hard, heavy with sorrow!"

Now may all earls
Be bettered in mind,
May the grief of all maidens
Ever be minished,
For this tale of sorrow
So told to its ending.

# THE LAY OF HAMDIR

GREAT deeds of bale
In the garth began,
At the sad dawning
The tide of Elves' sorrow
When day is a-waxing
And man's grief awaketh,
And the sorrow of each one
The early day quickeneth.

Not now, not now,
Nor yesterday,
But long ago
Has that day worn by,
That ancientest time,
The first time to tell of,
Then, whenas Gudrun,
Born of Giuki,
Whetted her sons
To Swanhild's avenging.

" Your sister's name
Was naught but Swanhild,
Whom Jormunrek
With horses has trodden !—
White horses and black
On the war-beaten way,
Grey horses that go
On the roads of the Goths.

" All alone am I now
As in holt is the aspen;
As the fir-tree of boughs,
So of kin am I bare;

As bare of things longed for
As the willow of leaves
When the bough-breaking wind
The warm day endeth.

"Few, sad, are ye left,
O kings of my folk!
Yet alone living
Last shreds of my kin!

"Ah, naught are ye grown
As that Gunnar of old days;
Naught are your hearts
As the heart of Hogni!
Well would ye seek
Vengeance to win
If your hearts were in aught
As the hearts of my brethren!"

Then spake Hamdir
The high-hearted:
"Naught hadst thou to praise
The doings of Hogni,
When they woke up Sigurd
From out of slumber,
And in bed thou sat'st up
'Mid the banes-men's laughter.

"Then when thy bed-gear,
Blue-white, well woven
By art of craftsmen
All swam with thy king's blood;
Then Sigurd died,
O'er his dead corpse thou sattest,
Not heeding aught gladsome,
Since Gunnar so willed it.

"Great grief for Atli
Gatst thou by Erp's murder,
And the end of thine Eitil,
But worse grief for thyself.

Good to use sword
For the slaying of others
In such wise that its edge
Shall not turn on ourselves!"

Then well spake Sorli
From a heart full of wisdom:
"No words will I
Make with my mother,
Though both ye twain
Need words belike—
What askest thou, Gudrun,
To let thee go greeting?

"Weep for thy brethren,
Weep for thy sweet sons,
And thy nighest kinsfolk
Laid by the fight-side!
Yea, and thou Gudrun,
May'st greet for us twain
Sitting fey on our steeds
Doomed in far lands to die."

From the garth forth they went
With hearts full of fury,
Sorli and Hamdir,
The sons of Gudrun,
And they met on the way
The wise in all wiles:
"And thou little Erp,
What helping from thee?"

He of alien womb
Spake out in such wise:
"Good help for my kin,
Such as foot gives to foot,
Or flesh-covered hand
Gives unto hand!"

"What helping for foot
That help that foot giveth,

Or for flesh-covered hand
The helping of hand?"

Then spake Erp
Yet once again
Mock spake the prince
As he sat on his steed:
"Fool's deed to show
The way to a dastard!"
"Bold beyond measure,"
Quoth they, "is the base-born!"

Out from the sheath
Drew they the sheath-steel,
And the glaives' edges played
For the pleasure of hell;
By the third part they minished
The might that they had,
Their young kin they let lie
A-cold on the earth.

Then their fur-cloaks they shook
And bound fast their swords,
In webs goodly woven
Those great ones were clad;
Young they went o'er the fells
Where the dew was new-fallen
Swift, on steeds of the Huns,
Heavy vengeance to wreak.

Forth stretched the ways,
And an ill way they found,
Yea, their sister's son[1]
Hanging slain upon tree—
Wolf-trees by the wind made cold
At the town's westward
Loud with cranes' clatter—
Ill abiding there long!

Din in the king's hall
Of men merry with drink,

[1] Randver, the son of their sister's husband.

And none might hearken
The horses' tramping
Or ever the warders
Their great horn winded.

Then men went forth
To Jormunrek
To tell of the heeding
Of men under helm:
"Give ye good counsel!
Great ones are come hither,
For the wrong of men mighty
Was the may to death trodden."

Loud Jormunrek laughed,
And laid hand to his beard,
Nor bade bring his byrny,
But with the wine fighting,
Shook his red locks,
On his white shield sat staring,
And in his hand
Swung the gold cup on high.

"Sweet sight for me
Those twain to set eyes on,
Sorli and Hamdir,
Here in my hall!
Then with bowstrings
Would I bind them,
And hang the good Giukings
Aloft on the gallows!"

.    .    .    .

.    .    .    .

.    .    .    .

Then spake Hrothglod
From off the high steps,
Spake the slim-fingered
Unto her son,—
—For a threat was cast forth
Of what ne'er should fall—

" Shall two men alone
Two hundred Gothfolk
Bind or bear down
In the midst of their burg? "

.    .    .    .

.    .    .    .

Strife and din in the hall,
Cups smitten asunder
Men lay low in blood
From the breasts of Goths flowing.

Then spake Hamdir,
The high-hearted:
" Thou cravedst, O king,
For the coming of us,
The sons of one mother,
Amidmost thine hall—
Look on these hands of thine,
Look on these feet of thine,
Cast by us, Jormunrek,
On to the flame! "

Then cried aloud
The high Gods' kinsman,[2]
Bold under byrny,—
Roared he as bears roar;
" Stones to the stout ones
That the spears bite not,
Nor the edges of steel,
These sons of Jonakr! "

.    .    .    .

.    .    .    .

### QUOTH SORLI

" Bale, brother, wroughtst thou
By that bag's[3] opening,

[2] Odin, namely.          [3] " Bag," his mouth.

Oft from that bag
Rede of bale cometh!
Heart hast thou, Hamdir,
If thou hadst heart's wisdom
Great lack in a man
Who lacks wisdom and lore!"

HAMDIR SAID

"Yea, off were the head
If Erp were alive yet,
Our brother the bold
Whom we slew by the way;
The far-famed through the world.—
Ah, the fates drave me on,
And the man war made holy,
There must I slay!"

SORLI SAID

"Unmeet we should do
As the doings of wolves are,
Raising wrong each 'gainst other
As the dogs of the Norns,
The greedy ones nourished
In waste steads of the world.

"In strong wise have we fought,
On Goths' corpses we stand,
Beat down by our edges,
E'en as ernes on the bough.
Great fame our might winneth,
Die we now, or to-morrow,—
No man lives till eve
Whom the fates doom at morning."
At the hall's gable-end
Fell Sorli to earth,
But Hamdir lay low
At the back of the houses.

Now this is called the Ancient Lay of Hamdir.

# THE LAMENT OF ODDRUN

THERE was a king hight Heidrik, and his daughter was called Borgny, and the name of her lover was Vilmund. Now she might nowise be made lighter of a child she travailed with, before Oddrun, Atli's sister, came to her,—she who had been the love of Gunnar, Giuki's son. But of their speech together has this been sung:

I have heard tell
In ancient tales
How a may there came
To Morna-land,
Because no man
On mould abiding
For Heidrik's daughter
Might win healing.

All that heard Oddrun,
Atli's sister,
How that the damsel
Had heavy sickness,
So she led from stall
Her bridled steed,
And on the swart one
Laid the saddle.

She made her horse wend
O'er smooth ways of earth,
Until to a high-built
Hall she came;
Then the saddle she had
From the hungry horse,

457

And her ways wended
In along the wide hall,
And this word first
Spake forth therewith:

"What is most famed,
Afield in Hunland,
Or what may be
Blithest in Hunland?"

QUOTH THE HANDMAID

"Here lieth Borgny,
Borne down by trouble,
Thy sweet friend, O Oddrun,
See to her helping!"

ODDRUN SAID

"Who of the lords
Hath laid this grief on her,
Why is the anguish
Of Borgny so weary?"

THE HANDMAID SAID

"He is hight Vilmund,
Friend of hawk-bearers,
He wrapped the damsel
In the warm bed-gear
Five winters long
Without her father's wotting."

No more than this
They spake methinks;
Kind sat she down
By the damsel's knee;
Mightily sang Oddrun,
Eagerly sang Oddrun,
Sharp piercing songs
By Borgny's side:

Till a maid and a boy
Might tread on the world's ways,
Blithe babes and sweet
Of Hogni's bane:
Then the damsel forewearied
The word took up,
The first word of all
That had won from her:

"So may help thee
All helpful things,
Fey and Freyia,
And all the fair Gods,
As thou hast thrust
This torment from me!"

#### ODDRUN SAID

"Yet no heart had I
For thy helping,
Since never wert thou
Worthy of helping,
But my word I held to,
That of old was spoken
When the high lords
Dealt out the heritage,
That every soul
I would ever help."

#### BORGNY SAID

"Right mad art thou, Oddrun,
And reft of thy wits,
Whereas thou speakest
Hard words to me
Thy fellow ever
Upon the earth
As of brothers twain,
We had been born."

"Well I mind me yet,
What thou saidst that evening,
Whenas I bore forth
Fair drink for Gunnar;
Such a thing, saidst thou,
Should fall out never,
For any may
Save for me alone."

Mind had the damsel
Of the weary day
Whenas the high lords
Dealt out the heritage,
And she sat her down,
The sorrowful woman,
To tell of the bale,
And the heavy trouble.

"Nourished was I
In the hall of kings—
Most folk were glad—
'Mid the council of great ones:
In fair life lived I,
And the wealth of my father
For five winters only,
While yet he had life.

"Such were the last words
That ever he spake,
The king forewearied,
Ere his ways he went;
For he bade folk give me
The gold red-gleaming,
And give me in Southlands
To the son of Grimhild.

"But Brynhild he bade
To the helm to betake her,

And said that Death-chooser
She should become;
And that no better
Might ever be born
Into the world,
If fate would not spoil it.

" Brynhild in bower
Sewed at her broidery,
Folk she had
And fair lands about her;
Earth lay a-sleeping,
Slept the heavens aloft
When Fafnir's-bane
The burg first saw.

" Then was war waged
With the Welsh-wrought sword
And the burg all broken
That Brynhild owned;
Nor wore long space,
E'en as well might be,
Ere all those wiles
Full well she knew.

" Hard and dreadful
Was the vengeance she drew down,
So that all we
Have woe enow.
Through all lands of the world
Shall that story fare forth
How she did her to death
For the death of Sigurd.

" But therewithal Gunnar
The gold-scatterer
Did I fall to loving
And she should have loved him.
Rings of red gold
Would they give to Atli,

Would give to my brother
Things goodly and great.

" Yea, fifteen steads
Would they give for me,
And the load of Grani
To have as a gift;
But then spake Atli,
That such was his will,
Never gift to take
From the sons of Giuki.

" But we in nowise
Might love withstand,
And mine head must I lay
On my love, the ring-breaker;
And many there were
Among my kin,
Who said that they
Had seen us together.

" Then Atli said
That I surely never
Would fall to crime
Or shameful folly:
But now let no one
For any other,
That shame deny
Where love has dealing.

" For Atli sent
His serving-folk
Wide through the murkwood
Proof to win of me,
And thither they came
Where they ne'er should have come,
Where one bed we twain
Had dight betwixt us.

" To those men had we given
Rings of red gold,

Naught to tell
Thereof to Atli,
But straight they hastened
Home to the house,
And all the tale
To Atli told.

"Whereas from Gudrun
Well they hid it,
Though better by half
Had she have known it.

.        .        .        .

.        .        .        .

"Din was there to hear
Of the hoofs gold-shod,
When into the garth
Rode the sons of Giuki.

"There from Hogni
The heart they cut,
But into the worm-close
Cast the other.
There the king, the wise-hearted,
Swept his harp-strings,
For the mighty king
Had ever mind
That I to his helping
Soon should come.

"But now was I gone
Yet once again
Unto Geirmund,
Good feast to make;
Yet had I hearing,
E'en out from Hlesey,
How of sore trouble
The harp-strings sang.

"So I bade the bondmaids
Be ready swiftly,

For I listed to save
The life of the king,
And we let our ship
Swim over the sound,
Till Atli's dwelling
We saw all clearly.

" Then came the wretch[1]
Crawling out,
E'en Atli's mother,
All sorrow upon her!
A grave gat her sting
In the heart of Gunnar,
So that no helping
Was left for my hero.

" O gold-clad woman,
Full oft I wonder
How I my life
Still hold thereafter,
For methought I loved
That light in battle,
The swift with the sword,
As my very self.

" Thou hast sat and hearkened
As I have told thee
Of many an ill-fate,
Mine and theirs—
Each man liveth
E'en as he may live—
Now hath gone forth
The greeting of Oddrun."

[1] Atli's mother took the form of the only adder that was not lulled to sleep by Gunnar's harp-playing, and who slew him.